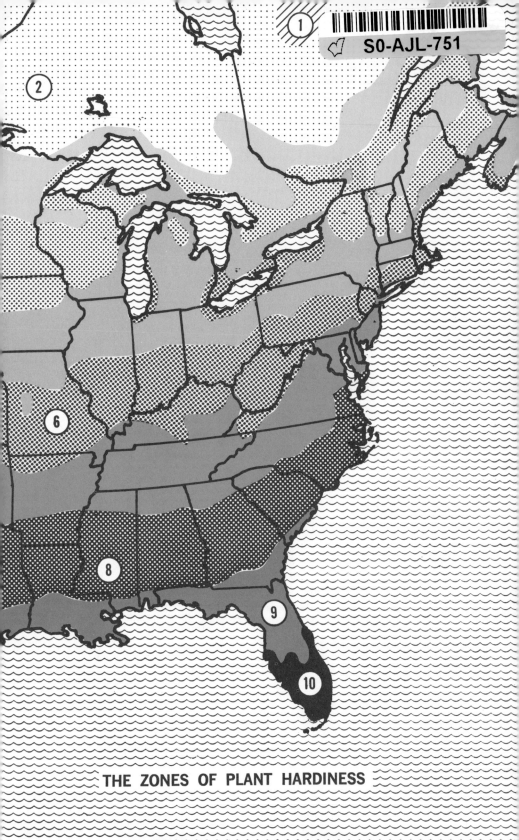

THE ZONES OF PLANT HARDINESS

THE YEARBOOK OF AGRICULTURE 1972

landscape
for
living

U. S. DEPARTMENT OF AGRICULTURE

From microscopic studies of
a bronze snapdragon and pink azalea
to moss on a stump and the
full glory of a lily blossom,
plants have beauty that eventually
is woven into the vast tapestry of
our landscape for living . . .

Colorful plants range from the native
paint brush growing among the gray rocks
of the High Sierras, and wisteria
in a cypress swamp down South,
to the single white flower of a clematis.

In their versatility,
plants propagated by cuttings
may be grown in jars
and bottles . . . Woody plants
like the widely grown
rose make a foundation for
gardens to delight
old and young alike,
and the southern camellia
offers a special contribution
to greenhouse and garden.

Blue and plum petunias,
zinnias, azaleas,
marigolds, star magnolias
can load home gardens
with color, edging
a lawn, making an
eyefilling display
before a pleasing fence,
enlivening a setting
of small boulders
and a walk.

Pyracantha lends drama to a house wall.
Rhododendron, another woody shrub,
can offer a wide choice of flower color,
leaf texture, and shape for a home yard.

Mulches, and a well-tended
compost pile, are aids
to good gardening.

Shrubs and compact trees like the Japanese maple
in its autumn splendor give interest, structure,
and background to home gardens and garden structures.

Vegetables provide fresh food,
and personal satisfaction
as shown by the boy with his
pumpkin grown in an
inner city garden project.

White dogwood and red azaleas in a
natural setting make a backdrop for
companion photos of a public
housing roof garden and a housing
development that saved existing trees.

Flowers and plants in action—
inner city youth gardens,
a classroom among azaleas,
and a Touch and See nature trail
for the visually handicapped.

Plants and lawns beautify our roads,
school grounds, and yards, and prevent
erosion eyesores . . . Crownvetch seed
can be planted on steep roadsides, and
mulch blown on. The end result is
a carpet of green and purple.

Landscapes to be seen
and experienced in the city.

Plantings at a museum,
apartment house,
public building, and
an indoor shopping mall.

Plants and pools enhance
downtown malls in the east and west . . .
Grasses and shrubs landscape a highway
median strip in the Southwest.

Science to improve
plants by breeding;
by using chemicals
to improve or change
plant color, size, and form;
and by comparing
the effects of clean and
dirty air on birch leaves
and potato plants to
develop pollution resistance.

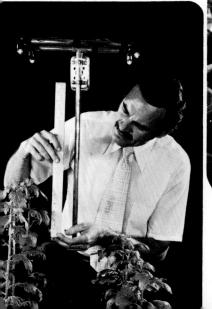

Controlled climate conservatories
are exciting places to visit
to see a variety of exotic plants
grown in or out of season,
to get ideas, to go on tours,
and to attend scheduled classes.

A commercial
chrysanthemum producer
knows how to grow his plants.
The hobby gardener can
obtain good plants, tools,
and advice at his local
nursery or garden center.

FOREWORD

EARL L. BUTZ

Secretary of Agriculture

If you put all the gardeners and all the other Americans concerned with our environment under one roof, you would really have a crowd. An estimated 80 million people garden as a hobby in the United States. They are all concerned with improving the environment, I feel sure. And most of the rest of our population certainly want a better environment. In fact, it would be no exaggeration to say that just about everybody would like to see our surroundings made more livable.

In a survey to determine which of 26 items people consider most important to their happiness, 59 percent of those answering checked "green grass and trees around me." Whether we live in urban areas or in the country, there's a touch of the farmer in most of us—a love for growing things. Greenery and flowers satisfy some psychological need we have. We join the poets in celebrating spring, while summer with its flowers and autumn with its colorful foliage touch our hearts in a special way.

This Yearbook, *Landscape for Living,* was produced to tell Americans about improving our environment with plants, and to give background information and how-to-do-it advice to home gardeners. In a low key way, too, it's a bit of a textbook on the biology of plants. But even beyond this, the book discusses land planning, redesigning downtown shopping areas, and new towns. Also covered is the vast subject of plants in action—helping raise the spirits of inner city residents, teaching youth about the environment, and providing new vistas for senior citizens. In short, this is a handbook with something for everyone on improving the quality of life in urban and suburban America, and in the countryside.

The book describes how our future growth centers can be designed for better living, and gives many examples. Citizen involvement is needed to make this a reality, and more of us must become involved. We need many more housing developments that provide open space and greenery, more shopping centers with trees and other plantings, more office buildings that have park-like surroundings, more planned new towns instead of towns that simply evolve from urban sprawl. A wealth of exciting possibilities are discussed in these pages.

Homeowners themselves can contribute significantly to a better environment, and many already do so. For instance, homeowners can help control soil erosion and water pollution with grass and other ground cover on their yards, and with mulches and terracing. Civic, business, and environmental groups can help control erosion by advocating roadside plantings, and plantings and other techniques to curb mudflows at new construction sites. Saving desirable trees in development areas also should be encouraged. A side effect of all these activities is a reduction of visual pollution, since greenery and flowers and trees make everything more attractive to the eye.

As one of the book's authors notes, nearly everyone can garden with satisfaction and delight. I might add, though, that a lot of hard work is involved, and that raking leaves, mowing lawns, and other garden chores can be physically fatiguing. But there's great satisfaction when a garden or lawn turns out well, while the exercise and mental relaxation are beneficial. *Medical Economics* made a survey of doctors' leisure pursuits, and found that "an astonishing 40 per cent" of those surveyed engage in gardening. In fact, more M.D.'s garden than play golf. Maybe this should be a tip to the rest of us.

Ornamental plants make up an important segment of American agriculture. Sales of ornamental plants and flowers are estimated at nearly $5 billion each year. The U.S. Department of Agriculture is constantly striving to develop better plants. Among our many goals are plants with special characteristics such as the ability to resist air pollution, to grow well within enclosed shopping centers, to control erosion better, and to reduce traffic noise.

Our scientists are finding new ways to combat plant diseases and pests. Among recent developments is a fungicide injection technique against Dutch elm disease and wilts of oak and maple. USDA has programs to guard against introduction of plant pests and diseases into the United States, and to control or eradicate those within our borders. Varieties of plants with built-in resistance to diseases and pests are being developed.

USDA's plant researchers have found ways of improving flower seed germination, changing flower color, controlling stem length, extending flowering periods, and increasing plant hardiness against extremes of temperature and moisture. Our plant explorers have traveled the far reaches of the earth, collecting plants that are new to the United States and will one day enhance our home gardens.

Our rapidly changing environment provides an added challenge to future generations of plant breeders to originate new and adaptive trees and shrubs for beautifying America. The need for better shade trees has been recognized, and breeding research is underway. With time, and increased effort, the city and suburban trees of tomorrow will be superior to today's.

Most plants start with seeds, and a vast amount of care goes into trying to make sure that the seeds you buy will yield disease-free plants, good wholesome vegetables, or beautiful flowers. Seeds are the product of the labor of many men. Research scientists, geneticists, plant breeders, and seedsmen all have a hand in improving the seed for your garden or lawn. Federal and State laws regulate the quality of most seeds, and required facts about seed quality on the label are a valuable aid to the purchaser.

Sound practices in gardening are outlined in a number of chapters in this Yearbook, and a good first step is to have your soil tested. Results of this test will give you a guide towards improving the soil for your lawn or garden. Chapters on practical gardening cover shrubs, perennials, annuals, lawns, and vegetables, fruits and herbs. Other how-to-do-it type articles discuss plant propagation, greenhouses, fertilizing, mulching, and composting.

All sectors of our population share in the joy and wonder of plants and flowers that uplift our spirits. Writing about public housing gardens in this book, an author notes that "in the ecology of the human spirit, the microclimate of a flower box or a flowerbed can contain a tremendous healing force." Inner city areas have been revitalized through neighborhood gardens and youth gardens. Improved morale of workers has resulted from attractive landscaping by their firms. Neighborhood plantings have given suburbanites stronger links to their communities. School children have developed new pride from schoolyard plantings— and incidentally learned valuable lessons in conservation at the same time. Use of horticulture as training, career opportunity, and therapy for the handicapped is on the increase.

All of these activities are good, and our only need is for many more of them. America's Landscape for Living is far from complete, but this book points to a multitude of ways of achieving a better environment for our generation and future generations. As the title of the book's closing chapter points out, "hope for tomorrow's landscapes depends on our acting now."

PREFACE

JACK HAYES

Yearbook Editor

For good tips on landscaping in your area, start near home. Neighbors, a garden club, the county extension agent, your local newspaper's garden column can steer you right. The chapter that begins on page 320, *current gardening information: where you can find it,* tells in considerable detail how to go about getting reliable help.

This Yearbook, *Landscape for Living,* contains a vast amount of practical, basic background information of value to all gardeners. But like most books, it cannot be localized enough to cover every aspect of your particular garden. Thus the suggestion to start near home for advice in your area.

If you already are a skilled gardener, you can do your bit by helping the beginners. A better looking neighborhood or community will result. Of course, you must be diplomatic. Some folks just don't take kindly to advice or other help, even though it may be obvious to you that they need it.

While this Yearbook contains basic material for both skilled and novice home gardeners, you may want additional information on particular subjects. As a help, many chapters in the book conclude with a short list of suggested further reading, often including U.S. Department of Agriculture publications. In some cases the USDA publications may be obtained free from USDA or your local county extension office; in other cases you can purchase them from the Superintendent of Documents, U.S. Government Printing Office. The USDA publications will help you in your special gardening concerns. Your own State extension service or State university may also be able to provide publications, and they will be designed for gardeners in the State.

Since popularly used plant names often vary from one part of the country to another, this book in many instances—in the text, in lists, in the index—gives the Latin name which will serve as a universal identification for a plant.

A number of chapters refer to plant hardiness zones, which is an indication of whether a plant is suitable for your region. The map just inside the front cover of the book shows these zones. It is a redrawn version of the far more detailed Plant Hardiness Zone Map, Miscellaneous Publication No. 814, which you can get for 20¢ from the Superintendent of Documents, U.S. Government Printing Office, Washington, D.C. 20402. Only the Yearbook chapter that begins on page 176 is keyed to a different type map, which is reproduced in that chapter.

This Yearbook's production was speeded up so that it might be available to gardeners earlier in the year than usual (many of the Yearbooks have been published in the late fall). Special credit should be given to the authors who prepared their material in a very short time, and to the Committee that planned the book under a tight schedule.

William A. Dalton of the *Animal and Plant Health Inspection Service* participated in the editing of chapters, and rewrote parts of a number of chapters. Frederick G. Meyer of the *Agricultural Research Service* standardized most of the plant names in the book, and verified them.

Indexer of the book was Mrs. Eunice A. Johnson of the *Office of Information,* editorial assistant in the Yearbook Office. Working with her was Mrs. Elaine

B. Hunt, editorial clerk. Rudolph A. Diamond, U.S. Government Printing Office, was involved in virtually all printing phases of the book.

George W. Irving, Jr., then administrator of the *Agricultural Research Service,* was chairman of the 1972 Yearbook Committee. He has since retired. Committee members were:

Kate Alfriend, Office of Information

William A. Bailey, Agricultural Research Service

Henry M. Cathey, Agricultural Research Service

H C Cox, Agricultural Research Service

John L. Creech, Agricultural Research Service

Jeanne M. Davis, planning consultant, formerly with the Economic Research Service

R. Stanley Dyal, Agricultural Research Service

Paul H. Harvey, North Carolina State University

Arthur E. Merriman, Forest Service

Albert A. Piringer, Agricultural Research Service

Robert B. Rathbone, Agricultural Research Service

Warren C. Shaw, Agricultural Research Service

Wilmer W. Steiner, Soil Conservation Service

William R. Van Dersal, Soil Conservation Service

Jan Van Schilfgaarde, Agricultural Research Service

David F. Warren, Office of Information, visual coordinator

Robert A. Wearne, Extension Service

CONTENTS

selecting and protecting plants

searching for, breeding, and propagating new plants

understanding plant growth

plants in action

who can help

planning for growth centers

PLANTS IN THE LIVING ENVIRONMENT

plants in the living environment
to lift the spirits of man

OUR VIEW OF EARTH from 100,000 miles in space shows a cloud-covered ball rotating in orbit. When the clouds part, we observe two areas covered with frozen water. The area in between is colored various tints of blue intermixed with gray and tan. Green plants are not detectable to the unaided eye.

Our view of earth from a car window in many cities shows terrain with most of the natural vegetation removed. Spaces are filled with buildings, roads, construction machinery; any open areas are tan and gray colored, or blacktopped and covered with parked cars. The blue sky is dulled with pollution haze. Green plants are forgotten in this landscape; the few present grow with difficulty.

This need not be the vista confronting Americans in their cities, or wherever they live and work. We must set new priorities for land use, we must create new landscapes through the many uses of green plants. We must educate the new generation to the benefits of having plants in their lives.

Green plants in the countryside seem so simple and abundant. They appear to grow everywhere, survive all kinds of changes.

Under the protection and comforts of indoor living we forget the ruthlessness of the outdoors. We retain only the memories of balmy days of late spring, the crisp days of autumn. We soon forget the driving rains of spring, the sudden chilling nights of fall. Plants growing in our landscapes are adapted to survive this fury.

A farmer knows how suddenly the weather can change. An emerging crop of seedlings or a field of maturing produce can be wiped out in minutes.

Thunderstorms, driving rains, and abrupt changes in temperatures are considered natural calamities. Man has made no progress in controlling them. Only a utopian dreamer visualizes the means whereby plants can be put into a manmade protective shell on a widespread basis.

Much of the information on the functions of plants is lost prior to reaching people. Most people know that plants are the counterpart of animals. They remember vaguely that if the two types of organisms are combined in some kind of an airtight fish bowl, the plants would sustain the life of the animals, and vice versa. Creation of a balance of nature is considered beyond the scope of a human being. And yet earth, somehow, must maintain its balance of nature.

Although our major recycling plants are the marine algae, land plants recycle water, oxygen, carbon dioxide, and almost all of the elements in the periodic table. Even what is left over— organic matter produced during each growth cycle of plants—becomes the beginning of mulches, protective covers, and ultimately one of the ingredients of all productive soils.

Many people have their roots in the land, through parents or grandparents. They learned at home that plants feed, shade, cool, color, scent, and protect man's environment. They remember that their yards are alive with fruits, vegetables, and flowers for every season. Beyond their yards were the weed trees left in the fields and pastures. The distant scenery of unmanageable land

Author HENRY M. CATHEY is Leader of Ornamental Investigations in the Plant Science Research Division, Agricultural Research Service.

flourished with native plants living in concert with all organisms.

The skills with plants were handed down in the family. Every trip meant that "the green thumb" people returned with new slips to root, new seeds to plant, and new ideas on how to raise plants.

Every neighborhood had at least one person who spent some or most of his spare time working with plants. The extra fruits, vegetables, and flowers appeared as gifts through the neighborhood. This person also acted as a consultant for novice gardeners. Young gardeners became involved in working with plants through the gift of a package of seed or through the demonstration that a specific plant could be grown in their neighborhood. The satisfaction to be obtained from growing plants was learned by trial and error.

Our weak memory retention permits us to forget the erratic and limited seasons of production. We also forget the seasons where certain kinds of plants failed to produce flowers due to severe winters, improper pruning, and epidemics of all kinds of pests and diseases.

We enjoy the legacy from the skills of previous generations—broad-reaching coverings of trees—parklands with mature plantings of trees, shrubs, ground covers, and grass—tasty fruits and vegetables, and fragrant flowers.

With the pressures of a growing population, the patterns of living in the seventies have used a million acres of land a year to make room for new homes, shops, and roads. Much of this land was formerly used for producing food and was located near cities. This land is now permanently lost from recycling our environment. We have pushed out of production some of the land best suited for plant growth, sealed it over with layers of asphalt and concrete. We have created vast areas of living space for man where plants need help to survive.

We have altered everything. We have bulldozed off the natural stratum of soil, reducing the soil's ability to absorb water. We have removed the natural channels of streams. We have even prevented the natural recovery progressions from simple plants to the intermeshing of many kinds of organisms into the living environment.

Green plants brought into city, town, or suburb have many advantages over their counterparts in the wild. We can select plants from a specific clone rather than randomly picking plants from a seedling population. We can train the plants for transplanting to a specific site. We can position the plants in their own especially selected microenvironment. All the skills of the grower can be brought to focus on adapting plants to sites.

Gardening is a hobby of over 80 million people in the United States. Many of them garden without a lawn or any natural soil, miles away from any field or woodland. They put their plants everywhere—on porches and balconies, windows and decks. They mix all kinds of plants together—vegetable, flower, fruit, and foliage. Not every plant persists under these conditions—some survive for years, others need frequent replacement. Gardeners need simple ways to extend the kinds of plants that may be grown and ways to protect them against the changing environment.

Knowledge about plants and their functions has become the concern of many more persons than the avid gardener with an interest in a specific group of plants. There are, of course, the traditional gardening groups. But there are also the action groups which strive to protect our national heritage of woodlands, wetland, coastline, and lakeshore. Many of the new gardeners want to know not only what color the flower will be but also how the plant will tolerate air pollution, hide litter, baffle sounds, serve as a fire resistant screen, or survive the intense heat and cold in our concrete canyons.

Skills of many kinds of scientists must be combined to create the information to help maintain plants in the urban environment. Then, it will be up to people to carry out the plantings and maintain them if plants are to succeed in the urban environment.

3

Top, lecture for inner city youths at U.S. National Arboretum, in Washington, D.C. Above, child in New York City public housing garden.

The number of people with plants in their lives is increasing as new uses are found for plants. Plants are becoming living forms of sculpture in the new landscapes. Plants reflect the changes of the seasons in their colors, texture, and smell. Plants are appearing in unexpected places and giving every person opportunities to be creative, even with few facilities and little experience.

This generation of young people should be made aware of the special experiences which come from having plants in their lives. They can learn the cycle of seed, seedling, cutting, plant, flower, and tree. They can learn that each stage of growth has the regenerating capacity to develop the new shoots which can become the beginning of new plants. They can learn that a person who plants a seed shares with the person who plants a 10-foot tree for continued life and growth.

A 4-year-old sums it up for me. I was working in my garden when it was dotted with hundreds of yellow daffodils. The strong voice of the young boy rolled through the yard: "It's spring, Dr. Cathey, and you are with it!"

It is people of all ages becoming involved in visualizing the new landscapes and then doing something about it that will make plants lift the spirits of man.

making our lives more pleasant—
plants as climate changers

PLANTS CAN MAKE our lives more pleasant. Besides beautifying our surroundings, plants can modify the climate. They don't modify it very much, mind you, but the little that they do can be felt immediately. Ever sit under a shady tree on a hot day? Or walk in the woods when the wind is blowing across open fields hard enough to make you squint your eyes? It's cooler under the trees and the wind doesn't blow nearly as hard in the woods as it does in the open.

Trees and shrubs can modify the climate in other ways, too. They can increase the humidity and they can dampen the movement of hot air from busy highways. They can control the drifting of snow in winter, and they can be the umbrella that protects you from a sudden summer shower.

To understand climate—and the way plants modify it—you should know about the earth's energy balance. The earth as a whole—its land, water, and air—is a great machine, and its fuel is solar energy. Each 24 hours the sun showers the earth with energy equivalent to that obtained by burning 5½ billion tons of coal. How the earth stores, transports, converts, and spends this energy determines our climate.

About 30 percent of the solar radiation that reaches the outer limits of the earth's atmosphere is reflected back into space; about 20 percent is absorbed by the earth's atmosphere; the remaining 50 percent is absorbed by the earth's land and water surfaces.

The total amount of heat absorbed by the earth is balanced by the heat lost through infrared and longwave radiation. Over an extended time, the two balance or else the world would gradually become hotter or colder. Recent measurements made by satellite have confirmed that the global temperature does remain fairly stable. This balance is called the energy balance or, sometimes, the energy exchange.

To modify climate, then, requires that the rate at which this energy is exchanged be slowed down or speeded up. Trees and shrubs can do this. Of course, the height, volume, and density of a plant strongly influence the extent of any effect it has on its immediate surroundings. A pansy may provide plenty of shade for an ant, but a man needs a tree or a large shrub.

Consider a grove of trees and its effect on its surroundings. Viewed from above, the grove will look like a leafy, green canopy covering the ground. About 90 percent of the solar energy received by a grove is absorbed by the topmost foliage. Of course, this energy raises the temperature of the foliage. The foliage then radiates this heat outward in the same way that heat spreads outward from a hot stove or radiator. This outward radiation of heat reduces by a significant amount the temperature we feel when we stand in the grove.

Trees do a better job of reducing the temperature than would a tent or umbrella covering the same area. This is because a tree has depth of foliage. That depth gives the tree five to seven times as much absorbing surface as an umbrella or tent.

Probably you always thought it was perspiration, but a scientist would elaborate. He'd call it the exchange of

---

Author RAYMOND E. LEONARD is a meteorologist in the Northeastern Forest Experiment Station, Forest Service, at the State University of New York, Syracuse.

5

Trees and shrubs protect homes against wind in Nebraska (top) and North Dakota.

energy between people and the environment. And he'd tell you that it goes on continually. Normally, because of our high body temperatures, we emit more radiant energy than we receive from the surrounding atmosphere; so the process of energy exchange is a cooling one. Under clear skies, incoming longwave radiation is small; at night, when solar radiation is not present, cooling of an outdoor exposed surface is rapid.

So here's another way trees modify the climate. They act like a blanket to decrease the longwave radiation cooling of objects—and people—beneath them. Night temperatures are higher under trees than in the open. Also, the frost-free period is longer under trees than in the open. While a tree may act like a blanket at night, during the day it is nature's own air conditioner. And this is where it has its greatest effect on the climate.

Trees move moisture from the soil to the atmosphere. Absorption of solar energy by the canopy sets up the process known as transpiration. During transpiration, vast amounts of moisture from the ground move upward through the plant stem to the surface of the leaves. The moisture then evaporates from the leaf surfaces into the atmosphere.

The transpiration process uses a large part of the solar energy absorbed by the canopy, thus removing this possible heat load from the area beneath the canopy. Water vapor carries away into the atmosphere about 580 calories of heat for each gram evaporated. A calorie is the amount of heat it takes to raise the temperature of 1 gram of water 1 degree centigrade.

Although measuring the effect of plants on air temperature exactly is fraught with complications, some assumptions can be made. I estimate that the overall effect of well-watered vegetation, mainly trees, would be to reduce air temperature on a hot dry day by about $3.5°$ centigrade ($7°$ Fahrenheit). Differences in temperature between a surface exposed to the sun and one protected under a canopy of trees may greatly exceed this.

The effect of a few trees may be fairly significant. However, doubling the area covered by the trees will not double the effect on the climate. Thus the planting of a single tree in an urban area can be fairly significant; such a tree will remove prodigious amounts of heat from the air and will use it to evaporate water.

Putting in another tree near the first one may double the area covered by vegetation, but probably would not double the amount of heat removed because the second tree is influenced by the first. So the effect of trees on air temperature will be most significant when they are planted in areas where there are no existing trees.

USDA Forest Service researchers have noted that transpiration from a single city tree may produce 600,000 B.t.u.'s per day for cooling. This is equivalent to five average-size room air conditioners running approximately 20 hours per day.

However, remember that plants transpire at a high rate only when they are well supplied with water. Most city trees, at least in the Northeast, do not appear to suffer from a shortage of water. I suspect that many trees in urban areas are able to tap underground sources of water such as sewers and storm drains. Also, many urban dwellers are compulsive plant waterers, and they provide the trees with enough water to allow a fair rate of transpiration.

There is another way that trees affect the climate. Trees and tall shrubs provide a mechanical obstruction to wind movement by blocking or deflecting air currents. This affects the force, direction, and speed of the wind. Naturally, the degree to which trees and shrubs influence the wind will vary with height, length, and width of crown as well as the densities of individual crowns and groups of plants.

When an air current reaches a group of trees or other tall plants, part is deflected upward with only a small change in speed. Another part passes under the crowns, but at a rapidly decreasing speed. When wind strikes an extensive forest, there is a marked reduction in wind speed close to the forest margin and only slight additional reductions within the forest.

Groups of trees planted as windbreaks are common in the Plains States. These windbreaks were designed primarily to keep bare soil from blowing away. Of increasing interest in urban areas is the potential use of trees and shrubs along busy highways to reduce sudden gusts of wind.

As an example, a double row of maple trees with a height of about 40 feet, and oriented perpendicular to the prevailing wind direction, will reduce wind speed by about 50 percent in the area immediately downwind. As might be expected, the effect of a row of plants on wind speed is greatest when the row is perpendicular to the prevailing winds. The effect decreases markedly as the wind angle to the vegetation decreases from 90 degrees.

Single large trees will provide an impermeable barrier against wind over a very short distance, but probably will not affect wind speed significantly. However, in urban areas, rows of trees and shrubs along busy highways have considerable potential. They will reduce the sudden wind gust and the high air temperatures over the pavement as well as diminish the amount of dust and debris transferred from the highways to adjacent living areas.

The effect of plants on precipitation has been somewhat overrated. I think this is because trees or shrubs have offered most of us some protection in

Trees between north and south lanes on this freeway in New York State reduce wind and dust activity, and lower the noise levels, as well as creating a scenic drive.

a downpour at one time or another. At the onset of a storm, leaves and branches intercept the rain and keep it from falling to the ground.

The tree crown canopy has a total leaf surface that is often five to seven times the canopy area as we view it from the ground, so it has a great deal more surface on which to hold rain water than the ground area it covers. After the surfaces of the leaves are covered, though, the canopy can hold additional rain only as water is evaporated from the plant surfaces. In general, high vegetation intercepts approximately 15 to 20 percent of the rainfall.

Another important and often overlooked aspect of plants in relation to climate is the effect they have on snow. Trees retain more snow than rain on the surfaces of their branches and needles and hold snow longer, particularly when the weather is extremely cold and the wind is light. Trees are planted in watershed areas to shade the snow on the ground and thus retard melting of the snow and subsequent runoff. This technique is important to the city dweller because it assures a constant water supply and reduces the likelihood of floods.

If properly used, trees and shrubs can reduce the drifting of snow around dwellings or on highways. I believe the use of plants to affect snow deposition

Trees and shrubs provide a cool retreat in urban areas.

8

may also be of considerable importance in ski areas where the proper location of trees may provide a channeling of snow to desired areas on a ski slope.

In conclusion, the effects of plants on climate will seldom be dramatic. However, plants can have a very positive effect in modifying the microclimate of an area. The esthetic aspects must also be considered in assessing the effects of plants on man. The cool, peaceful setting of a small group of trees in an urban area provides benefits in climate control and mental well-being.

The type of trees or shrubs used can have an effect on the modification of climate. Large conifer trees will tend to make the area cooler in both winter and summer; deciduous or leaf trees will tend to reduce temperature only in the summer.

For most of the temperate areas, a mixture of both needle trees and leaf trees or shrubs will probably be most beneficial. The evergreens such as arborvitae, and spruce types used in conjunction with the maples or oaks, should provide a workable combination.

 # gardening to help solve your erosion problems

PLANTS AND TECHNIQUES developed to conserve soil and water on farms and ranches are fast finding their way into our cities and suburbs.

Add these to the more sophisticated urbanized plant species and methods already available or in use around town. You will find you have an imposing list from which to choose solutions to the erosion control problems that may be plaguing you.

You may be having trouble every time it rains with that high steep bank behind your house which cascades mud into your window wells or onto an irate neighbor's lawn. Or, possibly you have deep gullies forming in low bare soil areas where excess storm waters rush off your property.

Have the children worn big bare areas in that pretty bluegrass lawn with all their romping? Perhaps you get a swirling cloud of dust and dirt every time the wind blows. And, do the rocks seem to grow faster than the plants in your rock garden because the soil is washing away? All of these are erosion problems faced by Mr. Average Homeowner, and most can be solved with the right plants.

Selection of proper plants, choosing the best ways to get them established, and then deciding on treatment measures for long-term management of the protective vegetation are all important steps in developing and maintaining erosion-resistant vegetative cover.

In selecting the plant for your job, be sure it is well adapted for the purpose and to your area. The plant should be able to grow well in the type of soil you have, and need only modest additions of lime and fertilizer. It must thrive under your climate and rainfall. It should have the vegetative characteristics to carry moving water, protect slopes from raindrop impact, provide attractive long-lived cover, and be reasonably easy to establish and maintain.

You may even want plants to serve as windbreaks to prevent soil blowing, or to drift snow where the accumulated moisture will be beneficial.

Fortunately, plants often have multiple uses. So it is possible to pick a variety that will provide good erosion control, food and cover for wildlife,

Author WILMER W. STEINER is Chief Plant Materials Specialist, Plant Sciences Division, Soil Conservation Service.

9

and beauty for your property if that is your wish.

The huge grass family offers some of our most valuable and versatile conservation plants. There are sod formers with dense surface growth and fibrous root systems that make up our lawns, carry storm water safely, and cover play areas with wear-resistant turf. Then there are bunchy grasses that are long-lived and require little maintenance when used on cuts and fills along highways, in housing projects, and in urban industrial areas. Bunch grasses add beauty to the landscape with graceful foliage and seed stalks of every shape, size, and hue.

Many of the grasses we use for conservation of soil, water and wildlife are native, but others come from the far corners of the earth. Weeping lovegrass from South Africa is as equally at home tying down blowing mid-Atlantic sandy soils as are our native switchgrass and coastal panicgrass.

We have grasses at our beck and call that will grow in soils which are variously wet, dry, acid, alkaline, sandy, clayey, rich, or infertile. Some grasses are exceedingly heat tolerant, some withstand excessive cold. Many can help you combat erosion if they are properly used.

Among the sod-forming grasses, common Kentucky bluegrass and its varieties are widely used for turf for carrying water safely down slopes and through manmade ditches and channels or natural watercourses. Creeping forms of red fescue are also good in the cooler parts of this country as a wear- and water-resistant turf, and are often used in mixtures with Kentucky bluegrass to give added strength to the sod. Reed canarygrass is a big coarse grass, with creeping underground stems, that is well adapted to wet soils and is often planted by seed, sprigs, or sod in seepy waterways and on the banks of ditches or streams to protect the soil from washing away.

'Kentucky 31' tall fescue has an important niche in the conservation hall of fame. It is tolerant to imperfectly drained soil, withstands drought and

wear, and is widely adapted throughout the Eastern United States, the Midwest, and the Western Gulf States. Although it is a bunchy grass, thick stands safely carry heavy storm runoff and take a great deal of punishment on recreation areas and home lawns. Many miles of highway banks are seeded to this versatile grass.

As we look at the hotter and drier situations from the mid-Atlantic States to the South and West, other grasses take their place in conservation. Good stands of Bermudagrass varieties have very high resistance to foot and vehicular traffic and the scouring of moving water. 'Tufcote' is an example of a recently developed Bermudagrass that is proving useful in lawns, watercourses, and play areas such as football fields.

The 'Wilmington' and 'Pensacola' varieties of bahiagrass and 'Amcorae' brunswickgrass are new promising erosion control plants in the Southeast. They were developed for forage but are now used in lawns, highway bank plantings, and recreation areas. 'Wilmington' bahiagrass has found special favor in Florida, where it seldom produces seed heads to mar its appearance as a turf. It is also resistant to the chinch bug, which is a damaging pest in heavily-used St. Augustine grass.

Buffalograss, sideoats grama, and blue grama are useful in dryland situations of the West. They will form protective cover at very low rainfall rates. Where more moisture is available, western wheatgrass is a good sod-forming grass for use in waterways and on critical slopes.

Two grasses developed in the West for particularly tough sites are 'Sodar' streambank wheatgrass and 'Critana' thickspike wheatgrass. They are both drought-tolerant sod formers, but you can use 'Sodar' on lawn areas, parking lots, and playgrounds because of its low maintenance requirements and wear resistance.

In the Great Plains some introduced grasses such as smooth bromegrass are used for conservation, but the natives are of dominant importance. Big, little,

and sand bluestem, indiangrass, and switchgrass are used in pure stands or mixtures for many conservation jobs.

These natives usually have rather narrow ranges of adaptation, but you can get selections suited to the soils and climate of your locality. They even range into the East and local types are being developed for use there. They give long-term, low maintenance protection to erosive soils and provide excellent wildlife cover. And of course, they are excellent forage grasses.

A group of annual or short-lived perennial grasses and legumes can be seeded to give quick cover and protect the soil from washing until the desired permanent species take over. They can also provide temporary seasonal cover until the time is right to seed the plant

Above, mixture of seed, fertilizer, water, and compost material is sprayed on highway bank in Georgia. Right, roadside stand of tall fescue in West Virginia.

11

that you hope to maintain permanently. Then you can mow the temporary cover for "grown-in-place" mulch and seed over it, or work it into the soil when you prepare the final seed or plant bed with spade or tiller. Some of this plant group are winter annuals and some summer growers, so you have a choice depending on seasonal need.

Good temporary species include annual or perennial ryegrass, sudangrass, rye, field bromegrass, redtop, and Korean lespedeza.

While grasses are tremendously important in a program of soil and water conservation in both city and country, another huge group of plants can be used to tie down the soil. Also, they add utility and beauty to our surroundings through different textures, shapes, fruit crops and colors. These are the herbaceous and woody plants categorized variously as trees, shrubs, vines, and groundcovers.

Groundcovers as a class may include vines, herbaceous perennials, and prostrate forms or species of woody plants.

Some vines are used effectively as groundcovers but they will often cause you more work to contain them than will other types. A good example is English ivy. It is a very effective, beautiful, dense evergreen cover in sun or shade, but continually climbs or intrudes where it is unwanted unless pruned or otherwise removed.

Groundcovers such as periwinkle and pachysandra are also dense and attractive shade-tolerant plants but they stay in bounds for urban use with a minimum of maintenance.

Then, you have a choice of densely canopied groundcovers that spread by shoots from underground stems and roots and grow lushly through the summer, but dieback to the ground over winter. Dwarf Japanese fleeceflower is one of these which produces attractive growth and bright red fruiting stalks.

Crownvetch is one of the most effective and widely used species, with dense top and root growth and a profusion of pink flowers. Those who have travelled along highways in the East and Midwest have probably noticed great stretches of roadbanks covered with this legume.

Three varieties of crownvetch are available. 'Emerald' was developed for use in the Midwest, while 'Chemung' and 'Penngift' were selected in the East.

Both the Japanese fleeceflower and crownvetch give winter protection to slopes because the dead stems mat down to form a mulch.

Woody and evergreen herbaceous

Periwinkle groundcover in front of a Michigan residence.

Planting of woody plants—green ash, caragana, honeysuckle, and cotoneaster—in North Dakota.

plants that qualify as groundcovers and give excellent protection to sloping banks or rock gardens include many spreading forms of junipers and other needled evergreens, as well as leafy plants like cotoneasters. 'Blue Rug' juniper is a fine example of an attractive low spreading selection which grows into a dense mat of bluish erosion-resistant foliage. Rockspray cotoneaster grows flatly with dense shiny green foliage, and produces many bright red berries to add color to erosion control plantings.

In California, many low-growing plants are used effectively to cover slopes and hold the soil. One of much interest and versatility is iceplant. It is attractive and the dense growth holds the soil from washing.

One of iceplant's important other features, however, is its resistance to fire because of its succulent foliage. A band of iceplant slows the spread and lowers the intensity of wild fires. And, if not too badly damaged, it continues to provide soil protection while recovering.

Groundcover-type plants are many and varied. By the very nature of their growth habit and dense stems and leaves or needles, most are good plants to use to conserve soil and water. Many are described elsewhere in this book.

When you develop conservation plantings on your property, you will no doubt want to use trees and shrubs along with ground hugging species. That's just fine, because the taller growing plants have their role in reducing erosion. They still the wind, reduce the impact of falling raindrops, provide room and board for wildlife, and beautify the environment.

You still need turf or low growing

Above, steep bank between industrial plant and parking lot in Tennessee was seeded to fescue and crownvetch, mulched with straw and emulsified asphalt, and then protected with a mulchmat. Right, grass grows through loose netting. Below netting holds straw mulch in place in Missouri.

companion plants under the taller species, or else you can use mulches. This surface protection keeps the soil where it belongs and provides maximum entry of water into the soil.

Many trees and shrubs have particular values for soil-conserving work. Some will grow in very infertile soils with little care because they are so-called nitrogen fixers. Actually, these plants have bacteria and tiny fungi attached to their roots, and these little helpers can take nitrogen gas from the air and change it into a form the host plant can use. Nitrogen is needed by all plants for good growth. The fixed nitrogen also encourages weedy species to invade and provide protective cover to bare areas beneath the trees or shrubs.

'Cardinal' autumn-olive and 'Arnot' bristly locust are two nitrogen-fixing plants. They can even be used to cover and beautify raw coal stripmine banks or acid infertile highway cuts and fills. 'Cardinal' can also be used as a screening plant on your property, and its heavy fruit crops will attract and hold birds for your enjoyment.

Nationally, there are many such plants to choose from. All you need is competent local help to select the right ones suited to your area and need.

Earthworms in a wood chip mulch are good for your soil.

If you have a conservation job to do, site preparation and protection may be just as important as species selection for good establishment and maintenance. Before you seed or plant your areas you should find out what your soil needs to have added to give plants a chance to grow. Get a soil test if at all possible. (Your county extension agent or State university can tell you how to take soil samples and where to send them for testing.) Then, add the recommended organic matter, lime and fertilizer, and work them into the soil well. If your area is steep and the soil is erosive, this action becomes all the more important to give your plants a quick start and keep them growing.

Then after you seed or plant, you must immediately protect slopes and waterways by applying mulch over the seedbed and tying it down so it will not wash or blow away.

Straw is an excellent mulch, and should be applied over the seedbed at a rate of not more than 70 to 90 pounds per 1,000 square feet if you want good emergence of grasses and legumes. Hay, excelsior, glass fiber, and other materials are also used effectively.

Several netlike materials made of paper or other fibers are on the market. These can be stretched over the mulch and pinned or tied down to hold it securely until your new planting is alive and well.

There are also heavy jute nettings and mats made of glass or wood fibers that you can apply right against the bare soil after you have seeded. The nets or mats act like a mulch and prevent the seed and soil from washing away until the plants grow and take over the job of protecting the soil.

I cannot overemphasize the importance of mulching seed and plant beds where washing and blowing may take place. In addition, seedings of certain species such as crownvetch have given more failures than successes where a mulch was not used, even when the seed or little plants were not washed or blown away, because the mulch kept the soil cool and moist to suit the seeds' needs for sprouting and growing.

Mulch bare areas where trees and shrubs are the only cover. Even slight slopes may lose considerable soil to runoff when bare.

Wood chips are excellent mulch material. They permit rapid infiltration of water, cool the soil, encourage earthworm activity, decompose to add organic matter and nutrients to the soil, and reduce the weeding job.

Rotted sawdust, shredded paper, straw, hay, and even byproducts such as cocoa shells are beneficial. Some folks use crushed stone or gravel. Although stones provide no organic matter, they do protect the soil surface, conserve moisture, reduce weed competition, and are attractive in the right place.

It has only been possible here to give an insight into some of the plants and methods used to conserve soil and water in this broad and diverse land. If you have conservation problems, seek local help from your soil conservation district, or from Soil Conservation Service and Extension Service offices.

Many nurserymen and landscape firms can help you with your erosion problems.

plants that will withstand pollution and reduce it

THE AIR IN OUR CITIES that smarts our eyes and chokes our lungs also damages —and sometimes kills—our shrubs and trees. Runoff of salt spread on streets to melt snow and ice in winter harms lawns and other growing things. Plants are needed that will survive, even thrive, amid smoke, grime, fumes, chemicals.

Plants absorb carbon dioxide and supply us with oxygen in the process of photosynthesis. At the same time, they reduce pollutants in water and soil. They also remove significant amounts of gaseous pollutants and particles from the air. The microscopic plants in soil also reduce air pollutants and degrade many toxic chemicals that enter the soil.

Plants hold topsoil in place. Thus, they reduce sediment and excess nutrients which pollute water. Plants also make effective sound barriers, and so reduce noise pollution.

In the United States, ozone is the major pollutant that affects vegetation.

Other air pollutants of concern to plant scientists are peroxyacetyl nitrate (PAN), sulfur dioxide, and fluorides. Nitrogen dioxide and ethylene are not as likely to cause acute injury, but they may stunt the growth of plants and cause their premature old age.

Ozone and PAN are photochemical oxidants formed by sunlight acting on products of fuel combustion, particularly the nitrogen dioxide and hydrocarbons that come from motor vehicle exhausts.

Ethylene is also a product of fuel combustion, and to a very minor extent it is produced by vegetation.

Sulfur dioxide results from smelting ores and from burning fuels containing sulfur—such as coal and crude oil.

Fluorides are emitted in the production of aluminum, steel, ceramics, and phosphorus fertilizers.

Some of the injuries caused by air pollutants are given on the next page.

———

Author H. E. HEGGESTAD is Leader in Charge of the Plant Air Pollution Laboratory, Plant Science Research Division, Agricultural Research Service (ARS).

Coauthor F. S. SANTAMOUR, JR., is a Research Geneticist, U.S. National Arboretum, Plant Science Research Division.

Coauthor LEON BERNSTEIN is a Plant Physiologist, Soil and Water Conservation Research Division, ARS.

Left, sulfur dioxide injury to white birch leaf. Right, normal leaf.

Ozone causes many small irregular lesions, called fleck or stipple, on the upper leaf surface of broad-leaved plants. Injury can develop on both leaf surfaces on upright growing species like grain or grass. Veins of the leaves tend to remain green unless general yellowing (chlorosis) occurs. Chlorotic lesions occur also on pine needles, along with tip dieback. Injury occurs primarily on lower leaves of plants.

Peroxyacetyl nitrate (PAN) causes collapse of tissue and silvering, glazing, or bronzing usually of the lower leaf surface. The injury may appear as transverse bands. PAN affects younger leaves than are affected by ozone.

Sulfur dioxide causes irregular blotches between the veins of leaves. These blotches show on both leaf surfaces. Injured tissue is white, gray, or ivory with larger veins remaining green. On grasses and similar plants with parallel veins, injury appears as streaks and general blight on leaf tips.

Nitrogen dioxide suppresses plant growth without marking the leaves when concentrations are low. High concentrations may produce leaf markings resembling sulfur dioxide injury.

Fluoride causes necrosis (death) of leaf margins and tips. On some plants— for example, citrus, poplar, and corn— chlorotic patterns on the leaves may be the principal symptoms.

Ethylene causes wilting of blossoms and drooping of the younger leaves, followed by premature yellowing and defoliation.

Pollution in towns and cities is seldom from a single pollutant. Usually there are many pollutants and their total effect is often much greater than you would expect, knowing their individual effects. There are also symptoms that mimic air pollution injury. They may be caused by insects and diseases or by poor nutrition, soil compaction, drought, cold, and high salt content in soil. Injury from air pollutants may make plants more susceptible to injury from some diseases and insects.

Premature aging of leaves caused by air pollutants is often confused with natural aging. The best way to know the full effects of photochemical oxidant air pollutants on plants is to grow the same plants in greenhouses in both unfiltered air and clean filtered air. Scientists have done this, with remarkable results.

17

Left, a potato plant grown in air filtered through carbon to remove oxidants. Right, plant of same age grown in nonfiltered air.

For example, studies near Los Angeles with citrus showed that yields of fruit were only about half as much in unfiltered air as in carbon-filtered air, even though the leaves were almost free of injury in the unfiltered air. Ozone was considered the primary cause of the reduced yield. It and other oxidants are effectively removed by activated carbon filters. Special filters are required to remove pollutants such as fluoride and ethylene.

Other studies, at Beltsville, Md., have shown that many plants benefit from air filtered through carbon to remove oxidants. Certain varieties of potato, onion, radish, and beans almost doubled their growth in greenhouses with carbon-filtered air. And they were free of the injuries observed in unfiltered air.

Sycamore seedlings in the carbon-filtered air were 25 percent taller than those in unfiltered air.

Levels of the photochemical oxidants at Beltsville and along the East Coast are only about a third of those in the Los Angeles basin. But plants grown in the East, with its higher soil and air moisture content, are much more sensitive to pollutants than plants grown in the arid West.

Losses from air pollutants can be serious or minor, depending on the variety of crop planted. One variety of potato, Norland, showed severe leaf injury and marked reduction in yield of tubers in unfiltered air, whereas another variety, Kennebec, did not.

Eventually, there will be increased demand from the public for plants that tolerate air pollution. The greatest need will be for plants tolerating photochemical oxidants. Levels of these pollutants are increasing, and their distribution is widespread.

Scientists know that genetic variation in resistance to pollutants occurs in many species of plants. One plant survives; another does not. So, they identify and save seed from the one that does on the theory that the plant has a natural tolerance to air pollution. The widespread use of tolerant varieties will do much to reduce losses.

Losses from air pollutants may be further reduced by breeding plants to increase tolerance. This has been done successfully for cigar-wrapper tobacco in the Connecticut Valley.

To some extent, the breeders of crop and horticultural plants unknowingly have developed pollution-tolerant plants when selecting plants most free of the leaf injury. For example, the alfalfa variety Team developed at Beltsville has greater tolerance to ozone than varieties developed in other parts of the country with less air pollution. The cotton variety Acala SJ–1, developed and used in California, has more tolerance to ozone than varieties from the Southeastern United States, where levels of these pollutants are much lower.

Plants are good air pollution detectives, and their use for this purpose will increase. West Germany requires planting of forest species around certain industries as a check on emission of toxicants. Sensitive plants may show visible effects of pollution long before their effects can be observed on animals or materials.

Plants are cheaper than specialized instrumentation as pollution detectives. They respond to several pollutants—effects can be additive—and they indicate whether pollutants of biological significance are present.

Of course, we also need instrumentation including, for some pollutants such as photochemical oxidants, a national grid of devices with the information summarized by computers and made available immediately to the public. The monitoring is primarily needed from June through September when oxidant levels are highest and vegetation is making most of its growth. In the Los Angeles basin the need is almost year round.

When plants are injured by pollutants we know they are, at the same time, removing some pollutants. In the case of fluoride pollution, leaves of tolerant species may contain several hundred parts per million of fluoride without visible injury. Leaves also remove pollutants, such as ozone and dust particles, just by contact with leaf surfaces. But more of the gaseous pollutants are removed when stomata or microscopic pores are open. There are several thousand of these pores on each square inch of leaf surface. Normally they are open in the day and closed at night.

Lower forms of plant life also remove pollutants in air, soil, and water. For example, some of the micro-organisms in soil remove carbon monoxide and hydrocarbons, such as ethylene, when the air above the soil surface mixes with air in the soil. Other micro-organisms degrade toxic chemicals so residues do not build up.

Chemical reactions seem to be primarily involved in soil removal of other pollutants such as sulfur dioxide and nitrogen dioxide.

Maintaining an abundance of vegetation is essential for pollution control. Top soil should be kept in place, and we need to propagate more plants than we destroy by our activities.

Trees and pollution could almost make a separate chapter. Although trees generally live a long time, air pollution can kill them.

For more than 95 years the sulfur dioxide spewed out by smelters in the United States and Europe has been killing trees, mostly the conifers, like pines, spruces, and firs. Extreme damage to conifers by sulfur dioxide was found in timbered areas around smelters, but losses also occurred in urban industrial centers where sulfur dioxide was the major pollutant.

In 1924, after a long struggle with conifer culture, the Royal Botanic Gardens decided to concentrate its future conifer plantings in rural Kent rather than at Kew, near London. Ozone and sulfur dioxide cause chlorotic dwarf disease and other ailments of white pine in the Eastern United States. Some of the affected white pines are in rural areas far removed from industry and urban centers. However, during periods of air stagnation the blanket of polluted air may cover a whole region from Maryland to Massachusetts.

But these are trees of the forest. In the East or the West, or anywhere in between, we might plant a Douglas-fir, a ponderosa pine, or an eastern white pine as an ornamental to grace our home grounds or to landscape a factory site, but they are not the usual trees of urban areas. What about the shade trees—elms, oaks, maples, planes; what about our ornamental trees—cherries, magnolias, flowering crabapples? We do not know the extent that these trees, which make life so much more livable, are suffering because of a polluted environment. Both acute and chronic injury are known to occur on some of these species because of pollutants.

Especially in our cities, trees are of inestimable value as they reduce noise, produce shade, filter out dust particles, and perhaps most importantly, provide an esthetic link between urban man and his wilderness heritage.

Reducing air pollution at the source will help to maintain the trees, but pollution probably cannot be eliminated.

Therefore, we must find ways for man and trees to live better under urban conditions.

Any reduction in vitality of a tree makes it a more likely host for insect and disease attack and lowers its resistance to other environmental stresses such as drought. What can be done to improve the resistance of trees to pollution?

As with horticultural and crop plants, trees must be found that are sufficiently tolerant of pollutants so as to be free of acute injury. Also, they must maintain satisfactory vigor when exposed to existing pollution levels. Even if pollution is reduced significantly at the source, tolerant trees will still be needed to thrive at the reduced pollution levels.

How can we select pollution-resistant trees? One obvious technique is to survey urban trees to determine which species have endured on our city streets over the years.

Two species immediately come to mind. These are the ginkgo and the Chinese tree-of-heaven (Ailanthus), the tree that grows even in Brooklyn. The ginkgo is an acceptable shade tree, especially the male trees that do not produce the characteristic odoriferous fruit. Ailanthus, however, cannot be considered at all desirable, except perhaps in the most desperate situations.

Reports of "natural" resistance vary from one region to another, and a tree species deemed resistant in Houston may be quite susceptible in Buffalo.

But town and city streets are not an ideal laboratory. Growing conditions vary tremendously, even from one side of a street to the other, and may influence a tree's response to gaseous air pollutants. Furthermore, since urban air pollution—especially photochemical smog—is a rather recent manifestation of civilization, there has not been sufficient time for any significant degree of natural selection for pollution tolerance to have taken place.

We can select for resistance by subjecting young tree seedlings or detached plant parts to measured amounts of pollutant gases under controlled conditions. Special fumigation chambers are being used to study the effects of various gases, alone or in combination, on trees as well as other plants. Even with the limited facilities available at the present, some progress is being made.

What has been found? Certain relationships between species have been established. For instance, European linden is more tolerant of ozone than is white ash. On the other hand, linden is more susceptible to salt in the soil. But the most important finding of the fumigation studies, exceeding even the differences between species, is the significant differences in resistance among *individual* plants within a species.

Urban tree culture is rapidly turning from dependence on particular species to the use of selected clones. All the members of a clone are propagated vegetatively from an individual tree (by grafting, budding, or rooted cuttings) and have the same genetic constitution, like identical twins.

It is in individual selection that our greatest hope lies. The selection of pollution-tolerant trees, and the combination of air pollution resistance with other desirable characteristics such as disease resistance and tolerance to drought and salts, is possible by selective breeding. Trees could be developed also for efficiency in removing pollutants from the atmosphere.

Trees live a long time; tree breeding takes a long time. But the improved trees resulting from today's research will last a long time—to enhance our towns, suburbs, and cities for the good of the people.

Salt Pollution

Salts occur naturally in soils and waters and may be considered pollutants only when man introduces extraneous salts. This obviously occurs when salt is used to de-ice city streets and highways.

Salts supply plants with mineral nutrients essential for their growth. When present in excess, however, salts are injurious.

In humid regions, rain readily leaches salts out of the soil, and salinity is not normally a problem. In subhumid and arid regions, plants must be watered, and salts present in irrigation waters are the main source of salt accumulation in the soil. Many irrigated areas in modern as well as in ancient times have been "salted out" or severely damaged as a result of salt accumulation.

When you water your plants they absorb water, but leave behind in the soil most of the salts that were in the water. The only way to remove these salts is to use more water than that which evaporates and is used by the plants. If the excess water can drain away below the roots, it will carry with it the excess, unwanted salts. This is called leaching.

Leaching with a 6-inch depth of water, for example, will reduce the salinity of the top foot of soil by 50 percent, and a 12-inch depth of water will reduce it by 80 percent. Chemical amendments, such as gypsum, are needed to reclaim sodium-affected soils. Subsoil drainage must be provided if it is not naturally adequate.

What are the symptoms of salt injury? As the level of salinity increases, leaves, stems, flowers, and fruits are generally smaller. Stunting and, in extreme cases, death of plants are usually the only observable effects on most *nonwoody* plants. *Woody* plants—that is, trees, shrubs, and vines—are damaged by accumulations of sodium or chloride in the leaves. Characteristic tip or marginal leaf burns develop. Burned leaves often drop off the plants, and this may be followed by dieback of stems and eventual death of the plants.

Plant species exhibit a wide range of salt tolerance. The most tolerant economic species, such as Bermudagrass, are able to tolerate salt concentrations about 10 times as great as those tolerated by the most sensitive species—African-violet, rose, and strawberry for example.

Some idea of the salt levels tolerated by plants can be given in terms of the total salt concentration in soil water bathing the roots. Sensitive species are affected when the soil water contains more than 0.2 percent total salts in solution. Moderately tolerant plants are affected above 0.5 percent, and tolerant plants above 1 percent. For comparison, sea water has a salt content of 3.5 percent, and saturated brine a concentration of 35 percent.

Most nonwoody flower crops are moderately salt tolerant. Shrubs vary widely in salt tolerance. Natal plum, bougainvillea, oleander, dodonea, bottle brush, and the ground cover, rosemary, are quite salt tolerant. Most shrubs are moderately tolerant. The most sensitive shrub species include Algerian ivy (a groundcover), Burford holly, pineapple guava, and rose.

Trees from normally saline habitats, like the tamarisks and mangroves, are highly tolerant. Other tolerant species include the black locust and honey locust. Coniferous trees, such as the blue spruce, white pine, and Douglas-fir, are relatively sensitive, but ponderosa pine and eastern red cedar are moderately tolerant as are also white oak, red oak, spreading juniper and arborvitae.

Plants normally absorb salts through their roots, but many will take up salts directly through their leaves if the foliage is wetted by sprinkling. Fruit trees, such as plum and other stone fruits, and citrus absorb salts so readily through their leaves that sprinkler systems usually must be designed to avoid wetting the foliage of these trees. Uptake of salt by the leaves of shrubs has not been studied, but salt-spray damage has been observed in coastal areas of Florida and Australia where sea spray wets the foliage. Leaf damage from salt-water spray has also been noted for trees and shrubs planted along highways that were de-iced with salt.

The extensive salt damage to trees, shrubs, and grass along streets and highways de-iced by salt is harder to control by plant selection. Salt concentrations in water draining off the highway can be so high that no plant adapted to northern conditions may be able to survive. Further, the loss of magnificent roadside trees may not be acceptable, even if some humble salt-tolerant replacement species is available.

It would be better to install drains to carry the brine solutions away from the highway without damaging roadside trees. Design of new highways and roadside plantings should take into account the effects of de-icing by salt.

Land will be increasingly used for the disposal of liquid and solid wastes to reduce contamination of our waterways and to take advantage of the exceptional capacity of soil to remove and decompose many waste materials. Tolerance of plants to salinity, as well as other pollutants, will have to be taken into account.

Salinity, like air pollution, cannot be completely eliminated. However, if adequately salt tolerant plant species are readily available, the salinity may not be damaging.

 # plants for easing visual pollution, or ways to overcome ugliness

WASHINGTON, D.C., is constructing its subway system, a truly awesome task. Everything is a mess. They've cut gaping holes in the ground; they've demolished buildings. Many streets are blocked. Giant unmuffled diesel engines drive compressors. Jackhammers chatter, and men shout at one another. The noise is amplified by the stifling closeness of the crowded buildings. Cranes swing wrecking balls. Huge noisy trucks come to haul away the debris. You are overwhelmed by the noise and ugliness. But such is the price of progress.

Someday the subway will be built. The men and machines will be gone. So will their noise. But will the ugliness? It's hard to say. Right now it could go either way. Subway stations are necessary. They can either be attractively designed buildings surrounded by attractive plantings, or they can be like those giant ugly gaping mouths of the subway systems of many other cities that swallow and disgorge hundreds of thousands of people every day. Progress is necessary; ugliness isn't.

The Washington, D.C., subway is only an example of what is being repeated in hundreds of different ways in other cities all across the country.

The screaming noise of jet engines at big city airports, parking lots full of automobiles, highways with no relief for fatigued eyes—these are just a few examples.

There are other forms of ugliness, too. Forms that most of us are painfully aware of. Trolley wires for buses, transformers, electric wires, and the utility poles that support them. And to what purpose? To provide enough electricity to light the wearisome neon signs that abound everywhere.

Try to drive out in the country for a little peace and relaxation and what do you find. Billboards and junkyards, unattractive gas stations and used car lots and thousands of automobiles.

Everywhere there is clutter. The clutter of construction crews, the clutter of automobiles, the clutter of unrelated building styles. The clutter that jangles the mind and disturbs the soul. Can anything be done about it?

All these have one thing in common. Their effect on us can be mitigated through the knowledgeable use of flowers, vines, shrubs, and trees. Then, you might ask, why don't we do it? Good question.

We have the knowledge. We know how to use plants to good advantage to screen out ugliness, to lead the eye away from ugliness, and to pleasingly unify different types of architecture. Maybe we don't do it often enough be-

Author GARY ROBINETTE is Executive Director of the American Society of Landscape Architects Foundation, McLean, Va.

Plantings serve as a unifying element for different types of architecture.

cause it's too costly, or maybe because many of us just plain don't care enough.

It's a different story with the average homeowner though. Here there is willingness, but often a lack of knowledge. Plants are everywhere, and yet they are, for the most part, the least understood method of screening.

If you tell a person to use a fence, a wall, a hill, or a gully to hide his air conditioner, his garbage cans, a basement entrance, or something else ugly or bothersome, he'll understand pretty well what is necessary. But if you tell him to do it with plants, usually he won't understand. He'll plant the wrong plant, or he'll put it in the wrong place. He'll probably spend too much money. He may even lose the plant.

But the techniques that landscape architects have developed over the years for dealing with the larger problems of ugliness in the city can be just as valuable to the homeowner.

The landscape architect employs many different methods and materials to screen out unsightliness. He makes use of walls, fences, the natural shape of the land, and even architectural elements. But with all of these, he will use plants.

Plants possess beauty of form, shape, color, texture, and scent. Some plants are more beautiful at certain seasons of the year than they are at others. Some are beautiful when planted as specimens by themselves, some are better used in conjunction with other plants. Landscape architects have categorized and analyzed plants for their

23

impurities from the air, and they influence climate.

Here are several of the ways that landscape architects use plants to beautify the environment.

First, they use them for outright screening. To screen something unsightly from view, say a parking lot full of automobiles, they use plants that keep their foliage year around and that are tall enough to block the line of sight of the viewer to the objectionable element. In this instance, evergreens about 4 feet tall would be necessary.

Screening can be useful to you in your home if you want a private place where you don't have to look at your neighbors or have them look at you. Or, if you live near a busy highway, you can not only screen the traffic from sight, you may even be able to reduce its noise level as well.

Another way in which plants can be used is by putting to work their ability to soften their surroundings. They can

qualities in beautifying the environment. You can benefit from what they have learned.

A plant is a natural element in the middle of manmade ugliness. In addition to some of the qualities previously described, plants have other uses. They help reduce noise levels, they remove

Above, the background and foreground plantings lessen the visual impact of electrical equipment. Left, plants enhance the appearance of a filling station. Below, plants used in conjunction with architecture help screen a parking area.

Pattern, reflection, and silhouette, with a major contribution by plantings.

mitigate the intrusion of concrete, steel, and woven wire typified by modern building and modern fencing, or they can enliven the drabness of a masonry wall.

Plants can be used for enframement. It is often necessary to distract attention from an objectionable view by directing our attention toward a more favorable one. The ringmaster at the circus does this by spotlighting the ring he wants you to look at and dimming the lights on the other rings. Landscape architects do the same thing with plants. They select those that lead the eye toward the more pleasing view, and cover the objectionable one.

Other ways in which landscape architects make use of plants are (1) as a unifying element and (2) to provide scale and softness. These techniques are particularily useful in cities where many types of architecture compete for our attention.

The mere naturalness of a few well chosen trees can serve to unify different architectural styles. Instead of the buildings competing like a classroom full of children all trying to get the teacher's attention, they sit quietly, minding their manners.

A plant can be effectively used as a structural element in a landscape. It can be planted as a single specimen or it can be used with other plants.

The most complicated way in which landscape architects use plants to beautify is through a technique called "progressive realization." This technique takes into account the fact that plants may be relatively invisible in and of themselves. By the careful placement of plants, views of objects, areas, or activities can be progressively revealed. In this fashion, the view through the plants becomes more important than the plants themselves.

At the other end of the spectrum, consider the effect of a single tree. A single tree in the middle of the concrete jungles we call cities has a fantastic effect upon its surroundings. Read the chapter, "Making Our Lives More Pleasant—Plants as Climate Changers,"

and you'll see what a single tree can do.

These are a few of the ways that ugliness can be removed, hidden, or lessened through the use of plants. Will the Washington, D.C., subway system present an eyesore even though 99 percent of it is underground? It needn't, and this is true of any other example of the progress of modern man.

Men need only remember that when one attractive environment has been destroyed to make way for progress, another attractive environment can always take its place.

Plants provide a foreground for the view beyond.

trees and shrubs can curb noise,
but with quite a few loud 'ifs'

YOU LIVE in a relatively quiet residential area for years, then a truck stop is established about 1,000 feet from your home. The noise volume rises, sometimes to annoying levels, especially at night when other background noises are lower and atmospheric conditions favor the transmission of sound. What can you do to lower the noise level, short of moving out of the area?

Someone in the community has heard that trees and other forms of vegetation are known to have some effect as sound barriers. You investigate and find the proper authorities that can offer advice about alleviating the situation.

A solution is recommended. It calls for a 75-foot-wide belt of trees to be planted between the residential area and the truck stop, with the trees as close as possible to the truck stop. Suitable evergreens will be planted with a minimum spacing, and a soft ground cover of taller grasses or other vegetation will be maintained between the truck stop and the residences. A solid wall close to the noise source and high enough to screen the trucks could be a possible temporary measure, removable when the trees reach a height of 15 to 20 feet.

The noise level would be decreased substantially, except during occasional periods of unfavorable atmospheric conditions. Though still audible outdoors most of the time, it should not be objectionable to most people.

This is a hypothetical case, but research is proving the effectiveness of trees and shrubs as noise abaters—research prompted by the growing awareness that excessive noise is a form of environmental pollution. The average community noise level has risen fourfold in the past 20 years with jet aircraft, the heavy vehicular traffic, and domestic power equipment contributing to the problem. It is likely to go higher if it is not checked.

Noise is a subjective quantity and therefore difficult to measure. Sound, however, which is caused by a variation in air pressure, may be measured accurately and is usually expressed in decibels. A device often used to measure loudness is the decibel A-weighted scale (dBA) of the precision sound-level meter, which approximates human response to loudness. This scale gives a relatively high correlation with subjective loudness estimates of broadband noises, such as vehicular traffic.

A zero decibel level corresponds to the threshold of hearing. Most ordinary sounds we hear fall in the range of 25 decibels, as in a quiet library, to about 80 decibels at a noisy street corner. A difference of one decibel is the smallest change in loudness that can be easily detected by the ear. An increase of 10 decibels corresponds to approximately doubling the apparent loudness of a sound. In residential areas, a level of 55 to 60 dBA is desirable during daytime, and 50 to 57 dBA during the evening hours.

Although trees and other forms of vegetation have some effect on the transmission of sound, precise information on their use as noise screens is

Author DAVID I. COOK, Professor of Engineering Mechanics at the University of Nebraska, and coauthor David F. Van Haverbeke, Research Forester at the Forest Service's Rocky Mountain Forest and Range Experiment Station, coauthored *Trees and Shrubs for Noise Abatement*, the research study referred to in this chapter.

Scientists tape-record truck noise in preparation for studying the passage of sound through belts of trees and shrubs.

somewhat meager. A recent cooperative study made by the Forest Service and the University of Nebraska attempted to derive accurate useful information on such usage and to add to the knowledge about sound propagation. Actual plantings of trees and shrubs in the form of shelterbelts on the Nebraska plains were studied, as were screen-plantings of shrub-tree combinations in urban areas.

Traffic noises produced by trucks, cars, and city buses were recorded on magnetic tape to provide the sound source. These prerecorded sounds were played back through tree and shrub barriers, and the sound level was measured behind the barriers at varying distances. This procedure was repeated at nearby locations, but without the trees, to evaluate the effectiveness of trees in reducing the noise level.

Many of the shelterbelts had been planted during the Dust Bowl days of the late 1930's and early 1940's under the Prairie States Forestry Project directed by the Forest Service. They had been established to reduce loss of topsoil from wind erosion, and to provide man, animals, and crops with protection from the wind. Now they were being used for noise tests in rural areas where trucks account for much of the vehicular traffic.

The potential value of vegetation as noise abaters, as determined by the study, was deemed very good. Findings showed that reduction of sound values in the order of 5 to 10 decibels are not unusual for wide belts of tall, dense trees. Species did not appear to differ greatly in their ability to reduce noise levels, provided the deciduous varieties were in full leaf. However, evergreens are favored for year-round noise screening. A supplementary study of various surfaces indicated that, from a noise-reduction standpoint, surfaces covered with trees were the best.

Screening of urban residential property was effective with a single row of dense shrubs backed by a row of taller trees, totaling a depth of 20 feet. Screening for rural areas or freeways where truck traffic is heavy requires wider belts consisting of several rows of tall trees in dense plantings.

29

Distances of 100 feet or more between the noise source and the area to be protected were found desirable.

Recommendations arising from the study that may be applied to some current noise problems include:

—To reduce noise from high-speed car and truck traffic in rural areas, plant 65- to 100-foot-wide belts of trees and shrubs, with the edge of the belt within 50 to 80 feet of the center of the nearest traffic lane. Center trees should be at least 45 feet tall. Consult local nurserymen and landscape architects for specific varieties at a given locality.

—To reduce noise from moderate-speed car traffic in urban areas where the interaction of tires and roadway is the principal cause of noise, plant 20- to 50-foot-wide belts of trees and shrubs, with the edge of the belt from 20 to 50 feet from the center of the nearest traffic lane. Use shrubs 6 to 8 feet tall next to the traffic lane, with backup rows of trees 15 to 30 feet tall.

—For best results, trees and shrubs should be planted close to the noise source rather than to the area that needs protection.

—Where possible, use taller varieties of trees that have dense foliage and relatively uniform vertical foliage distribution, or combinations of shorter shrubs and taller trees to give this effect. Where the use of tall trees is restricted, use combinations of shorter shrubs and tall grass or similar soft ground cover in preference to paved, crushed rock, or gravel surfaces.

—Trees and shrubs should be planted as close together as practical to form a continuous, dense barrier. The spacing should conform to the established local practices for each species.

—Where year-round noise screening is desired, evergreens or deciduous varieties that retain their leaves throughout most of the year are recommended.

—The planted belt should be approximately twice as long as the distance from the noise source to the receiver. When used as a noise screen parallel to a roadway, it should extend equal distances along the roadway on both sides of the protected area.

Screening is most effective when trees and shrubs are combined with soft rather than hard surfaces, such as pavement or gravel. This can result in a 50 percent or more reduction in the apparent noise.

Certain natural and practical considerations limit the use of trees and shrubs as noise screens. Due to the physical nature of sound and the extreme sensitivity of the human ear, sound cannot be brought below the threshold of hearing, no matter how extensive the natural vegetation. Very thinly planted trees, or trees in poor condition as a result of neglect or of an unfavorable growth environment, offer little resistance to the passage of sound. Ground forms are frequently limiting, as when elevated highways are above the treetops so that there is relatively minor sound absorption from below. Also, a right-of-way or land area requirements may prevent an effective noise screening, especially where belts of 75- to 100-foot widths are needed.

Although the limitations are formidable, trees and shrubs can effectively reduce noise levels. However, they will not do so in all situations. A knowledge of out-of-door sound propagation, aided by experience, is necessary to make valid judgments on the use of trees and other plants as sound barriers.

A planting of shrubs, backed by taller evergreens, provides noise protection as well as a visual screen against urban arterial traffic.

some cardinal techniques
for attracting birds

FOOD AND SHELTER for birds are mainly a matter of vegetation. Plants therefore are essential to your efforts to improve your land for birds.

Plantings can beautify your property as well as attract birds. Birds often feed on berries, and many of their favorites are bright hued and decorative. Hedges and dense shrubs provide nest sites and shelter and also a landscape background. Trees for nesting and singing offer shade and beauty to the householder. Sunflowers and other colorful annuals are seed producers and some provide nectar. A small wildlife pool or a bird bath is an attractive addition to the landscape.

Birds are an important part of city and country living. Their coming and going, their bright colors, and their singing are so delightful that many people often wonder how to assure their presence and increase their numbers.

It's easy to attract birds. You do it by providing more of the things they need most. Birds require food, water, and shelter for nesting, resting, and safety. If any of these are absent or in short supply, birds will be scarce. By providing for their needs, you can increase the numbers and even the kinds of birds that will visit your yard.

Birds like variety—so remember this when deciding what plants to use in your wildlife landscaping. Create a varied pattern by intermingling plant species, sizes, and shapes. Give birds a choice of places for their activities— shrubs, trees, flowers, and grasses. Give them a choice of food sources—seeds, nuts, fruits, berries, and flower nectar. Many songbirds combine these plant foods with insects, worms, and other animal foods.

By knowing the wildlife value of plants now on your property, you can make plantings that will add diversity to the landscape and at the same time provide needed food and shelter for birds. Many common shade trees and landscape shrubs, for example, yield little food for birds. Autumn-olive, cherry, and fruit-bearing shrubs are helpful additions. Yards and grounds that have only deciduous trees and shrubs are usually short on winter shelter for birds. They can be improved by adding junipers, cedars, yews, and other evergreens.

You have endless choices of combinations to consider in creating a landscape that attracts birds: hardwoods and conifers; vines, shrubs, and low trees; grasses and flowers. If your yard is small, you may be limited to single specimens of different plants. With larger grounds, you can use hedges, clumps, food plots, and other massed plantings. If you have a wooded area, a clearing within it can create more edges for birds and lend variety to the landscape.

Hedges and rows of trees screen off unpleasant views and reduce noise from highways. In crowded neighborhoods they offer privacy for your backyard. And they attract birds to your place year after year.

Conifers, autumn-olive, dogwood, cotoneaster, or a combination of these make good living screens.

Open stretches of lawn and fields with few if any trees or shrubs are favored

Author LAWRENCE V. COMPTON is Chief Biologist of the Soil Conservation Service (SCS).

Coauthor WADE H. HAMOR is Regional Biologist for the Midwest region of SCS, with headquarters at Lincoln, Nebr.

by meadowlarks, bobolinks, and several kinds of sparrows. In seldom-mowed open areas, try planting a variety of native grasses. They protect the soil, and birds and mammals like the variety of foods. A windbreak of red cedar, spruce, or pines, with a crabapple tree tucked in on the sheltered side, gives birds a warm, safe place to rest when the snow is deep. A food plot or feeder nearby helps keep the birds with you through the snowy months.

Living fences or hedges of honeysuckle, dogwood, or autumn-olive can reinforce and even replace wire fence along property lines, and can protect the house area. Cardinals, brown thrashers, and mockingbirds find living fences ideal.

Food plots of millets (browntop, foxtail, or proso), grain sorghum, corn, or sunflowers will attract the "seedeaters," such as goldfinches, cardinals, juncos, and sparrows. Wild bristlegrasses and ragweeds also attract many birds. A food plot can be small, perhaps several short rows, or large if you have the space.

When planting for birds, you need to consider soil, slope, drainage, exposure, and climate as well as your personal wishes. Added benefits occur if plantings provide shade, stabilize the soil, and control potentially damaging water runoff.

In general, trees and shrubs that attract birds grow satisfactorily on well-drained, fairly fertile, somewhat loamy soils not particularly suited for vegetables and flowers. The ideal soil has a loose, loamy upper layer 18 inches or more deep, and is neutral or slightly acid.

Use plantings of annuals, such as coreopsis, marigolds, sunflowers, or petunias, to provide more kinds of bird feeds, to balance landscape spacing, or to fill in along walks and other man-made structures.

Open water of some kind is needed by most birds. A small pool with stones in the shallow edges draws birds to drink and bathe. They use the dry tops of the rocks for preening sites after bathing. A conventional birdbath may be put on a pedestal or set on the ground.

Despite your best planting efforts you may not be able to provide a year-round supply of food for birds nor a full variety of nest sites. And there may be times when the birds have eaten

Autumn-olive berries, in Pennsylvania

Martin house in Arkansas is mounted on a telescopic pole to facilitate cleaning.

every dogwood berry, autumn-olive, crabapple, or other fruits and seeds of your plantings. So plan to use bird feeders, nest boxes, and birdbaths to supplement your plantings and landscaping.

Feeders stocked with fruits and grains are welcome food sources in late winter after fruits from your plantings have been depleted. Scattering food on the ground will attract birds such as bobwhite, mourning dove, and others that rarely go to feeders.

Certain kinds of nesting boxes, houses, and shelves attract certain kinds of birds. The ones to choose depend on what kinds of birds nest in your neighborhood.

Select feeders and boxes of materials and design that blend with your landscaping. The more simple and natural they look, the better they are.

Be sure your landscaping allows you to *see* the birds. Put plants, feeders, and bath or pool where they can be seen from windows, patio, or terrace. Choose the kinds of plants reported to have high bird use and adapted to your area. Attention to periods of blooming and fruiting makes possible a succession of floral displays and bird foods.

You can get further information on suitable plants from your local soil conservationist or county extension agent. Nurserymen, landscape architects, and bird societies can also help.

Your local library will have useful books and leaflets on attracting birds.

Some Plants Attractive to Birds

Autumn-olive—*Elaeagnus umbellata*
Bird use: 15 species
Ornamental value: Large, spreading shrub with gray-green foliage, fragrant, small, yellowish blooms; abundant red fruits.
Adaptation: Moist to dry soil; sun to light shade; Cardinal variety, winter hardy.
In bloom: May–July. *In fruit:* September–December.

Height: 8 to 15 ft.
Sources: Commercial nurseries, several State nurseries.

Dogwood—Cornus spp.
Bird use: 47 species
Ornamental value: Variable forms: small to large shrubs, small trees; leaves strongly veined, red to bronze in the fall; whitish to yellowish blooms; fruits bunched or clustered—red, blue, or white.
Adaptation: Moist to well-drained soil; sun to shade.
Height: shrub, 5 to 8 ft.; tree. 20 to 30 ft.
In bloom: April–June. In fruit: August–February
Sources: Commercial and State nurseries, wild transplants, cuttings.

Mountain-ash—Sorbus spp.
Bird use: 20 species
Ornamental value: Medium-size trees with compound leaves; flat, white flower clusters; bright red to orange berry clusters.
Adaptation: Moist to dry soil; sun; cool climate.

In bloom: May–June. In fruit: August–March
Height: 20 to 40 ft.
Sources: Commercial nurseries, wild transplants.

Russian-olive—Elaeagnus angustifolia
Bird use: 31 species
Ornamental value: Large shrub to small tree; introduced species widely established in dry alkaline sites in West; silvery yellow to pink fruits persist nearly all winter; narrow green leaves silvery below.
Adaptation: Well-drained to dry soil; sun.
In bloom: June–July. In fruit: September–February
Height: 15 to 25 ft.
Sources: Commercial nurseries and wild transplants.

Firethorn—Pyracantha spp.
Bird use: 17 species
Ornamental value: Medium to large shrubs; white blooms; showy, orange to red fruits.
Adaptation: Moist to well-drained soil; sun to partial shade.

The fruit of mountain-ash is available to wildlife even after heavy snow has covered other food sources in this Michigan scene.

In bloom: June. *In fruit:* September–March
Height: 6 to 12 ft.
Sources: Commercial nurseries.

Sunflower—*Helianthus* spp.
Bird use: 52 species
Ornamental value: Tall annual plant; has large yellow flowers.
Adaptation: Well-drained soil; sun.
In bloom: June–August. *Ripe seed:* August–September
Height: 4 to 8 ft.
Sources: Commercial seed stores.

Crabapple—*Malus* spp.
Bird use: 29 species
Ornamental value: Small to medium-size trees; showy, white to pink blooms; red, purple, orange, or yellow fruits.
Adaptation: Well-drained soil; sun and light shade.
In bloom: April–May. *In fruit:* September–April
Height: 10 to 30 ft.
Sources: Commercial nurseries, grafting, budding.

Elderberry—*Sambucus* spp.
Bird use: 50 species
Ornamental value: Tall shrubs; flat, whitish flower clusters; red to purple-black fruits.
Adaptation: Moist to well-drained soil; sun to shade.
In bloom: May–July. *In fruit:* July–October
Height: 5 to 8 ft.
Sources: Commercial nurseries.

American Cranberrybush—*Viburnum trilobum*
Bird use: 28 species
Ornamental value: Tall upright shrub; showy flat clusters of whitish flowers; glossy scarlet fruit clusters.
Adaptation: Deep, moist to well-drained soil; sun to light shade.
In bloom: May–June. *In fruit:* September–May
Height: 8 to 12 ft.
Sources: Commercial nurseries, some State nurseries, wild transplants or cuttings.

Cherry—*Prunus* spp.
Bird use: 49 species
Ornamental value: Variable forms; shrubs, small to large trees; small fine-toothed leaves, yellow in fall; showy white flower clusters or drooping spikes; small, bright-red to black fruits.
Height: shrub, 5 to 15 ft.; tree, 20 to 75 ft.
Adaptation: Moist to dry soil; sun to light shade.

In bloom: April–June. *In fruit:* Variable with species, June–November.
Sources: Commercial nurseries, wild transplants.

Wild Plum—*Prunus americana*
Bird use: 16 species
Ornamental value: Large shrub to small tree; suited to large yards or fields; spreads by suckers to form clumps; fragrant pink and white flowers; hardy red or yellow fruits.
Adaptation: Moist to well-drained loamy soil; sun.
In bloom: April–May. *In fruit:* July–October
Height: 10 to 30 ft.
Sources: Commercial nurseries, wild transplants.

Cotoneaster—*Cotoneaster* spp.
Bird use: 6 species
Ornamental value: Medium-size shrub; usually planted as a hedge but also as ground cover; dark-green leaves turning red-gold in fall; small pink or white flowers; showy red, orange, or black fruits.
Adaptation: Moist to well-drained soil; sun.
In bloom: May–June. *In fruit:* September–November
Height: 2 to 10 ft.
Sources: Commercial nurseries.

Tatarian Honeysuckle—*Lonicera tatarica*
Bird use: 18 species
Ornamental value: Large shrub; pink to yellow-white blooms; yellow to red fruits.
Adaptation: Well-drained to dry soil; sun to light shade.
In bloom: May–June. *In fruit:* July–September
Height: 5 to 15 ft.
Sources: Commercial nurseries.

Redcedar—*Juniperus virginiana*
Bird use: 25 species
Ornamental value: Medium-size coniferous tree (many varieties); dense, green to blue-green needles; small, dusty-blue, berrylike cones.
Adaptation: Moist to dry soil; sun to light shade.
In bloom: April–May. *In fruit:* September–May
Height: 15 to 40 ft.
Sources: Commercial nurseries, some State nurseries, and wild transplants.

Bittersweet—*Celastrus scandens*
Bird use: 12 species

Ornamental value: Twining vine; pale-green flowers; bright-red berries in yellow or orange husks.
Adaptation: Well-drained to dry soil; light shade.
In bloom: May–June. *In fruit:* September–December
Height: Climbs to 25 ft.
Sources: Commercial nurseries, some State nurseries, cuttings.

Holly—*Ilex spp.*
Bird use: 20 species
Ornamental value: Variable forms: upright rounded shrubs, small to medium-size trees; many varieties; dark green foliage, evergreen or deciduous; small whitish blooms, bright-red, black, or yellow fruits (very persistent).
Adaptation: Moist to well-drained soil; sun to shade.
In bloom: April–June. *In fruit:* September–May
Height: Shrub, 5 to 15 ft.; tree, 30 to 50 ft.

Sources: Commercial nurseries, wild transplants, cuttings.

Hawthorn—*Crataegus spp.*
Bird use: 19 species
Ornamental value: Small trees; pale-green toothed leaves; abundant, clustered, white flowers; orange to red fruits (very persistent).
Adaptation: Deep, moist to dry soil; sun to shade.
In bloom: May–June. *In fruit:* October–March
Height: 15 to 30 ft.
Sources: Commercial nurseries.

For further reading:

U.S. Department of Agriculture, *Conservation Plantings for the Northeast: Invite Birds to Your Home.* PA 940, Washington, D. C. 20250, 1969.

————, *More Wildlife Through Soil and Water Conservation.* Agriculture Information Bulletin 175, Washington, D. C. 20250, 1971.

 bees, butterflies, and blossoms: our useful garden insects

MOST OF OUR GARDEN PLANTS have flowers at some time during their growing cycle. Many, of course, are ornamentals planted primarily for the flowers they produce. Many useful insects find the flowers just as attractive as we do, but for different reasons.

Flowers originally developed as showy changes to attract the attention of insects for pollination. Later modifications adapted some flowers for pollination by birds, and even bats. Many flowers returned to dependence upon the original agent of pollen dispersal, the wind. These have usually lost the eye-catching colors, forms, and odors that characterize flowers as most of us know them. Although some of these (like the grasses) are important in the garden, we grow them for other features than flowers.

Fundamental to all flowers are the floral structures required for reproduc-tion. The female elements (stigma, style, and ovary) and the male elements (pollen, anther, and stamens) may be on the same or different plants. If on the same plant, they may be in the same or different flowers. In general, the farther apart the sexual parts are, the more dependent the plants become upon an agent of pollination to distribute the male pollen to the female pistil.

Hummingbirds and other birds provide this service for a few plants, bats also are known to pollinate some plants, but the most abundant and important pollinators are the insects that visit the flowers for food.

The pollen usually available in flowering plants provides the protein food required by many insects, particularly the bees. It is often produced in great quantity. Many kinds of bees depend upon it for supplying their young with protein, lipids, vitamins, and minerals.

Supplemented with nectar (often converted to honey), pollen thus becomes a necessity for bees, and they have evolved many remarkable structural adaptations to help them collect and handle pollen. Plants too have changed in complicated ways to take advantage of the visits of bees and other insects.

One of the most interesting of the many complicated relationships between plant and insect is that which has developed between the yucca plant of the Southwest and the yucca moth. The showy white flowers are visited by the yucca moth which purposefully scrapes pollen from the stamens and stuffs it into the funnel-shaped stigma after inserting eggs in the ovary below. This procedure guarantees food for the moth offspring which feeds on the developing ovules. The plant loses a few seeds, but is guaranteed pollination.

Other groups of insects show strong attractions to certain types of flowers. These may be roughly grouped in the following way:

Insects attracted to pollen flowers. Syrphid flies, colorful soldier flies, pollen-feeding beetles, and many pollen-collecting bees are often seen on poppy, rose, potato, elderberry, and similar flowers that provide pollen but no nectar. Male bees, moths, butterflies, or hummingbirds, interested only in nectar collection, are not usually attracted to these.

Insects attracted to flowers with exposed nectar. Short-tongued bees, flies, and many kinds of wasps are frequent visitors to the flowers of carrot, maple, saxifrage, euphorbia, poison-oak, and grapes. The flowers are usually inconspicuous, but it is easy for these insects to obtain the nectar.

Insects attracted to flowers with partly concealed nectar. Syrphid flies, short- and long-tongued bees, honey bees, and a few butterflies are attracted to the moderately showy flowers of

Author MARSHALL D. LEVIN is Chief of the Apiculture Research Branch, Entomology Research Division, Agricultural Research Service.

stone fruits, strawberry, raspberry, cactus, buttercups, and cruciferous plants.

Insects attracted to flowers with concealed nectar. Many sorts of bees, wasps, and butterflies are attracted to the generally conspicuous flowers of currant, blueberry, onion, melon, and citrus. Although the nectar is hidden there is often a copious amount.

Insects attracted to social flowers. A large variety of both nectar and pollen collecting insects, including long- and short-tongued bees, showy butterflies, flies, and colorful beetles are frequent visitors to the conspicuous composites such as dandelion, sunflower, and aster. The showy "petals" are actually sterile flowers used to attract insects to the many tiny fertile florets of the central disk. The nectar in these "flowers" is usually hidden in narrow corolla tubes and the insects usually have to force their tongue past the stigma and stamens to reach the nectar.

Flowers adapted for bees. Only medium- to long-tongued bees can operate the sometimes complex mechanisms protecting the pollen and nectar of legumes, mints, sages, violets, delphinium, iris, etc. These flowers are sometimes visited by butterflies and moths for nectar, but the insects generally do not operate the pollinating mechanism. Some flowers have nectar so deep that only bumblebees can reach it. Others have tough mechanisms requiring large powerful bees for pollination. Sometimes bees will bite holes in the flower tubes to "steal" nectar without pollinating.

Flowers adapted for butterflies and moths. Large, conspicuous, strongly perfumed flowers with nectar at the base of long narrow corolla tubes or spurs are visited principally by butterflies and moths, although some are also utilized by long-tongued bees and flies. Hummingbirds and honey birds are important pollinators in tropical areas. Examples in this group include honeysuckle, trumpet flowers, tobacco, phlox, and many orchids.

Flowers visited mostly by moths are generally open or fragrant only at night and are white or pale colored. Butterflies, on the other hand, visit flowers which are generally open and fragrant during the daytime and are variously colored.

Insect pollinators, most of which are bees, are directly beneficial to the plants they visit and as a result many are also indirectly of great benefit to man. Visits of pollinating insects to flowers usually result in the production of seeds and fruits. These seeds and fruits are very important elements in our diet and in our agricultural economy.

A partial list of crops known to require or benefit from insect pollination includes almonds, apples, cherries, cranberries, cucumbers, canteloups and watermelon, and strawberries. Lima beans, buckwheat, celery seed, mustard, rape, and sunflower are other seeds consumed by us that result from pollination.

A large number of seeds used for propagation require insect pollination. Some of the more important ones are alfalfa, asparagus, cabbage, broccoli, cauliflower, carrot, clover, onion, radish, rutabaga, and turnip. It has been conservatively estimated that bee pollination is essential to the production of $1 billion worth of agricultural crops. No one has been able to put a price tag on the value of pollination to wildflower seed production or conservation-plant maintenance.

In your own garden, visits by honey bees and other bees to your fruit trees, holly trees, pyracantha shrubs, cucumber, muskmelon, watermelon, squash plants, blackberry, raspberry, and strawberry patches are to be greatly encouraged. They are making vital contributions to the decorative or edible fruits and berries in your garden. To prove this, put cheesecloth or other screening material around some of these plants or flower clusters so that bees cannot visit the flowers. No bees; no fruit!

Many people are disturbed at the presence of bees and wasps in their garden because of the rather common fear of being stung. It is true that bees and wasps have stings and do use them in defense of their nests. However, very rarely are their protective instincts aroused while they are visiting flowers. It is extremely unusual for anyone to be stung by a foraging bee or wasp unless the insect is sharply disturbed—accidentally or otherwise.

Bees or wasps around their nests are much more easily aroused to defend the nests. If you have such nests in your garden, they should either be avoided or eliminated.

One group of bees may prove annoying in another way. Leaf-cutter bees snip circular pieces of tissue from the leaves of roses and other ornamentals. They use these to fashion cells in which they store pollen and lay eggs and in which their offspring develop. Some varieties of roses are very attractive to leaf-cutter bees and are sometimes almost defoliated. However, most leaf-cutter bees are excellent pollinators and we ought to overlook the occasional damage they do to some of our plants.

Since the pollinating insects described here make such an important contribution to our food production and ecology, we should make some compromises in our attitudes towards them. Even if the ones in your garden are not helping you, they, their relatives or offspring may be making some important visits to plants in your neighbor's garden. Since bees are known to forage up to three miles; their environment encompasses a large area. Careless or uninformed use of insecticides can thus have far-reaching effects.

Some of the honey bees visiting your flowers may come from the colony of a neighbor who keeps bees as a hobby, as a 4–H or merit badge project, or for honey for his table or to sell. His bees are at the same time spreading the benefits of their activity indiscriminately around the neighborhood within a 3-mile radius. Considered in this light, we should find it easy to put into proper perspective their occasional misplaced defensive activities.

container gardening offers
something for everyone

CONTAINER GARDENING is especially adapted to contemporary living. Plants in containers are compatible with any decor, be it the straight horizontal and vertical lines of contemporary architecture or the more comfortable lines of the early American home. Plants display great variety of form and texture. They can be used to create instant indoor gardens; they can be moved from one home to another; and they can be moved outdoors in the summer and indoors during the cooler months.

Space is not a problem. Container gardening can be conducted in a single pot on a table or windowsill, in a more elaborate room divider, or in a built-in planter.

Just as there are many kinds of plants, there are many kinds of containers. Plants can be grown in any container that will hold a growing medium. The choice ranges from the common clay pot to cans, jars, boxes, baskets, and tubs. Containers may be made of wood, plastic, glass, metal, and glazed ceramics. They can be portable or built in.

Most people select containers for both their practical and esthetic qualities. These include cost, availability, weight, strength, durability, attractiveness, and decorative and sentimental value.

When you choose a container, its size and shape should be consistent with the plant's size and shape. Tall, tapering plants are more attractive in tall, relatively narrow containers. Short, compact plants appear more at home in shallow, wide containers.

Particularly important considerations for good plant growth are the volume and depth of the container, plus some provision for drainage. Select containers that have drainage holes in the bottom for removal of excess water. Watertight containers are difficult to manage; excess water will accumulate at the bottom of the container and injure plant roots by excluding oxygen. Container volume and depth become critical in relation to the quantity of available water and nutrients.

Although the evaporation of water through the container walls is not critical, plants in porous containers will require more frequent watering to maintain moisture levels than will those in nonporous containers.

Besides the right kind of container, some fundamental requirements for plant growth must be provided if you are going to be a successful indoor gardener. Plants need light, water, nutrients, and a satisfactory temperature range.

Light is the most critical requirement. The levels of all the other requirements are adjusted in relation to the amount of light that plants receive. When plants don't have enough light, they grow slowly and become tall and spindly; it becomes difficult to avoid overwatering them. Plants are easier to maintain in good condition when their light requirements are met. You can use fluorescent lamps to supplement or replace natural light. Or you can select plants to fit the level of light that is available in a particular location.

The majority of the plants grown in containers will thrive at temperatures ranging from 60° to 75°F. In poorly

Author JOHN W. WHITE is Associate Professor of Floriculture at The Pennsylvania State University, University Park.

Coauthor JOHN W. MASTALERZ is Professor of Floriculture at the University.

lighted locations, you should keep the air temperatures as low as people will tolerate. As the amount of available light increases, higher temperatures can be used.

Plants will benefit if moisture is added to the air to increase relative humidity. Plants will grow under conditions of low humidity, but a more frequent watering will generally be necessary.

Let's say you have a location with enough light and a satisfactory temperature range, and that you've purchased a few good containers. There's not much more to indoor gardening except making sure that you have a good growing medium and keeping your plants well watered.

Growing media can be purchased at nurseries and garden centers. Special kinds are available for acid-loving plants, for orchids and for cacti, but it is fun to make your own growing medium. You can either follow another person's recipe, or you can experiment and develop your own special blend.

A good growing medium does four things. It anchors roots and provides physical support for the top; it stores nutrient elements (fertilizer); it stores water; and it is a source of oxygen for root growth.

These last two items—water and oxygen—are the cause of most problems people have with indoor gardening. Plants can very easily get too much of one and not enough of the other. Part of the job of a good growing medium is to make sure that plants have a chance to get enough of both.

For this reason, soils containing large quantities of clay and silt should not be used. Because the particles of clay and silt are very small, they clog up air pores in the soil and keep the plant's roots from obtaining enough oxygen. When this happens, the plant usually will die.

Many people have excellent results with good garden soil. But if you don't have much experience with plants, you

Above, modular plant boxes made of plywood. Right, rhododendron and English ivy in a cement planter.

will probably be better off using a good mixture.

In general, a mixture has three parts—soil, organic matter, and coarse aggregate.

Soil is not essential for plant growth. However, soil is usually the largest portion of most mixtures simply because it is inexpensive and readily available.

Organic matter adds air space, reduces the weight, and keeps a mixture from compacting. In other words, it has just the opposite effect of clay and silt. However, should the organic matter decompose too rapidly, these properties will be lost. Thus, if you add organic matter, use a kind that is resistant to rapid decay.

Sphagnum moss peat, peat humus, sawdust, bark, hulls, straw, cobs, compost, manure, and animal byproducts are the major types of organic matter used in mixtures for container gardening. Sphagnum moss peat is excellent because it is readily available in several grades, slow to decompose, low in mineral elements, and chemically stable when steam pasteurized.

Coarse aggregates are used primarily to improve pore space and drainage and sometimes to reduce weight. Since they are either of mineral or synthetic origin, they are generally very resistant to decomposition. Sand, gravel, vermiculite, perlite, calcined clays, cinders, and shredded plastics are examples.

When soil is placed in a shallow container, the water-holding capacity of that soil is increased and the amount of pore space occupied by air is decreased. Consequently, the soil must be amended to increase the size of the soil pores and decrease the ability of the soil to hold water. This is the reason that a mixture of ingredients is recommended as a growing medium for plants in containers.

Sometimes the medium itself plugs the drainage holes, and sometimes the roots of the plant do. To prevent this from happening, put some stones or curved pieces of broken clay pots over the drain holes. Special plastic drain pieces also may be used.

Here are some soil mixtures that will work quite well for most indoor gardening projects. The ingredients are expressed as parts by volume.

General purpose medium
  2 parts sandy loam soil
  1 part organic matter
    (medium to coarse grade)
  1 part coarse aggregate

Add superphosphate and pulverized or dolomitic limestone according to results of soil tests.

Some people add organic or complete inorganic fertilizers to their mixtures. This practice can result in root loss from excess fertilizer (soluble salts) unless you are quite knowledgeable of the correct kinds and amounts to add. If you are not sure, start out experimenting with a small batch and see how the plants do. Keep in mind that what works well for one plant species may not work at all for another. Also remember that many organic fertilizers vary greatly in chemical composition from batch to batch and from year to year.

A table has been included to give you some idea of how much fertilizer to use.

Acid lovers
(azaleas, camellias, gardenias, heathers)
  1 part organic matter (preferably one with a low pH such as sphagnum moss peat)
  1 part coarse aggregate

Some of these plants grow very well in only organic matter. The low pH of some peats requires the addition of limestone before growing most plants (pH indicates the intensity or strength of acidity or alkalinity in the soil. A pH of 7.0 is neutral, below 7.0 is acid, and above 7.0 is alkaline.)

Fine-rooted plants
(annual seedlings, begonias, many foliage plants, African-violets)
  1 part sandy loam soil
  1 part organic matter (fine grade)
  1 part coarse aggregate

Cacti and succulents
(crassulas, echeverias, sedums)
  2 parts sandy loam soil
  1 part organic matter (fine grade)
  2 parts coarse aggregate

All of the previous mixtures contained soil. Here are some soilless mix-

Slowly Soluble and Slow-Release Fertilizers With Trial Rates of Application for General Purpose or Fine-Rooted Media

Fertilizer	Ounces per bushel [1]
Nitrogen	
Urea-Formaldehyde [2] (38% N)	2 to 3.
Blood meal [2] (13% N)	1 to 2.
Fish meal [2] (11% N)	1 to 2.
Hoof and horn meal [2] (13% N)	1 to 2.
Castor pomace [2] (6% N)	2 to 3.
Osmocote 14–14–14 [2] (14% N)	3 to 6.
Osmocote 18–9–9 [2] (18% N)	4 to 8.
Mag Amp 7–40–6 (7% N) (14% Mg)	6 to 12.
Phosphorus	
Single superphosphate (20% P_2O_5)	2 to 4.
Treble superphosphate (45% P_2O_5)	1 to 2.
Potassium	
Fritted potash (Dura–K)	1 to 2.
Magnesium and calcium	
Pulverized dolomitic limestone	3 to 6.
Calcium and sulphate	
Gypsum	3 to 6.

[1] Use the lower rates for slow growing plants and sensitive plants like African-violets, azaleas, begonias, orchids, and ferns.

[2] Do not heat treat (steam pasteurize) soils containing these materials. They can be added safely after steaming as a 3- to 4-month source of fertilizer.

tures that are easy to prepare and give good results.

University of California Soil Mix
1 part fine sand (preferably around 0.5 to 0.05 mm in diameter)
1 part finely shredded peat (Canadian or German sphagnum or California hypnum)

With fertilizer formula I (given below) this mix may be stored indefinitely.

Fertilizer formula I for U.C. Soil Mix

Add to each bushel of mix 2 ounces of 20 percent superphosphate, 6 ounces dolomitic limestone, and 2 ounces pulverized limestone, 5 grams potassium nitrate, and 5 grams potassium sulfate.

Cornell Peat-Lite Mixes
1 part vermiculite (No. 2, 3, or 4 grade) or perlite (horticultural grade)
1 part shredded sphagnum moss peat

Add to each bushel of mix 3.5 ounces

of pulverized dolomitic limestone, 1.5 ounces of 20 percent superphosphate, ¾ ounce potassium nitrate, and 1 gram chelated iron.

A key to success with any medium, but especially with soilless media, is thorough mixing of the fertilizers into the medium. Peat moss is often difficult to wet. Using warm water will make it easier to wet. The superphosphate and limestone are best added dry before the peat moss is wetted. But the potassium nitrate and chelated iron are easier to add in solution with a sprinkling can because of the small quantities needed.

Orchids and Bromeliads
3 parts bark (fir or redwood)
1 part sphagnum moss
1 part coarse aggregate

Camellias and Gardenias
2 parts ⅛- to ¼-inch pieces of fir bark (not tanbark)
1 part organic matter (fine grade and acid)
1 part coarse aggregate

The amount of water available to a plant for growth is affected by volume and depth of the container, physical properties of the growing medium, and the amount and distribution of roots. Growing media described previously were designed to allow water to be applied frequently without danger of killing plant roots because of a lack of oxygen, assuming that adequate drainage out of and away from the container is provided. Therefore, the major concern is determining how frequently to irrigate to prevent a water deficiency.

The number and distribution of roots determines how much of the total volume of medium is being used by roots in absorbing water. A small seedling will absorb very little water because the number of roots are few and they occupy a relatively small amount of the medium. Small quantities of water must be added frequently for small plants because of their shallow root systems.

A large succulent plant, such as a geranium with foliage overlapping the sides of the container, will use as much as 20 ounces of water on a bright sunny day. Thus, on a bright day a

Above, geraniums in built-in planter at entrance to a home. Below, geraniums in ceramic urns on a doorstep.

large geranium in a 6-inch pot of general purpose growing medium would have to be watered four times a day to maintain rapid growth and development. Surface mulches will reduce these rates of water loss; this is more true for small plants in large containers than for large plants in small containers.

You can reduce the frequency of watering house plants by filling an indoor planter with peat moss and inserting the pots up to the rim in the peat. Water is applied to the peat moss and is absorbed through the walls of the containers.

Clay pots evaporate 50 percent of the water applied directly through the pot walls. In contrast, glazed clay pots and plastic pots lose no water through the pot wall. Nonporous pots will cut the frequency of watering about in half.

One inch of rainfall into a 6-inch container supplies about 15 ounces of water. If all the rainwater went into the container (most of it runs off the foliage onto the ground), 1⅓ inches of rain would be needed daily to grow the geranium. Obviously, supplemental irrigation will be necessary under these conditions.

It is usually best to apply water in excess of container capacity to be assured that the entire medium is wet. Many people double water (that is, they water twice within a half hour) to accomplish thorough wetting. Double watering also helps to expand the medium so that it seals against the container wall. This prevents water from running between the container and medium where it is lost without a chance of soaking into the medium.

Accumulation of soluble salts is another factor affecting the amount of water used. As water evaporates from the surface of the medium, salts (unused fertilizers) are left as residues. If these residues are not flushed out of the medium, they eventually accumulate to toxic amounts. Periodic additions of more water than the medium can hold are necessary to flush out these salt residues. This is called leaching. The plant symptoms of salt buildup are wilting when the medium is wet, loss of

roots, and eventual drying out and necrosis (death) of the leaves.

You can apply water manually using a sprinkler can or hose with a water breaker, an attachment which reduces the force of water applied to the soil. Many people enjoy this daily task. Or, you can purchase irrigation pipe systems for use with containers. These systems are easily automated using solenoid valves and timeclocks. Such automation simplifies irrigation and removes the human factor, making it easier for you to schedule weekend trips and vacations. Also water delivered automatically can be applied more slowly, with less force, and more frequently than is convenient manually.

In some areas water quality may be a problem and may vary from season to season. As a general rule, water safe for human consumption is usually safe for container plants. One exception to this rule is that water softeners should not be used in water for irrigating plants. The reason is that water from softeners has a high sodium content which destroys soil structure. (Most water softeners are installed in homes at the point where the water line is attached to the municipal supply.)

Also, you should be wary of watering plants with a hose that has lain in the hot sun all day. It may contain water hot enough to scald both plants and root systems.

Never repot a plant into a container with more than 4-inch clearance between root ball and container wall. Excess medium in oversize containers can stay too wet and sour when out of reach of roots for very long. Toxic substances build up and damage the plants.

Some indoor gardeners have poor results with their plants despite being conscientious about using the right mixtures for the kind of plant they are growing, making sure their containers are the right size, and seeing that the plants are properly watered and drained. What's wrong? Well, it could be that one or more essential nutrient elements may be missing from the mixture.

Sixteen elements are accepted generally as essential for plant growth.

Container Plant Suggestions for Various Conditions

Plants for Low Temperature (50°–60° F. at Night)

Australian laurel	Citrus	Jerusalem-cherry
Azalea	Cyclamen	Kalanchoe
Babytears	Easter lily	Miniature holly
Black pepper	English ivy cultivars	Mother-of-thousands
Boxwood	Fatshedera	Oxalis
Bromeliads	Flowering maple	Primrose
Calceolaria	Fuchsia	Sensitive plant
Camellia	Geraniums	Spindle tree
Christmas begonia	German ivy	Vinca
Cineraria	Honeysuckle	White calla lily

Plants for Medium Temperature (60°–65° F. at Night)

Achimenes	Crown of thorns	Poinsettia
Amaryllis	Easter lily	Rose
Ardisia	English ivy cultivars	Shrimp plant
Avocado	Gardenia	Silk-oak
Bromeliads	Grape ivy	Ti Plant
Browallia	Hibiscus	Tuberous begonia
Chenille plant	Hydrangea	Velvet plant
Christmas cactus	Norfolk Island pine	Wax begonia
Chrysanthemum	Palms	Wax plant
Citrus	Peperomia	Yellow calla lily
Copperleaf	Pilea	

Plants for High Temperature (65°–75° F. at Night)

African-violet	Chinese evergreen	Golddust plant
Aphelandra	Croton	Philodendron
Arrowhead	Dracaena	Scindapsus (Pothos)
Australian umbrella tree	Episcia	Seersucker plant
Banded Maranta	Figs	Snake plant
Cacti and succulents	Gloxinia	Spathyphyllum
Caladium		Veitch screwpine

Plants That Will Withstand Abuse

Arrowhead	Fiddle-leaf fig	Pleomele
Australian umbrella tree	Grape ivy	Snake plant
Cast-iron plant	Heartleaf Philodendron	Spathyphyllum
Chinese evergreen	India-rubber plant	Trileaf Wonder
Crown of thorns	Jade plant	Tuftroot (*D. amoena*)
Devil's ivy	Ovalleaf Peperomia	Veitch screwpine
		Zebra plant

Plants for Extremely Dry Conditions

Bromeliads	Crown of thorns	Snake plant
Cacti	Ovalleaf Peperomia	Scindapsus (Pothos)
		Wandering-Jew

Vines and Trailing Plants for Totem Poles

Arrowhead	Grape ivy	Philodendron
Black pepper	Kangaroo vine	Scindapsus (Pothos)
Creeping fig	Pellionia	Syngonium
English ivy cultivars		Wax Plant

Plants for Hanging Baskets

African-violet	Fuchsia (some cultivars)	Philodendron (some species)
Anthericum	German ivy	Saxifraga
(Spider plant)	Goldfish plant	Scindapsus (pothos)
Asparagus fern	Grape ivy	Syngonium
Begonias (some types)	Honeysuckle	Trailing-coleus
Black pepper	Italian bellflower	Wandering-Jew
English ivy cultivars	Ivy geranium	Wax plant
Episcia	Peperomia (some species)	

Container Plant Suggestions for Various Conditions—Continued

Suggestions for Large Tubbed Specimens

Australian umbrella tree	Fiddle-leaf fig	Philodendrons
Dracaenas	India-rubber plant	Silk-oak
False-aralia	and cultivars	Tuftroot
Fatshedera	Palms	Veitch screwpine

For Special Exposures
SOUTH OR WEST WINDOWS

Amaryllis	Coleus	Oxalis
Azalea	Cyclamen	Poinsettia
Begonia (in winter)	Easter lily	Rose
Bloodleaf	Gardenia	Sweetflag
Cacti and succulents	Geranium	Tulip
Calla lily	Lily	Velvet plant

NORTH WINDOW

African-violet	Dracaena	Philodendron
(in summer)	Dumbcane	Piggyback plant
Anthericum	Fern	Pleomele
Arrowhead	Ivy	Rubber plant
Australian umbrella tree	Mother-of-thousands	Scindapsus (Pothos)
Babytears	Norfolk Island pine	Snake plant
Cast-iron plant	Peperomia	Tuftroot
Chinese evergreen		Wandering-Jew

EAST WINDOW

African-violet	Gloxinia	Serissa
Banded maranta	Ivy	Silk-oak
Caladium	Peperomia	Tuftroot
Dracaena	Philodendron	Veitch screwpine
Fatshedera	Rubber plant	Wandering-Jew
Fern	Scindapsus (Pothos)	Wax Plant

They are carbon (C), hydrogen (H), oxygen (O), phosphorus (P), potassium (K), nitrogen (N), sulfur (S), calcium (Ca), iron (Fe), magnesium (Mg), chlorine (Cl), molybdenum (Mo), boron (B), copper (Cu), manganese (Mn), and zinc (Zn). If you want to memorize these elements, here's an easy way. Learn this sentence:

The mob comes in to see Cl. Hopkins, cafe manager.

MoB CuMn Zn C Cl HOPKNS CaFe Mg

These essential elements are present in the atmosphere or growing medium most of the time. For instance, carbon and oxygen are supplied as carbon dioxide (CO_2) from the air. Hydrogen enters the plant as water (H_2O).

The other 13 elements enter the plant through the roots, although some can be absorbed through the leaves. These 13 elements can be added to the growing medium as fertilizers (salts).

Phosphorus, sulfur, and calcium usually are applied prior to planting as 20 percent (single) superphosphate ($CaH_4(PO_4)_2$ and $CaSO_4$), calcium and sulfur as gypsum ($CaSO_4$), calcium as pulverized limestone ($CaCO_3$) and calcium and magnesium as dolomitic limestone ($CaMgCO_3$).

Iron, chlorine, molybdenum, boron, copper, manganese, and zinc are present in sufficient quantities in most soils to supply the needs of a container-grown plant for several months. However, the soilless media do require applications of these elements. Some of these elements are added as impurities in low analysis complete fertilizers such as 5–10–5 or 10–10–10. Some must be added as separate fertilizers.

Plants use more nitrogen and potassium than they do other elements, so these must be applied at more frequent intervals. Nitrogen and potassium can be applied prior to planting in organic fertilizer forms or as slow-release inorganic chemicals, or after planting in a quickly available dry or liquid form.

To maintain good fertility, you need to take into consideration the plant species and its stage of development, plant size, season of the year, the growing medium, and irrigation practices.

Small, slow growing, reproductive plants, seedlings, and most fine-rooted plants will require less fertilizer than large, rapidly growing, highly vegetative, coarse-rooted plants.

Fibrous-rooted begonias and wandering-Jew in a lamp post planter.

Three basic approaches are used for fertility control. These are: a standard fertilization program; chemical analysis of the growing medium and plant tissue; and visual appearance of the plant.

Fertilization programs may range from very dilute daily applications with each irrigation to yearly top dressing with low analysis (5–10–5) slow release or organic fertilizers. For example, you can fertilize potted chrysanthemums at every irrigation with 1 level teaspoon (3.8 grams) per gallon of water using a 20–20–20 fertilizer, or once every 3 months using 1 level tablespoon per 6-inch pot of a 14–14–14 slow-release fertilizer. Additional slowly soluble fertilizers and rates of application are

listed in the table on page 43. Many annuals require about one-half of these amounts; azaleas, begonias, and foliage plants need about one-fourth.

The home gardener will find that the following dry mixture is safe and easy to use on trees and shrubs grown in containers:

6 parts hoof and horn or bloodmeal
1 part ammonium nitrate
1 part treble superphosphate
1 part sulfate of potash
6 parts gypsum

Apply this mixture once monthly during the early part of the growing season at the rate of 1 level teaspoon per 4½-inch pot, 2 teaspoons per 6-inch pot, or 3 teaspoons per 7-inch pot. Narrow-leaved plants require less fertilizer than broad-leaved plants.

You should avoid midsummer applications because they encourage soft growth in late fall which winterkills easily. Some nurserymen recommend applications after leaf drop. At that time the tops are dormant, but the roots are still active and capable of absorbing nutrients which may be stored until needed for growth in the spring.

Variation in fertilization levels can be used to just maintain a plant with little or no growth, or to force a plant to grow rapidly. Large and frequent applications of nitrogen and water produce the most rapid growth. Reduction in amounts of nitrogen and water slow down the rate of growth. Use a 5–10–10 for maintenance, a 10–10–10 for moderate, and a 20–10–10 fertilizer for rapid plant growth.

Soil analysis programs are available in most States either through the county extension agent's office, the State university, or commercial laboratories. Tissue analysis programs are less widely available. All growing media should be tested prior to use each year, especially for pH and total soluble salts. Most laboratories also test for phosphorus, potassium, and calcium, and some for nitrogen and magnesium. Be sure to send in a sample representative of the total contents of the container and specify on the sample that recommendations should be made for container growing and not for growing in the ground.

Tissue samples are used primarily to help diagnose problems when the plants do not look healthy. Contact your local laboratories about sampling procedures.

Visual appearance of the plant can offer clues to the trained diagnostician when a plant is not healthy. However, a visual diagnosis can also be misleading since many different causes (insects, disease, air pollution) can produce similar effects.

Visual diagnosis should always be combined with soil and tissue analysis.

Many houseplants die while the owner is away from home on a vacation or business trip. The best way to prevent loss of plants while you're away is to get a friend to look in on them now and then and give them any care they need.

Watering plants during your vacation is not a difficult problem to solve. If you have time before leaving, decrease the frequency of watering for several weeks. By allowing plants to reach the wilting point several times, the need for water can be reduced. Plants will adjust to lower moisture levels without suffering permanent harm.

An alternative method is to water the plants thoroughly, seal them in clear polyethylene plastic bags, and place them in a cool location out of direct sunlight.

If your plants are in porous containers, stand them on clay bricks placed in a watertight container. Bring the water level up to the top of the bricks. Reduce the light intensity to decrease evaporation. Plants in porous containers can be taken outdoors and buried up to the rim in soil or saturated peat moss. A shady location is best.

Plants usually can get along satisfactorily by themselves for about 2 weeks. If you must be away for more than 2 weeks, reconcile yourself to loss of some of your plants. Flowering plants in particular are likely to die.

For further reading:
U.S. Department of Agriculture, *Selecting and Growing House Plants.* Home and Garden Bulletin 82, Washington, D.C. 20250, 1968.

landscaping limited areas
such as terraces, patios

ORNAMENTAL GARDENS have always been an important part of our American culture. Since the time of the first settlers, the character of the home landscape has gone through many changes from the dooryard garden of herbs and flowers to the intricate fussy details of the Victorian era and finally to the garden as an extension of the indoor living environment into outdoor space.

Now urban living with its high density housing and minimal outdoor space is creating another kind of change in garden style. This change brings a greater emphasis on intensive use of limited space. This kind of gardening can be the most exciting and the most enjoyable.

Not only has the landscape changed but people too have changed as a result of this life style. Today there is less concern with traditional garden designs of heavy flower and shrub massing. Instead the design must have dramatic visual appeal. One way to achieve this visual appeal is to use natural or man-made landscape elements to complement your plants.

Before discussing the various elements available for creating a landscape, let us first consider our basic goal—to create space for people and for people's activities. Each time trees, shrubs, fences, walls are placed on the land, space has been created. The size and visual quality of this space determines its success. Therefore, as you plan your landscape, think of it as if you are creating a room outdoors. This room, like a room in your house, must have a floor, walls, and a ceiling.

The floor is the stage upon which all of your activities are organized. This ground surface might be paved, covered with gravel or other loose aggregate, planted to ground cover or grass. Which of these elements to select depends upon the intended use of the area.

Walls of the room are created by vertical elements (trees, shrubs, fences, walls). Not only do they define the space but they also provide an enclosure for privacy that is essential for outdoor living. Human nature is such that many people are not comfortable pursuing outdoor activities if they feel they can be seen or watched by others. To effectively provide a privacy screen, the material used should be above eye level.

Even in situations where privacy is not a primary concern, enclosure elements are still important to give organization to the space. In this case height is not important. In fact the effect of enclosure can be achieved through using elements only 12 to 24 inches high. This is an implied enclosure rather than the complete enclosure you would have with the privacy screen.

The final unit of your outdoor room is the ceiling. Unlike the rooms of your home it does not have to be total and complete. The ceiling may be the canopy effect of the spreading branches of a tree combined with the sky, or it may be an overhead structure over the patio or terrace. The structure may have a solid roof for complete weather protection or be partially open or louvered for filtered light and shade. Most important, there should be a partial overhead definition combined with the sky. In either case the ceiling effect

------

Author WILLIAM R. NELSON, JR., is Extension Landscape Architect, University of Illinois, Urbana-Champaign.

should be sensed rather than seen. Therefore the design should be simple, not eye-catching or detailed.

For patios and limited space gardens, there are two primary types of space:
- Visual space—a landscape scene viewed from within or a landscape picture associated with a primary window. Visual space is created mainly through the use of plant material and it is not intended to accommodate outdoor living activities.
- Usable living space—designed for family use in entertaining, relaxation, or play. It, too, should be designed to be visually pleasing. However, it is composed of any of the landscape elements—natural or manmade—to assure that the design serves the family's interests.

Although not a part of this discussion, it should be understood that elements of both these types of space may be combined into a landscape composition. To successfully accomplish this, a larger area is required.

Both types of space are formed by using fences, walls, planting screens, trees, shrubs, flowers, ground covers, hard surfaced paving, loose aggregate surfacing, water features, portable or fixed planters, lighting, sculpture, and natural boulders. Not all of these elements can be used in any one design. Instead you should select those that will most effectively create the type of space and design you want.

Fences, walls, and planting screens not only define space but also provide privacy and screening where needed. For a landscape with limited space, fences and walls have greater value because they require a minimum of ground space to provide a 6-foot screen. To achieve the same effect with plants would require 4 to 6 feet of ground space to accommodate the mature spread of the plants.

Fences are easy to construct and they provide an immediate effect not possible with plants which often require 3 to 5 years to grow to the desired height. But don't feel compelled to surround your entire garden area with a fence.

This is monotonous and poor design. Instead, you should identify critical areas where screening or privacy are needed and then use sections or panels of the enclosure unit. These units can easily be tied together through the skillful use of flowering trees and shrubs.

You should avoid painting fences. The first stroke of a paint brush commits you to a high maintenance program that can be avoided by staining the fence instead. It's best to select neutral colors of stain that blend well with foliage colors. In this way the fence will blend with the rest of the elements and not dominate the scene.

Trees and shrubs are the bulk of the natural materials used in the landscape. Having a permanent woody structure and being vertical elements, they too create space. For this reason they must be selected on the basis of the function they will serve in this three-dimensional composition and not just because the plant is pretty.

Trees may be divided into two groups —the large shade tree and the smaller flowering types. In situations of limited size, it is unlikely that more than one large shade tree can be introduced into the design. At this point you must decide if a shade tree or an overhead structure is going to do the best job of providing shade and the ceiling to the space. You can choose from a great variety of trees. They vary in height, soil tolerance, hardiness, and rate of growth. Your county extension agent or nurseryman can assist you in making a selection suitable for your soil and climate.

Flowering trees are generally smaller, ranging from 8 feet to 35 feet. Many varieties in this group have not only showy flowers but also interesting fruit. They may be used by themselves or as part of a shrub border. Because of their smaller size, flowering trees are often planted in containers or planters. They are valuable for patios, terraces, and other small areas. Also, when combined with a fence or wall, the crown of the flowering tree added to the height of the fence adds considerably to the vertical

Walls, fountain, and paving make a setting for a low maintenance garden of rhododendrons and Ilex species with a ground cover of Baltic ivy.

screening in any areas where there are elevated views into your property.

Because of the wide variety of tree flower colors, be certain to select colors that will be harmonious both with other flowers blooming at the same time and with surrounding building colors.

Since shrubs bloom for only a short time, it is important to consider foliage, fruit, branching habits, and suitability for a specific location as well as their flowers. Because shrubs are smaller than trees, you can see them in much greater detail—hence the importance of other plant qualities besides flowers. In small gardens, avoid using too many different kinds. Your design will have a strong unity and be visually more appealing if you limit the number of varieties.

One type of plant that has particular value for the small-scaled landscape is called a specimen, which is a plant that is unique in form, color, or texture, or any combination of these three elements. When used by itself, either in a planter or in the ground, it becomes a dramatic unit with great dominance and visual appeal. Only one specimen plant should be used in a composition. Using

51

two or more is distracting and it diminishes the dramatic effect.

Flowers are not a permanent landscape element. Since they dieback to the ground during dormant seasons, they do not offer year-round structure or form to the landscape. Therefore, flowers should be considered as an accessory or embellishment. Flowers are classified as annuals and perennials. Annuals must be replanted each year whereas perennials, although they dieback to the ground each winter, do live for many seasons without replanting. In small areas, the annuals offer the most spectacular color and showiness. To be most effective they should have a background against which to be viewed.

Keep flower plantings simple. Plant flowers in masses and do not use too many different kinds or too many different colors. As a rule of thumb, small flower planting areas should include only one flower variety and all one color. When selecting your flowers, remember that most types require full sunlight. If yours is a shady situation, there are several types from which to choose. Consult your nurseryman or garden center.

Until now, consideration has been given only to the vertical landscape elements, but it is also important to consider what you will put on the floor of your landscape. In this case, the criteria for selection are based upon the intended use of the area. If the area must support heavy traffic or is an activity center such as a patio or terrace then a permanent, hard-surfaced material should be used. You may choose from concrete, brick, slate, flagstone, or wood.

Walks should be at least 4 feet wide so two people can walk side by side. The terrace or patio area should be at least 400 square feet. This will provide sufficient room for garden furniture and still leave space to move around.

Design of the terrace or patio should be carefully studied to develop a strong pattern. There are many possible shapes besides the typical square or rectangle. You may wish to consider a broad arc combined with straight (diagonal, horizontal, or vertical) lines or a straight-line design set on a 45° angle from the building. Rectangular and square areas can be made more interesting by using 2 by 4 wood divider strips to develop a modular pattern of 4- or 5-foot squares across the surface. Lawn or loose aggregates work well in areas with little or no traffic. If you use a loose aggregate for paths or walks, select a rounded rock of ¼- to ¾-inch screen size. Do not use pea gravel. It sticks to shoes and makes footing difficult. Loose aggregates such as gravel can also be used as a mulch in planting areas.

Ground cover plants do not tolerate any foot traffic, hence their use is restricted to planting bed areas. This group of plants offers a wide choice in texture and in height—from 6 inches to 18 inches. Some thrive very well in deep shade while others tolerate a hot, dry location. Be sure to select the right one for your situation. Ornamental ground covers are discussed elsewhere in this book.

In patio gardens and landscapes for limited space, special features such as water, planters, night lighting, and sculpture can enhance space whether it is visual space designed for window viewing or actually usable space.

Because the areas being discussed are assumed to be small in scale, the use of water must be controlled and obviously man designed. To try to introduce a babbling brook or a natural waterfall would be inappropriate and out of place. Your water design should have classic simplicity without superfluous decoration. The basic pattern may be straight lined or curved. In the latter case plan the design to be a "stylized" use of natural curves and not an attempt to copy nature.

The sound of water is very pleasant and has a psychological cooling effect. Sound may be achieved through the use of jets, bubblers, or sprays. If the area is breezy, the bubbler is better than the jets or sprays. Fine sprays can be carried some distance in a high breeze. Sound can also be introduced by having water fall from a higher basin into a lower one.

Water is also very effective for its reflective quality. To make the best use of reflection in water, paint the basin black. This will enhance the mirror-like qualities. Do not use jets or bubblers.

A great variety of planters is available for home use. Once filled with soil, a large planter is difficult to move. So study carefully where you need your planter for maximum effects, move it there, then fill it with soil.

Planters are available in concrete, fiber glass, and asbestos–concrete. Select them on the basis of their design and the soil volume in relation to the size plant you intend to use. If you have in mind a large shrub or small tree, a large volume of soil will be needed. Also keep in mind that it is important to select plants that are in good proportion and scale relationship with the planter. For example, a large, tall planter with only petunias in it lacks a good proportion and good scale relationship. It looks out of place.

In areas where cold winters may damage any permanent plantings, it's a good idea to line the inside of the planter with styrofoam sheets. This will reduce the effects of freezing and thawing.

Night lighting is no longer a costly or difficult project. New plastic insulated cable may be buried directly in the soil without using conduit. Conduit is required only where it comes out of the ground to attach to your fixture.

You can choose from a number of different light fixtures. Each is designed to achieve different effects. Consult your local power company or a local lighting store to determine which would be most appropriate.

Outdoor lighting can be used for three different purposes: to floodlight large areas; to spotlight specific features; and to illuminate areas softly by underlighting (directing the light upward into the plant or tree) to emphasize structure, form, and foliage. For small areas the last function fits best. However, there may be other features, sculpture, for example, that you may wish to spotlight.

Sculpture, murals or mosaics, and even boulders can enhance your design. These elements should be selected for form, color, texture, and interesting detail. Seldom can you ever use more than one of these elements effectively. To use more could clutter your design and result in visual confusion.

Selecting sculpture is a very personal thing. By including such an element you are creating an atmosphere expressing your tastes. For best results, you should carefully consider the scale of the piece. Small units usually need a plain, but complementary, base to elevate them to a level where the eye can appreciate the design. Usually sculpture is best set against a foliage or structural backdrop to show it to best advantage.

If you use large boulders, select specimens with unusual form, texture, and color. Place them carefully to show off their interesting qualities. This type of natural material can be most handsome. Boulders should look as if they logically belong where they are, not like they just fell out of the sky.

Successful landscape planning involves three considerations. First, consider your needs and determine how you plan to use the landscape. Second, carefully study your site for orientation, climatic factors, topography, and existing features. And finally, develop a scale drawing of the area you are going to develop.

Your family is the most important consideration in planning your landscape. Make a list of your family's needs. This will tell you which of the two types of spaces mentioned earlier will be most appropriate—a landscape scene or usable living space.

A list of family interests may help you to organize your thinking. Do you wish to extend your living activities into the outdoor area? Are there family hobbies which could be furthered by this development? Do you enjoy gardening or would you prefer a low maintenance design? How frequently do you entertain? Are the groups large or small? How often does your family cook out? Do family members enjoy sitting and relaxing outdoors? Do you wish to attract birds? Is there a need for space to store equipment?

A list, such as this, of your wants and needs will be most helpful in fashioning your final plan. It is the first and most important step to beginning your landscape, whatever the size.

Next, you need to carefully analyze your site because the character of the land, the climate, and the surrounding properties will determine the basic design and what landscape elements you should use.

Your design will be influenced by the property and its orientation to wind and sun. You should consider plantings or vertical structures that will give protection from the summer sun and also allow warmth from the winter sun, wind barriers to reduce the wind, and slopes to carry rain and melted snow from the house and the garden structures.

Identify sunny and shaded areas. You can then select plants that survive in either type of exposure. Find the average low winter temperature. Then you will know whether a plant will grow in your area. Hardiness is the word used to express a plant's tolerance to temperatures and climates. Your Cooperative Extension agent can tell you what plants are hardy in your climatic zone.

In your analysis, note the best natural resources of the site. Are there very good trees or interesting changes in grade? Carefully study good as well as bad views. Keep attractive views open. Screen out unattractive and objectionable views either by structures or by proper plantings. At the same time consider screening for privacy from your neighbors. One consideration is the height of surrounding land and buildings. You can screen by fencing and by skillful placement of shrubs and trees.

Finally, you will need to know the relative acidity or alkalinity, texture, humus content, and drainage of the soil. Soils that are extremely acid or alkaline restrict plant growth. A very heavy clay soil will drain poorly and keep needed air from the plant roots.

For easy maintenance, it is best to choose plants that will tolerate your particular soil condition.

With your list of family needs and your analysis of the site done, you are now ready to draw to scale a plan of the area. In a scaled drawing a fraction of an inch equals 1 foot. For example, ⅛ inch on paper is used to represent 1 foot on the ground; this is called a one-eighth inch scale.

To obtain the measurements for your scaled drawing you will have to make your outdoor measurements with a steel tape. First draw a rough sketch of the area and of the shape of the house on a sheet of paper. Allow enough space to jot down the measurements as you make them. Locate the position of the building in relation to the property boundaries and measure tree, walk, drive, sewer line, water line locations. Note also the location of power and telephone service, whether it's overhead or underground.

After locating all important features (don't forget windows and doors), you are ready to transfer this information to your base plan. A scale of ⅛ or ¼ inch equal to one foot will allow you to use a standard ruler. If you wish you may draw this to scale on graph paper. You can buy graph paper with various grid scales (1/16, ⅛, ¼) at most stationery and book stores.

You are now ready to start developing your design. The scale drawing will help you to visualize the space relationships and work out design patterns. It is amazing how mistakes and ideas will develop and show up on a plan. The more accurate you are, the more effective your plan will be. By fastening a sheet of tracing paper over your basic plan, you can try out various arrangements.

The first step in sketching out your design is to establish a basic ground pattern. There are no rules for developing a pattern. This is a personal thing. A rough guide is that lines near the building should follow the same regular pattern but as the pattern moves from the building it can become looser, more flowing and more informal.

Remember it is the shapes developed between the lines which are important —not the lines themselves.

Your final scale design will take the guesswork out of the project. And it will suggest to you additional landscape elements to combine with those previously selected. With this approach you have the blueprint for an organized, well designed landscape whether you complete it in planned stages or all at once.

plantings for the homeowner: down to earth advice

IN 1954, when I first came to Phoenix, Ariz., a total landscape project for the average home in this area consisted of the yard being bermed, or diked, for flood irrigation (a peculiarity of desert areas), a bermuda lawn seeded and topped with steer manure, and "FHA minimum" planting. This consisted of 15 small plants, six larger plants, and three small trees.

During 1972, only the tract homes are likely to get by with this formula. Many homeowners would not be caught dead without extensive landscaping, sprinkler-irrigation systems, and even swimming pools.

Naturally many expert "designers" have shown up during this evolution of landscaping, glibly selling the homeowner all sorts of fantastic plans. The homeowner is left unhappy, dissatisfied, and uncertain as to the reason.

Dissatisfaction can usually be traced to a nerve-jarring design in the yard, or poor selection of plant material, or both.

What can you do to save yourself from winding up in the same fix?

First, remember that good landscaping is mainly applying good common sense.

If you will sit down and determine the uses to which various areas around the home will be put, these uses will not only determine the sizes of the areas involved and the traffic patterns needed to serve them, but also dictate part of the yard design.

How does this relate to plantings?

Plants are used for several things:
• To define activity areas.
• To delineate traffic patterns.
• To screen or protect.
• To shade.
• To enhance.
I will come back to these items later.

Second, familiarize yourself with the plant material that does well in your area. I did say *does well*. If you want your project to be relatively free from failure, stay away from borderline plant material and exotics. The plantings in your yard are supposed to improve each year, not die out!

Wherever you live, plant material is divided roughly into these groupings:
• Conifers (spiny evergreens with cones)
• Broadleaf evergreens
• Deciduous (lose their leaves in winter)
Next, you have to know the various uses for plants, in some detail. Let's take them up one by one.

To define activity areas. Complete screening of such areas can be done by use of tall bushes, whether conifers, broadleafs, or deciduous. Deciduous screening can be used if you want to "open up" an activity area in the winter but screen it in the summer—a badminton court, for example. In the winter when badminton is impractical,

Author F. J. MACDONALD is Executive Vice President of the American Institute of Landscape Architects, with headquarters at Phoenix, Ariz.

EVERGREEN

CONIFERS

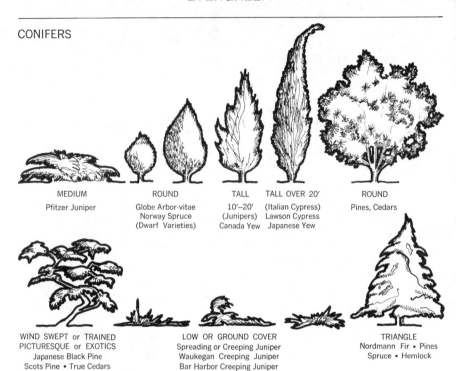

MEDIUM	ROUND	TALL	TALL OVER 20'	ROUND
Pfitzer Juniper	Globe Arbor-vitae Norway Spruce (Dwarf Varieties)	10'–20' (Junipers) Canada Yew	(Italian Cypress) Lawson Cypress Japanese Yew	Pines, Cedars

WIND SWEPT or TRAINED PICTURESQUE or EXOTICS Japanese Black Pine Scots Pine • True Cedars Eastern White Pine	LOW OR GROUND COVER Spreading or Creeping Juniper Waukegan Creeping Juniper Bar Harbor Creeping Juniper	TRIANGLE Nordmann Fir • Pines Spruce • Hemlock

BROADLEAF EVERGREENS

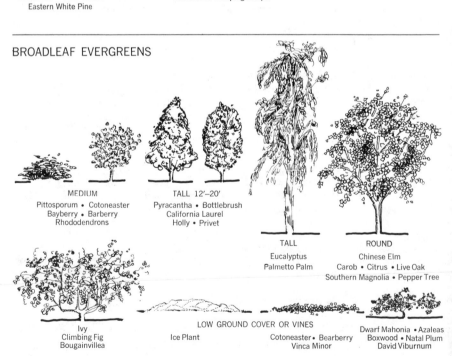

MEDIUM	TALL 12'–20'
Pittosporum • Cotoneaster Bayberry • Barberry Rhododendrons	Pyracantha • Bottlebrush California Laurel Holly • Privet

TALL	ROUND
Eucalyptus Palmetto Palm	Chinese Elm Carob • Citrus • Live Oak Southern Magnolia • Pepper Tree

Ivy Climbing Fig Bougainvillea	LOW GROUND COVER OR VINES		Dwarf Mahonia • Azaleas Boxwood • Natal Plum David Viburnum
	Ice Plant	Cotoneaster • Bearberry Vinca Minor	

56

DECIDUOUS

TREES

ROUND—GLOBE—SHAPED
Arnold Crabapple • Japanese Maple
Mulberry • Green Ash • Pistachio
Hawthorne Sycamore

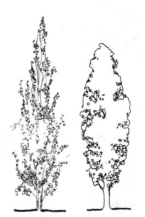

FASTIGIATE TREE OR COLUMNAR TREE
Dawyck Beech • Siberian Crabapple
English Oak • Poplar • Sargent Cherry
Sentry Ginkgo • Lombardy Poplar
Pyramidal European Birch
Linden

BROAD OVAL TREE
Bradford Pear
Sugar Maple • Labarnum
European Mountain Ash

FAN SHAPED—HORIZONTAL BRANCHING
Flowering Dogwood
Silk Tree • Redbud
Amur Maple

CONICAL TREE OR TRIANGLE
American Sweetgum
Pin Oak

SHRUBS

LOW 1½'–5'
February Daphne • Bush Cinquefoil
Anthony Waterer Spirea
Japanese Barberry

MEDIUM 5'–12'
Snowball • Forsythia • English Privet

TALL 12'–18'
Crapemyrtle • Spindle Tree
Russian Olive • Lilac

LOW, GROUND COVER OR VINES

Prostrate Pyracantha

Lantana

GROUND COVER 6"–18"
Cranberry Cotoneaster
Carpet Bugle • Memorial Rose
Aaronsbeard St. Johnswort

VINES
Wisteria • Passionflower • Bittersweet
Virginia Creeper • Clematis • Grapes

Azaleas used as foundation plantings next to a house, and as accent plantings on the lawn.

the yard will look much larger if all of it can be seen through the bare branches.

An optical or psychological screening of the same area can be done with the use of medium bushes—those that mature at about 3 feet in height. This will provide the feeling of a screen without obstructing vision to any extent. In addition, objects between the eye and the far boundary of a yard tend to make the yard look larger. The momentary interruption in the line of sight gives a much deeper feeling to the picture.

An even more subtle definition of activity areas can be accomplished with the use of low beds of ground cover plants, just to give an indication of a boundary.

To delineate traffic patterns. The same rules apply here as in screening activity areas except that, in many cases, you want paths, walkways, or drives to be seen: high plants would hide them. You should do much of the traffic delineation with very low plants —or none at all. Often an attractive walk or an interesting pattern of stepping stones is the most effective and

attractive way to carry out the traffic pattern.

To screen or protect. Here you are primarily interested in screening the yard from the various pollutions that have become so apparent during the past few years—noise pollution, dust pollution, visual pollution. If the yard is adjacent to anything unpleasant, you can use tall shrubs or small trees to form a barrier. Shrubs effectively cut down on noise as well as dust.

One other important barrier that can be helpful is a windbreak. You can use these same tall bushes and short trees to block off the prevailing wind in order to make your yard more livable. Keep in mind, however, that only evergreen plants are effective during the entire year. In many cases a screen or hedge of plants is preferred to a wall or solid fence, since the plants allow some air movement and do not reflect the sun's glare.

To shade. Most plants produce shade in varying amounts. If you want to reduce your electric bill, heavy shade on the house during the summer will show up as substantial savings. But the more subtle use of shade is accomplished through judicious placing of deciduous and evergreen trees in the same yard.

For example, a patio on the south or west side of a house will reflect heat and sunlight toward the house and increase the cost of cooling. However, this patio planted with an umbrella of deciduous trees will remain cool and shady all summer and help keep the house cool. Comes winter when the trees shed their leaves, the opening up of the patio to the warm winter sun will brighten the house and make the patio warmer for recreational purposes.

Just one other thing about trees and shade. If you really want significant results, both from a shade standpoint and an esthetic viewpoint, plant the trees *close* to the house. This means within 6 to 8 feet. Trees have a tendency to lean away from objects nearby; so the trunks will eventually have a small curve to them and the house will give the effect of being nestled between the trees.

Not all shade is accomplished with trees. Bushes can be trained to form a canopy and vines will climb trellises and pergolas. Palm trees give much more shade than one would imagine, but the eventual height of the trunk often puts the shade over in the neighbor's yard. This may be good public relations, but doesn't really save much on the electric bill.

One last word of caution concerning shade: Not all plants take sun and shade equally well. This applies also to grasses. So don't expect an evenly textured result from sunlight to shadow, even though you use the same plant variety throughout.

To enhance. This is the real problem, and should be attacked only after full consideration of the other four uses of plants have been thoroughly developed. Many times you see a plant of particular beauty and immediately want it in your yard, whether it belongs there or not. Also, it is difficult to believe that an exotic plant placed in your yard

will not look as breathtaking as the one in *Better Homes and Gardens* or *Sunset Magazine.*

The desire for the unusual and the beautiful is probably one of the great factors causing unbalanced (even downright weird) yards. Many such yards are a collection of struggling exotics, trying for survival, and existing in spite of numerous moves from place to place. (Many ladies do not fully realize that, unlike furniture, plants cannot be rearranged whenever the mood hits one!)

If you want your yard to be comfortable, as well as beautiful, you need to carefully limit plant selection to the few varieties that accomplish your main objectives. Then if you want to make a "splash," you can group the "iffy" exotics off to one side, discreetly screened, so that their struggle will not be witnessed by the entire world. Likewise, vegetable gardens, flower gardens, and roses should be kept behind the house so that their seasonal changes

SOLID SCREENING—TALL PLANTS

PARTIAL SCREENING—MEDIUM PLANTS

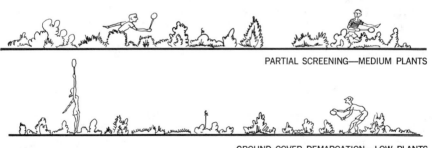

GROUND COVER DEMARCATION—LOW PLANTS

LOW SHRUBS

PATH OR WALK

STEPPING STONES

PLAN VIEW PATH, WALK OR STEPPING STONES

will not impair one's standing with the neighbors.

To do a complete job of planting around your home, you will have to design your front yard like the rear yard: Establish use areas, traffic patterns and views—and then accent these features.

Esthetically, you may find it easier to landscape in the front of the house. You can stand back and look at bare walls and decide if you want a vine or a bush in front of it. You can determine if you want a "woodsy" or "mountain" feeling—and use boulders and coniferous evergreens. Or you can achieve a more tropical feeling with the use of the large-leafed broadleaf evergreens.

Normally you wouldn't want too much deciduous material in front of the house, since these plants are completely bare for several months during the winter.

But, to get down to specifics, you need to apply what you know about plants toward the uses that they are best suited for, and work out a planting plan.

Let's play with a yard! We will make it 70 feet by 120 feet, an arbitrary city or suburban lot somewhere. Let's crowd the backyard full of activities and direct the front yard toward friends and neighbors.

In the backyard you will have badminton, horseshoes, a barbecue, a quiet area for reading, a patio for entertaining and—why not?—a swimming pool. (If you change your mind about the pool, you can convert this area to a lawn.)

Put the patio and barbecue right off the kitchen for convenience of food service, with the pool just beyond to keep swimmers within sight of the kitchen window.

Put the badminton far over to one side to keep the players from falling into the pool. Keep it to the rear of the lot to hold the noise level down. Horseshoes are tucked over against the fence to reduce the danger of an innocent swimmer being hit with a flying shoe.

'Way down in the corner, out of the way, put a little secluded quiet area.

These activities will generate traffic patterns which determine some of the lines and plantings.

Now the skeleton plan is taking on shape. You may want to change it later, but at least you have an idea of how things *could* be done.

In adding your plantings keep in mind that:

- The badminton court should be screened off. Since it's a small yard, a medium height screen will do the job.
- The quiet area should be screened for privacy and shaded from the sun.
- The pool should be sunny.
- The path needs more definition.
- The patio could use some summer shade, but away from the pool. You don't want to have to fish leaves out of the pool.
- The view from the family room could stand some help.

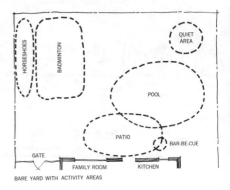
BARE YARD WITH ACTIVITY AREAS

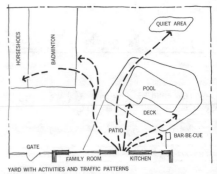
YARD WITH ACTIVITIES AND TRAFFIC PATTERNS

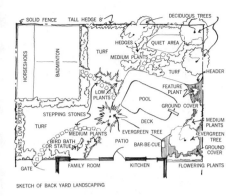

SKETCH OF BACK YARD LANDSCAPING

So let's draw up a sketch with plantings in it.

Perhaps you do not want your backyard to be this elaborate or busy. It is simple to eliminate unwanted items or make substitutions. For instance, if you don't care for badminton, you might want a vegetable and flower garden there. The pool could be eliminated and turf substituted. Stepping stones could be walks of concrete or brick.

All I am trying to do is develop a line of thought for locating your plantings, and have some sort of a reason for them being there.

How about that front yard? What will you use it for?

• An entrance to the house.
• An esthetic setting for the house.
• To complement the yards of your neighbors.

All these add up to a certain status symbol, whether you like it or not. In fact, the lack of a respectable-looking front yard may demote you to a lower status.

So let's sketch a front yard.

We will shade the front of the house, screen the dining room window, and develop a walk and some sort of a feature for the neighbors' edification.

We have used "headers" or "edgers" or "mowing strips" to delineate the lawn area. This helps in mowing as it eliminates many small corners and hard-to-mow areas, while establishing strong esthetic lines to the design. Unless a fence extends between your yard and the neighbors' yards out front, you should try not to delineate the front

yard borders with plants. In this way you can utilize, visually, some of the adjoining yards and make your own yard appear larger.

Again, these are only suggestions, but it certainly didn't take too long to lay out a front yard, did it? Or backyard either, for that matter.

If you can decide where the plants are going to be, and what they are to do, you can easily decide which plants to use.

Pick out a theme—a feeling—a motif. Do you want the front of the house to be northern mountains? Then go to your list of evergreen conifers, junipers and the like, and simply put them in the design where they fit the need.

Would you rather have a tropical effect? Use the broadleaf evergreens.

Or perhaps you like drastic seasonal change and would prefer to have the branches bare and laden with snow in winter. Then deciduous material is for you.

You can mix these very nicely, too. Just remember, at the same time, that each one has a job to fulfill.

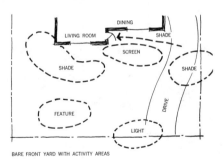

BARE FRONT YARD WITH ACTIVITY AREAS

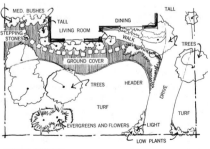

COMPLETED FRONT YARD

Incidentally, no one, but *no one* in the warmer sections of Arizona would landscape with deciduous material. Why man, all the friends and relatives (affectionately called "snowbirds") descend for the winter—and that's when the yard must look its best!

Then the backyard: it doesn't have to match the front, you know. All the front and back yards have to do is tie in at the sides of the house. So again you have to determine your motif for the backyard.

Just as the architecture and appearance of the front of the house will influence your choice of plants there, the decor of the family room, carried out onto the patio, will affect what you plant in the backyard.

Other than that, you are as free as a bird to establish any feeling you desire with your backyard plants. Keep in mind that each has a job to do.

I have not given you long lists of plants to work with. Geological and climatic conditions will govern plant selection wherever you live. So why try to second-guess the local nurseryman? He knows what will grow, and so will you when you look around the neighborhood and find out firsthand.

I have tried to give you general plant groups to choose from to accomplish desired results. This also gives you a very wide range from which to choose.

It really all boils down to this:
- Take your time.
- Decide what you want to do.
- Choose your material carefully.
- Use good common sense.

I should finish with this: Have fun!

For further reading:

U.S. Department of Agriculture, *Home Planting by Design*. Home and Garden Bulletin 164, Washington, D.C. 20250, 1969.

——————, *Gardening on the Contour*. Home and Garden Bulletin 179, Washington, D.C. 20250, 1970.

 # structures and equipment— from gazebo to barbecue

THERE ARE A GREAT MANY structures, equipment and garden designs to consider in landscaping your garden. Additional information on how to build these projects can be obtained from your library, book store, or retail lumber dealer. You should develop and draw up a master plan so that each project will be properly located and completed in the right sequence.

If you are handy with tools and want a garden of "your own design," then follow the principles of design and construction that are described, but add your own ideas. You may make a single structure do two or three things with a little imagination. For example, a gazebo can double as a children's playhouse during the day or it can be divided and partially enclosed to use for a tool shed, a potting shed, a bathhouse, or all of these at the same time. You can cover it with plastic or glass panels during the winter and spring to create a greenhouse to start garden plants early.

Therefore, as you read about the following structures and equipment, keep in mind how you want them to look and function because your garden should be your own creation for you and your friends to enjoy. It is your "heaven-on-earth", so take time to design and construct it right.

You may want to hire a consultant before starting construction. Consultants can save you much grief and expense by pointing out a hazardous or poorly designed garden or garden structure. In other words, a consultant lets you profit from other gardeners' experiences since one of his functions is to help you avoid pitfalls.

Now let's take a look at the various projects you can build or add to your garden. You might want to add one of these each year to enjoy the feeling of accomplishment, or you may wish to complete your whole plan at once.

Patios, terraces, and decks all have one thing in common—they are extensions of your living area to the outdoors. Their level areas may equal or exceed the size of your whole house. They are used as a house substitute in fair weather, especially for the kitchen, dining, and living areas. Generally they are located toward the rear of the house to insure some privacy and less street noise. They should be placed with the sun and prevailing winds in mind.

Depending on local weather conditions, you may want the patio to be in the sun or in the shade. You will probably want some shade in the latter part of the day when the hot temperature becomes uncomfortable.

The surface of the patio should be sloped away from the house or to a drain to keep water from flooding or seeping through basement walls. The patio surface should also be 6 or 8 inches below the level of the floor of the house.

Patios, terraces, and decks can be made from any of the present day construction materials that are weather proof or at least weather resistant. But regardless of the type of construction, a good foundation and subsurface that meet the local building codes are necessary to insure a long, serviceable life for your finished project. Provide

---

Author WILLIAM A. BAILEY is an Agricultural Engineer and Investigations Leader with the Livestock Engineering and Farm Structures Research Branch, Agricultural Engineering Research Division, Agricultural Research Service.

Coauthor HERSCHEL H. KLUETER is an Agricultural Engineer and Project Leader with the Farm Electrification Research Branch, Agricultural Engineering Research Division.

expansion joints where needed. Remember, temperature change, frost, and water can crumble a poorly designed patio in a few years.

The top surface can be made from wood boards or blocks, poured concrete, brick, concrete block, or patio or flag stones. The last three can be set in sand with an open space between each edge, or they can be set with mortar. Several patterns have been used for brick or block, such as herringbone, the basket weave, concentric squares, and flowing curves. There are several variations or combinations of the standard patterns and colors that can be employed to make your deck distinctive.

During warmer months of the year you may want a sunbreaker roof over your patio. Some gardeners combine a lath house and patio cover in one structure so that the shade-loving plants can be used to decorate the patio. Clear plastic film may be used over the top to shed rain when entertaining guests. In the winter, plastic covered panels can be added around the edge to enclose the patio to make a sun porch or temporary greenhouse.

Lawn and garden furniture should be spacious, rugged, and weather resistant. This furniture will last several seasons if properly constructed and cared for. It can be constructed in your workshop or purchased from the outdoor and garden center in your local store. However, you will take greater pride in using or displaying a piece of furniture that you have made with your own hands. You can add your own design by placing hinges, pins, or bolts in the right places for quick setting up or knocking down for storage. You can add wheels for easy movement to a sunny or shady spot.

Outdoor furniture plans may be obtained from books, magazines, State universities, lumber associations, and your own neighborhood lumberyard. The most popular construction material is wood, but you may want to use stone or concrete for some permanent items such as seats or tables. I prefer to keep my own furniture light

A well-equipped patio and lawn area.

enough to move around, since the garden is constantly changing as trees and shrubs grow.

The combination of increased leisure time and readily available gas or charcoal barbecue pits at reasonable prices makes outdoor or backyard cooking popular and fun. Just as the wife claims the kitchen as her domain, the husband claims the outdoor cooking area. It is easy to prepare meat, potatoes, and salads outdoors for family use or for your guests. A spacious patio and garden area provide a pleasant setting for entertaining either a few friends or a large group.

Three areas are required for an outdoor meal: cooking, serving, and eating areas. For a small group, a picnic table can be a combined serving and eating area. But the larger groups are handled better if the food is served in a central spot near the cooking area and then eaten in small groups elsewhere. The cooking area can include a preparation and washup site, but these chores are often taken care of in the regular kitchen.

Cooking equipment can be portable or permanently installed. The portable equipment is normally large enough to cook six to 10 steaks at one time. A brick barbecue center can be as small or large as desired. You may want a small grille for family cooking and a larger grille for entertaining. You may also want to include a warming oven and a smoking chamber in your design.

Consider where the smoke from your cooking area will go. Neither your guests nor your neighbors will appreciate having a smoke screen unless the mosquitoes are biting.

An important aspect of outdoor living is lighting. You would not think of building a home without careful consideration of lighting. The same holds true for lighting the outdoors. Whether you are building a new home or relandscaping an older one, lighting should be part of the master plan.

Lighting can be strictly functional, such as illuminating drives and walks, locating steps or landings, or for protection against unwanted visitors. It may be used to enhance outdoor living by providing light for parties, gardening, and sports activities. It may also add esthetic value by highlighting plants or areas of special beauty.

64

A wide variety of fixtures is available for all the purposes of outdoor lighting. Use the proper fixture and locate it in the least conspicuous manner. Lights should be placed so they illuminate the desired area and do not shine into the eyes of the observer or the neighbors.

You may wish to experiment with different lighting schemes sometime after dark to obtain the desired effect. Once this is done, the main lighting should be permanently installed, using buried 3-wire grounded cable and outdoor weatherproof fixtures. Additional weatherproof convenient outlets should also be installed at critical locations for special occasions. Check with your electric power supplier and a local electrical contractor, so that all electrical codes and safe practices are followed. For additional safety, low voltage lighting systems are available.

One of the easiest and most important garden structures to construct is the walk. Walks permanently divide the garden into individual areas and act as guides or roadways to your garden. Walks can be bold borders or inconspicuous or hidden paths to secluded garden sanctuaries.

Walks, like patios, can be constructed out of any durable building material which will hold up under temperature, moisture, and freezing stresses. Most walks are rather permanent, but flagstones can be easily moved to take out an old path or make a new one.

When laying out your garden plan, be careful to keep walks out of the lowest spots because nobody, excepting the preschool child, likes to splash through water. The walk should be built on a well-drained foundation of sand or concrete so neither soft mud nor upheaving frost can destroy your creation.

There are numerous standard patterns for designing your walk or you may want to create your own surface design. If you use standard brick, the end, edge, or side can be used for the top surface. By orienting any of these three shapes, parallel, perpendicular, or at some angle to the edge of the walk, you can create a large number of walk designs. Be sure to leave expansion room around each piece of material used. Mortar can be used to set the surface permanently and to eliminate water from the soil beneath the walk.

Care should be taken to allow good drainage for the whole garden. It may be desirable to provide an arched footbridge over a low area or a running stream. Several rustic bridge designs can be used. Some have wide banisters for sitting and viewing.

Most backyard gardens do not have natural running streams, but with the availability of plastic ground liners and submergible electric water pumps it is now possible for even the smallest gardens to have fish or reflecting pools, and running streams or waterfalls. You may want to have a spray fountain in your pool or in one corner of your garden.

Your local garden supply center or mail order catalog will display several kits or complete systems for using water to make your garden more enjoyable. Internal or external lights may be used to make your water display enjoyable after dark.

Of course the most enjoyable water project, especially in hot weather, is a swimming pool. Pools can be shaped and located to fit into your garden plans, so make your pool fit your plans for outdoor enjoyment and entertainment. Do not build a square pool and then try to landscape around it and force your patio and outdoor cooking area into an ugly design. A little pre-planning can fit everything you desire into a beautiful backyard garden.

The garden structure that fails most often and creates a dangerous situation when it does so is the garden wall. Whether it is a retaining wall or a free-standing wall, an adequate foundation below the frost line is necessary. If soil is placed against one side, then weep holes or tile drains are necessary. Otherwise, after a heavy rain or spring thaw, water pressure will cause the wall to collapse explosively. More than one person has been hurt when such a collapse trapped him.

Retaining walls may be covered by local building codes, and therefore you may need to file a blueprint with your local building inspector's office when obtaining a building permit. An inspector will probably keep watch over your construction. His purpose is to stop you from building a public hazard.

Before erecting a wall on or near your property line, be sure you know where your line is to insure that you do not encroach upon the neighboring property. Such an encroachment could cause a lawsuit or other unpleasantness and expense.

Like patios and walks, a wall can be built from a wide selection of materials, ranging from wood to stone. A large number of patterns is possible. Some are open to allow free airflow, while others are solid so as to insure privacy.

Walls were originally built to keep one's enemies away, but today they are used to separate one yard from another or to hide the home service areas. Inside the garden, walls may be built as a line of demarcation between two garden areas or as a backdrop.

The modern replacement for the bulky wall is a fence. Most homeowners install a fence around the edges of their property, but a fence can be much more than a boundary structure. It can be built from wire, wood boards or rails, plastic, glass, or fiber glass. It can be used as a decorative screen or backdrop, privacy screen, see-through screen for viewing, or as a solid wall to eliminate the view of a storage or service area such as around garbage cans.

Often the fence is an essential vertical element in the garden landscape just as trees and other ornamental plants are. Fences may be covered or screened by plants or vines. A fence may be a temporary screen until the tree or bush grows into a natural screen. The character of a fence can be changed more with planting arrangements than by construction.

The trellis is often used to substitute for a fence in the garden. A trellis is not a jungle gym, but it will be used for one by most young children. Make it strong enough to safely support a climbing child along with your climbing vines. Some gardeners cover a trellis with thorny vines to discourage adventurous children.

Trellises may be built from wood, metal, wire mesh, or some combination of these. If they are covered with annuals such as morning-glories, they can be repaired and repainted during the winter season. If you plan on this type of maintenance, design the trellises small enough to go through your workshop door and fit into the shop area.

With the urban areas expanding into the countryside, our wildlife friends are finding it more and more difficult to find natural food and family rearing areas. Each gardener who appreciates a colorful bird and its song or a squirrel's cavorting should build a feeding and watering station into his garden. Your wildlife neighbors can drink from a stream, waterfall, or pool if available. Animals cannot live long without water, especially during hot weather.

Feeders and nests can be purchased or built in your workshop. Each type of bird or animal requires a different house and feeder design. If you only want one type of wild native bird, then only supply feed and housing for that type. Birds will benefit your garden by eating large quantities of insects and worms.

For the best winter or summer viewing, place your feeders so that the wildlife can be seen through a kitchen or living room window.

Some gardeners in the warmer climates will want to build a screened-in aviary to raise canaries or other singing or colorful birds. If the wire is painted black, you can view your friends without being blinded from reflected light.

If you live in a low rainfall area, you will probably have to irrigate your grass, plants, shrubs, and trees on a regular basis. An automatic watering system that is controlled by a time-clock will water each plant according to your preset program. A soil moisture sensor can be used to lock out the irrigation whenever rainfall soaks the ground.

Gardens may be watered by flooding, sprinkling, subirrigation, soaker hose, or by individual tubes run to each plant.

Recently a plastic drip irrigator developed in Israel and based on a spiral metering design used to control refrigerant has shown great promise. It is economical and splices into a plastic water pipe. It can be adjusted for any flow desirable, and a small feeder tube can run to the base of each plant. The supply hose may be placed throughout the garden, either on the surface or underground. The water is turned on and left on for the whole dry season. Adjustments can be made on individual meters to increase or decrease the water flow.

Automatic watering will certainly help maintain your garden and yard plants in the best of condition whether you are at home or on a trip.

Optimum watering automatically increases the need for good drainage so that wet spots do not develop and drown your plants. Plant roots need oxygen just like people do, so be sure the soil is well drained.

Water-soluble fertilizer can be added to your irrigation water, but extra care should be taken not to over-fertilize particular plants. Besides, a vacuum breaker should be installed in the water supply line to keep the fertilizer from being siphoned into the home water supply.

As your garden develops, you will need one or more buildings for service and pleasure. The first building or shed needed is for storing the garden tools, equipment, boots, pots, and less rugged lawn furniture. This shed should be small on the outside but large on the inside. To enlarge the storage area,

Plywood tea house that also can serve as a tool storage shelter, or a poolside cabana and dressing room.

Above, outdoor storage center for garden equipment. Right, portable equipment and plant rack. Below, modular outdoor storage units of plywood, and greenhouse.

shelves and tool racks can be built on the walls. Hooks and hangers can be located across the ceiling or rafters.

If you do not have a workshop in your house, you may want to install electricity and a work bench in your garden storage shed. Garden supply centers can furnish knocked down tool sheds that are easy to assemble. However, these leave no room for changes in design. There are several build-it-yourself plans available from lumber suppliers.

The work bench can double as a repair bench during the winter and a potting bench during the spring planting season. A washup area near your storage shed will aid in keeping your tools and garden boots clean. It will also help keep the laundry area neater as dirty garden tools will be cleaned elsewhere.

The next building desired in a garden would probably be a greenhouse, which is described in another chapter in this book. That chapter also covers hotbeds, propagation cases, and coldframes. A third building project for the gardener might be a gazebo, which is a raised balcony with four, six, or eight open sides for resting and for viewing your garden and the scenery. Sometimes the following names have been applied to a gazebo—pavilion, tabernacle, or even a chummery.

Some gazebos are covered with a regular roof, while others have lattice framing that vines can fill in. The corners and sides can also be vine covered for added privacy. A gazebo may be closed in on two or more sides and used for several garden functions, such as a bathhouse or a storage area. Some prefer to roof only half the shelter, thereby letting the sun in to give you a private sundeck.

Insect screen panels and doors can be fitted for freedom from flies and mosquitoes. The same panels may be covered with plastic to make an additional winter storage area or temporary spring greenhouse when a heating system is added.

The following list of suggested further reading is only a small sampling of available literature on designing and constructing various backyard and garden structures.

Some projects such as bird houses or feeders may take only a few hours, while a large patio, terrace, or deck may take all your leisure hours for a summer.

Each project should fit into a master plan you have decided on for your property.

You will get much enjoyment out of planning and building your garden projects, but the real satisfaction will come when you see your family and your friends enjoying the finished project.

For further reading:

Brimer, J. B. *Homeowner's Complete Outdoor Building Book.* Popular Science Publ. Co., Harper and Row, New York. 1971.

Bruning, W. F. and others. *Minimum Maintenance Gardening Handbook.* Harper and Row, New York. 1970.

Eisinger, L. (ed.) *How to Build Outdoor Fireplaces and Furniture.* ARCO Publ. Co., Inc., New York. 1957.

Faust, J. L. (ed.) *The New York Times Book of Home Landscaping.* Alfred A. Knopf Publ. 1964.

Kramer, J. *Gardening and Home Landscaping Guide.* ARCO Publ. Co., Inc., New York. 1968.

Smith, A. U. *Patios, Terraces, Decks, and Roof Gardens.* Hawthorne Books, Inc., New York. 1969.

Sunset Books and Magazines, Lane Magazines and Book Co., Menlo Park, Calif.:
Building Barbecues
Decks for Outdoor Living
Fences and Gates
Furniture You Can Build
Garden and Patio Building Book
Garden Pools, Fountains, and Waterfalls
Garden Work Centers
Outdoor Lighting
Patio Book
Patio Roofs
Walks, Walls, and Patio Floors
Plans for plywood garden structures may be obtained from the American Plywood Association, 1119 A Street, Tacoma, Wash. 98401.

brightening neighborhoods
in suburbs and cities

FEW PROJECTS yield greater results for the expense and effort entailed than a community planting project. If shade and flowering trees are made a part of the planting scheme, their beauty and effectiveness will increase for many decades.

Most people are so resigned to seeing a capital improvement—a building or a machine for example—begin to deteriorate as soon as it has been erected or installed that they do not realize the trees or shrubs in a home or community planting increase in value long after they are put in. Community plantings of giant sequoias in England, live oaks in the Deep South, and sugar maples in New England are today in their full mature beauty after more than a century of growth.

What are almost certainly among the first camellias ever planted in this country, the four giant specimens on Middleton Plantation near Charleston, S.C., are covered with flowers each winter, more than 150 years after they were set out! The cost-yield ratio of such plant material is fantastic. Assuming a present day retail cost of $50 for a sizable young tree or $10 for a well grown camellia, a useful life span of 100 years would give an annual cost of 50 cents per year for the tree and 10 cents per year for the camellia.

In a community planting project, neighbors band together to plant one or several distinctive kinds of trees or shrubs both in their own yards and in public parks or recreational areas, creating a unifying and unusual plant theme.

The idea is not new, but it is remarkably effective. For many generations the city of Tokyo in Japan has special-ized in the Yoshino cherry. The week that this tree is in bloom is now a traditional spring festival time. A gift from the people of Japan has established a similar tradition in Washington, D.C. The town of Millville, N.J., has featured American Holly for many years. Because holly is slow growing it will still be some time until the trees become fully effective, although they get more beautiful every year.

Towns in Virginia have featured flowering dogwood and others in the Midwest have done the same thing with crabapples. The city of Victoria in British Columbia was decorated with hanging baskets of annual flowers for a special celebration and they were so popular that they have been a distinctive feature of this city ever since.

To start a community project you need some small group of dedicated local citizens, perhaps a garden club or service club. This small group can serve as a catalyst in getting the program started and it can see to it that the program is publicized and continued for many years until a real effect is achieved. Brief talks illustrated with colored slides are extremely effective in arousing general interest, especially if good slides can be obtained showing mass plantings of the species suggested for use.

Originally, special plantings for community beautification usually emphasized a single species, as for example

Author WILLIAM FLEMER III is president of Princeton Nurseries, Princeton, N.J. He is a past president of the American Association of Nurserymen and a member of the advisory boards of the Arnold Arboretum, Jamaica Plain, Mass., and the U.S. National Arboretum, Washington, D.C.

the forsythia plantings featured in Ithaca and Brooklyn, N.Y., in former years. Now special projects for unified planting are more likely to include several varieties of plants with varying seasons of interest, rather than a single one which may be at its best only for one week each year.

As a prerequisite, the plants selected must be ones which thrive in that particular soil and climate. Virtually no species is at its best throughout the entire country. An experienced local nurseryman, landscape architect, or professor of ornamental horticulture can give good advice that will prevent the disappointment of putting a lot of effort into planting a species which is not reliably hardy in the area or well adapted to local conditions.

By choosing several plants you can have two or more seasons of blooms, colorful fall foliage, and winter effects. If for example the neighborhood is located in plant hardiness zone 7 in the Middle South, a neighborhood planting project might involve the use of Kurume azaleas, crapemyrtle, and the southern magnolia (see map inside front cover of this book for boundaries of plant hardiness zones). The azaleas give an early spring display, the magnolias bear extremely fragrant white flowers in May and June, and the crapemyrtle blooms later in the summer. Evergreen foliage of the magnolias is also decorative in winter.

A community planting in colder parts of the Midwest (plant hardiness zones 3 and 4) might feature French hybrid lilacs, one or two varieties of crabapples for both spring flowers and fall fruits, and a spruce or pine species for winter color. If dogwoods were chosen for a community feature planting because they thrive in a particular section, the cornelian cherry (*Cornus mas*) could be planted for its very early yellow flowers and bright red fruits in August, the flowering dogwood (*Cornus florida*) for a mid-spring floral display and fall fruits combined with red leaves, and the Japanese dogwood (*Cornus kousa*) for a spectacular show of flowers in June, a month after the native species has bloomed.

On the East and West Coasts, an early Japanese cherry variety such as the single white Yoshino cherry, the later double pink Kwanzan cherry, and Japanese maples for summer and spectacular fall leaf color would provide a succession of beauty.

Don't overlook the merits of really durable and spectacular perennials like peonies and daylilies in planning a neighborhood feature planting. Durable bulbs such as daffodils and narcissus are also excellent choices. For special effects, you should choose only a very limited selection of the finest and most vigorous varieties. In these popular groups of garden plants literally hundreds of named varieties exist, all differing in color and blooming time, and too many variations create a less dramatic and unified effect than a carefully planned and limited selection.

Bradford ornamental pear in blossom, University Park, Md.

Sample Plant Combinations for Neighborhood Beautification

Common names	Botanical name	Plant hardiness zone	Good qualities
	For New England		
Japanese flowering crabapple	Malus floribunda	Zone 4	Red buds develop into fragrant white flowers. Fruits are fine bird food.
Grafted red maples ..	Acer rubrum 'October Glory' or 'Red Sunset'	Zone 4	Fuzzy red flowers in early spring. Brilliant red fall color.
French hybrid lilacs .	Syringa vulgaris— 'Charles Joly'—Red 'Ellen Wilmott'—White 'President Poincare'— Purple	Zone 3	Deliciously fragrant double flowers opening in May.
	For the Central Atlantic States		
Kwanzan cherry	Prunus serrulata 'Kwanzan'	Zone 5	Double pink flowers are borne in May. Pale orange fall color.
Saucer magnolia	Magnolia soulangeana	Zone 5	Large pink tulip-shaped flowers borne in late April.
Japanese dogwood ..	Cornus kousa	Zone 5	Large white flowers are borne in June. Red fall color.
	For the Middle South		
Southern magnolia ..	Magnolia grandiflora	Zone 7	Huge and fragrant white flowers in May and June. Glossy evergreen foliage.
Crapemyrtle	Lagerstroemia indica— 'Wm. Toovey'—Red 'Ingleside Pink'—Pink white varieties	Zone 7	Large clusters of colorful flowers borne throughout the summer.
Kurume azaleas	Rhododendron obtusum 'Hino-Crimson' Red 'Delaware Valley White' 'Rosebud' Double Pink	Zone 6	Evergreen foliage. Masses of brilliant flowers are borne in April.
	For the Deep South		
Live oak	Quercus virginiana	Zone 7	Shiny evergreen foliage. Broad spreading branches.
Common camellia ..	Camellia japonica— 'Prof. C. S. Sargent'— Red 'Chandleri Elegans'— Pink 'Alba Plena'—White	Zone 7	Glossy evergreen leaves. Double flowers produced through a long period in winter and spring.
Indian azalea	Rhododendron simsi— 'Fielder's white' 'President Clay'— Orange Red 'Pride of Mobile'— Rose Pink	Zone 7	Evergreen. Large flowers on bushes which reach great size.

Common names	Botanical name	Plant hardiness zone	Good qualities
For Southern California and Florida			
Cootamundra wattle	*Acacia baileyana*	Zone 10	Fine textured, silvery foliage and clouds of clear yellow, fragrant flowers.
Orchid tree	*Bauhinia variegata*	Zone 10	Large lavender flowers resembling florist's Cattleya orchids. There is also a white variety.
Canary island date palm	*Phoenix canariensis*	Zone 9	Short, sturdy trunk and immense crown of long graceful leaves.
For the North Central States			
Radiant crabapple ..	*Malus* 'Radiant'	Zone 3-4	Upright habit of growth. Rosy red flowers and small red fruits.
Hybrid french lilacs ..	*Syringa vulgaris—* 'Charles Joly'—Red 'Ellen Wilmott'—White 'President Poincare'— Purple	Zone 3	Fragrant double flowers opening in May.
Herbaceous peonies ..	*Paeonia lactiflora—* 'Karl Rosenfield'—Red 'Festiva Maxima' white 'Mons. Jules Elie'—Pink	Zone 3	One of the most permanent of all perennials. Showy fragrant flowers.
For the Pacific Northwest			
Pacific dogwood	*Cornus nuttalli*	Zone 7	Large white flowers with 4 to 6 bracts. Orange-scarlet fall color.
English holly	*Ilex aquifolium*	Zone 6	Glossy evergreen foliage and brilliant red berries which last all winter.
Hybrid rhododendrons ...	*Rhododendron* 'Loder's White' 'Jean Marie de Montague'—Red 'Scintillation'—Pink	Zone 6	Evergreen leaves. Enormous round clusters of flowers borne in May.
For Northern California			
Deodar cedar	*Cedrus deodara*	Zone 7	A rapid growing, graceful conifer. One of the best for hot climates.
Yoshino cherry	*Prunus yedoensis*	Zone 6	Single white flowers are borne in great abundance in late March.
Floribunda roses ...	*Rosa* 'Europeana'—Red 'Fashion'—Salmon Pink 'Circus'—Yellow & Pink blend	Zone 5-6	The flowering of roses is especially profuse and they are particularly healthy in this area.

The unity also extends in unexpected ways into community life when many people plan and work together in the common project. Not only home gardeners are involved, but merchants and businessmen can add plantings of the chosen species to landscape their commercial establishments.

With proper selection, planting, and subsequent maintenance, the entire community can take on a singular and unusual beauty which makes it more than "just another town."

Costs need not be high, because by combining and concentrating purchases on a few species or varieties of plants you can obtain volume discounts from nursery suppliers.

Remember that besides purely decorative aims, neighborhood plantings can accomplish utilitarian goals.

If a heavily travelled highway passes through or alongside a neighborhood, well-designed and dense barrier plantings can do much to absorb and reduce traffic noise and the dust and fumes traffic creates.

Tall trees closely planted in "thicket" style are frequently used in Germany for noise reduction. They can be faced down with borders of tough but colorful shrubs on the residential side of the barrier.

Such plantings reduce the noise level, but in addition they eliminate the psychological effect of having the highway so close. They replace the nerve wracking sight of an endless, hurrying procession of cars and trucks with a restful bank of green leaves and colorful flowers.

The illusion of isolation is as much a visual as an aural effect.

A jointly executed barrier planting of this kind has more than once lessened the impact of a highway upon a neighborhood, to the great benefit of the inhabitants and the preservation of the value of their homes.

In a similar way, city neighborhoods benefit from parks, even if they are only "vest pocket" parks no larger than a city lot in size. One of the charms of London is the multitude of tiny parks scattered through the city's residential areas. They are often only an acre or less in size, but the few stately shade trees and tiny patches of lawn or of ground cover within them create a distinct break in the nearby buildings.

Many of these little English parks are privately and jointly owned by the surrounding neighbors and maintained by them. In this way the cost, which would be too much for any one individual, is manageable by the entire group.

In areas where housing is so dense that there is just no room for individual gardens, the neighborhood can share a small but important spot of greenery.

The sum of many such little oases, added to the larger municipal parks, is of enormous benefit to the city. Prototypes of this urban form of neighborhood planting are gaining favor in Boston and in Washington, D.C. They require some property tax shelter on the part of the municipality, but the general public benefits enormously. In this way more vital open space can be created in an era of tightly stretched city budgets.

Neighborhood planting in highly urbanized residential sections can make a real contribution to the quality of life within them even if no space can be found for small parks. Establishing shade trees on the streets, either in planting pits or in large planter boxes, is a first step.

As an example, New York City has a tree planting program administered by the park department which greatly extends the limited municipal funds available.

The city arranges the purchase and planting of badly needed shade trees on the streets, but such planting is not limited by the municipal budget. Private citizens or neighborhood groups of citizens can request and pay for trees to be planted in front of their own homes.

Trees are planted as part of the city's annual park program and the cost is much lower than it would be if the plantings were done on an individual basis. New York City assumes ownership and care of the trees but the neighborhood benefits from quick results rather than waiting for regular city funds to become available.

Neighborhood projects in urban areas can also include planting flowers in window boxes and in planter boxes on sidewalks. These tiny areas of color and greenery play a surprisingly large role in converting a drab city street into one with beauty and charm. Joint projects of this kind have long been extremely popular and effective in Europe, and they are becoming increasingly popular in this country. If neighbors combine their efforts and resources, the costs of materials, soil, and plants can be greatly reduced.

Best results are obtained if the group settles upon a limited selection of flowering annuals which repeat a theme of color and texture. Marigolds, petunias, geraniums, and similar tough but freely blooming flowers give excellent results.

Whether the neighborhood is a city block, a newly built housing project, an older residential section, or a whole town, a planting task force might well be established in the following steps. The timing and order of procedure will of course be varied by local considerations, and this plan is only suggested as a guide.

1. A few interested people may meet in a home for preliminary discussion and to set up an organization procedure.

2. Each of the founding group then invites a few friends to attend a second gathering at which the general project idea is explained in further detail. If there is no local garden club or other formal sponsor, a guiding organization can be formed to provide continuity for future years' activities.

3. Informational sessions can now be held, inviting such speakers as an experienced local nurseryman, a landscape architect, an extension specialist in ornamental horticulture, or a horticulturist from the State university or city botanical garden. Topics for discussion should include plants which thrive in that local area, preferably illustrated with colored slides because they will show clearly what effects can be obtained. Other sessions can be devoted to soil preparation, to a planting demonstration, to watering, and to aftercare.

Such talks provide good winter programs to build interest prior to spring planting. Financing should be arranged and volunteer or municipality funds committed.

4. If special plants are to be featured in the community, they can be decided upon, nursery suppliers located, and an order placed well in advance of the spring planting season. If a special project is to be done such as the beautification of a public area (covered elsewhere in this book), a plan should be drawn up by a qualified designer. Then the material can be ordered, or bids can be sought and a contract let for the project if it is a large one involving grading and other site work.

5. When planting time arrives, the material should be delivered and stored temporarily in a central location. Bare rooted trees or shrubs should have their roots covered with moist peat, sawdust, or soil. Much valuable time will be saved if the planting holes are dug and the excavated soil is mixed with peat or humus prior to the delivery date. If amateur planting is done, the more experienced of the members should circulate and aid the others.

Planting too deeply is the most common error.

6. After planting, a small group of people should circulate each weekend to see that the newly planted stock does not dry out during the first season of growth.

7. At the end of summer the entire group should gather to review the experience of the past season, make any changes which seem advisable, and to plan meetings and extensions for the next year's program.

With this kind of enjoyable but necessary planning and attention to detail, remarkable results can be achieved in turning a neighborhood into a distinctive and beautiful community where it is a joy to live.

parks, malls, roadsides:
public area plantings

IN A SURVEY to find out which of 26 items people consider most important to their happiness, 59 percent of those answering checked "green grass and trees around me." This, together with the active interest being taken in combatting air and water pollution, points up the fact that growing plants are extremely important and greatly desired by all groups of Americans. This is especially true of urban dwellers, many of whom have far too few opportunities to walk among trees and on grass.

Americans have an inbred love of the forest with its green trees, fresh air and water, and the springy carpet of rich forest soil. It is part of our heritage. Yet in the work-a-day world of our manmade urban centers, it has been pushed aside by huge concrete and steel monuments to man's great engineering ability. Urban dwellers are beginning to realize what is missing in the city scene and how "civilization" has abused air and water to such an extent that their very health is jeopardized.

It has taken centuries to make us appreciate the true value of the forest in everyday living. Now that it is nonexistent in too many places, the best we can do is to plant trees and flowers wherever they can be worked into our modern way of living. Our task is to make room for them in the concrete and steel tabernacles which millions of us call home.

Plantings in public urban areas, though particularly desirable, are difficult to come by because of limited space, poor growing conditions, polluted air, and the high cost of maintenance. These are the always present limiting factors that keep plantings to a minimum. The proper selection of low maintenance trees, resistant to polluted air and tolerant of salt (used in de-icing city streets in winter), is the objective of every individual who plants in public areas such as parks, malls, roadsides, and open spaces.

Limited space is an obvious difficulty. But trees can be planted even in the centers of our great cities, as at Rockefeller Center in midtown New York City. There are ways of working around the space problem although in such areas they are expensive.

Planters—large concrete boxes—are often used, with varying success. The larger the planter (and the smaller the tree) the better.

Soil in small planters can dry out easily in summer and trees can suffer and even die before the damage is corrected. Also, since the trees remain in planters over winter, the smaller the amount of soil, the more susceptible the roots are to rapid variations in temperature. Roots of trees in the ground are usually much warmer than the surrounding air and so can survive winters. Roots of trees in small planters are often very near the air temperature; hence they are subject to low temperatures and quick changes and so are more susceptible to injury.

But planters *are* being used, even if they have to be picked up (by machine equipment) and stored in protected places over winter. Planters with a volume smaller than 64 cubic feet are frequently not conducive to reliable overwintering of trees in the Northern United States. In warmer climates, the root injury factor in winter is not so important.

_____

Author DONALD WYMAN is Horticulturist Emeritus, the Arnold Arboretum of Harvard University, Jamaica Plain, Mass.

Plantings in Lloyd Center, Portland, Oreg., above, and in Montgomery Mall, Bethesda, Md., below.

Trees that are tried in planters should be small and rugged, like hackberries, Washington hawthorn, oriental crabapple, and the little-leaf European linden.

Evergreen trees should not be used because their leaves remain all winter and continue to collect soot and dust which clog the stomates and greatly retard growth. Evergreen shrubs such as yews, some junipers, and forms of the Japanese holly have been used, however. If these are planted, it's a good idea to wash the foliage periodically. This lets the stomates function properly.

It is best, wherever possible, to plant trees and shrubs in the ground. Planters should not be considered as the final answer to urban planting problems.

Space can be used more efficiently in urban areas by planting columnar or globe shaped trees. Examples of these are the columnar and globe shaped forms of the European hornbeam; the thornless, single-seed hawthorn (*Crataegus monogyna* 'Inermis'); the Bolleana or the pyramidal Simon poplar; upright forms of several lindens; and the columnar form of Ginkgo.

When trees are planted in the soil, there should be at least 64 square feet of open ground about the base of each tree. This will permit water and air enough to reach the roots. Any tree has a difficult time in limited soil, and polluted air makes a bad situation worse. Iron gratings are sometimes placed over the soil surface in order to prevent continued packing of the soil by pedestrians.

Low maintenance trees resistant to air pollution should be used, especially those that, when mature, are less than 30 feet tall, unless they are to be planted in open park space. Smaller trees are much easier to plant, care for, and remove when necessary. Before planting, poor soil should always be removed from a large planting hole. The hole should then be filled with good soil containing a lot of humus. Frequently, smaller trees—planted carefully and in good soil—outgrow large trees that are too quickly planted in the poor soil available at the site.

It is not practicable to lay down hard and fast rules about the distance to plant from the curb on city streets, because all too often there is only one place for the tree. However, trees planted at the curb, with modern traffic what it is, might just as well be omitted for sooner or later their trunks will be skinned of bark and they will have to be removed because of serious injury. The farther they can be planted from the curb, the better.

Many of the newer housing and office developments in our larger cities include malls between the larger buildings, where motor traffic is restricted or prohibited. These places are excellent for planting trees. They can also be used for beds for flowers and grass. In fact, two-row planting with a walk between allows pedestrians to acquire the feeling of walking under a forest canopy of branches.

Soil conditions here are much better than along busy streets but the air is still polluted. Large trees have a more difficult time than small trees. Therefore, designers—who too frequently can merely envisage their massive buildings with massive trees—should keep in mind the practical facts of tree growth. Even here, evergreen trees are not advised. Malls in the suburban parking plazas might be embellished with a few of the most resistant evergreen species, the white fir, for example. Some of the best trees for urban malls are the Amur and Tatarian maples, globe hornbeam, Washington and cockspur hawthorns, and several varieties of the oriental crabapple, Idaho locust, blackhaw and Siebold viburnum.

Any tree should be given a space in good soil at least 8 feet by 8 feet, but 12 feet by 12 feet is better. This amount of space is often hard to provide. But urban planners should realize at the time plans are drawn that wellgrown trees in these malls are decided assets. A sickly or dying tree is an eyesore and detriment to the buildings nearby.

Urban parks are always desirable yet they are among the first areas to be considered for building purposes. Keeping growing trees and shrubs in urban parks is often none too easy. But with the selection of trees like the honey-locust, lindens, oriental crabapple, red oak wherever possible, hawthorn, Norway maple and others already mentioned, beauty spots can be made available to city dwellers. A tree canopy for pedestrians can be a reality.

Shrubs can be grown in the city park. But rugged, free flowering, disease resistant, low maintenance shrubs like forsythia, mock orange, spirea, privet, and barberry should be chosen. Even though these shrubs are common to people fortunate enough to live in the suburbs, nevertheless they are also the ones that stay green and flower under the adverse conditions of a city. Of course, shrubs are more often injured by urban vandals than are sturdy trees. But where possible, shrubs should be combined with trees and grassed areas. They bring the feeling of the forest down to eye level proportions and are certainly helpful in teaching city-bred youngsters an appreciation of growing things.

Growing green plants along the streets and in the public areas of suburbia is far easier than it is in the city. If plans are properly made at the start, there should be an 8- to 12-foot strip of grassed area between the sidewalk and the edge of private property. This area should be reserved by the town for planting trees. Planners should also take care that utility wires, above and below ground, are not an obstruction. The property owner cares for the grass, while the town cares for the trees. Certain town ordinances must be passed to make this work, but it can be and is being done.

Town trees can also be planted on private property (backed up with the proper town ordinances) when the 8- to 12-foot strip of land between the sidewalk and the private property is not available. Once agreed to by original property owners, subsequent purchasers will seldom object.

No tree should be closer to the curb (in suburbia) than 3½ feet, and 12 feet is much better. The farther from the street the tree is planted the less the danger of injury from salt used in winter to melt snow.

Sugar maple, hemlock, white pine, and red pine are most susceptible to salt injury; red oak, white oak, and black cherry are among the native trees most tolerant of salt. Research workers in several states are trying to find other native and exotic trees that are salt tolerant. Unfortunately, some of the trees most popular for street planting—Norway maple, linden, elm, and red maple—are only moderately tolerant of salt.

Drainage problems should be studied carefully so that, wherever possible, drainage water with dissolved chemicals is directed away from the area where the tree roots are.

Trees planted on either side of streets should not be planted opposite each other. Rather they should be alternated, allowing for proper development of the tops without too much crowding. Small trees should be at least 35 feet apart and large trees 75 feet or more.

It is much easier to buy, plant, and care for a new tree 1½ inches in trunk diameter than one 4 inches. And experiments have shown that with trees of the same species and with intelligent care, the smaller tree will usually outgrow the larger tree.

If arrangements were made in suburban towns for cooperative tree planting and management, many of our suburbs would be much more beautiful than they are.

Special street trees such as the Sargent cherry, common dogwood, Japanese dogwood, oriental crabapple, Kwanzan cherry, sourwood, willow oak, linden, and mountain-ash could be chosen for planting on different major streets. These could easily become prime displays for viewing at different times throughout the year. In the South, some of the small-leafed maples, fringe-tree, silverbell, glossy privet, redbud, and southern blackhaw are a few of many selections possible.

This type of tree planting gives a diversified interest to the streets of the town. Also, it increases the desire on the part of private property owners to plant good ornamentals on the many small side streets where town tree programs do not reach.

Open-space planting off our major highways has become a science in itself. In recent years, highway beautification has been greatly implemented by the Federal Aid Highway Act of 1938, by a law in 1940 allowing for purchase of land for preserving natural beauty within the highway corridor, and, of course, more recently by the Highway Beautification Act of 1965.

With our large, high-speed, dual highways running across the Nation, motorists travel normally at 60 miles an hour. Trees near such highways increase the seriousness of accidents. For this reason, legislation is now being passed in some areas to remove most of the trees within 30 feet of the highway's edge.

Now the policy is to plant only trees native to the area along the highway, and to leave large expanses open so that speeding motorists can see and appreciate the view.

Trees should not be regularly spaced in the open country for at high speeds this makes driving very monotonous and after several miles a driver quickly gets sleepy. Trees can, however, be regularly spaced on some of the parkways where speeds are slower and the roads are carefully policed. High-headed trees should be selected when possible, to allow mowing equipment ample space underneath. Of course, there should be no planting under (or over) utility wires.

Low-maintenance trees should be selected since the highway maintenance of trees is always minimal. When you see crews at work pruning trees along the highways, look a second time if you think the trees are receiving special care. Nine times out of 10, the pruning crews are merely doing line clearance work. For the most part, once trees are planted, they must fend for themselves.

Allowances should always be made in every highway planting project to water the trees and shrubs for the first 2 years after planting, to insure proper growth at the start. Watering, and even the fertilizing of newly planted trees, should be written into the planting contract and rigidly enforced. The first 2-year period after planting is critical in the life of any tree, and those planted in the open along our major highways get the least maintenance.

Planting along the highway is often necessary to screen objectionable views, such as town dumps, from the motorist's view.

In memorial highway plantings (the Blue Star Highway from Florida to Maine is one example) committees raise money for plantings and give the trees selected careful scrutiny. Occasionally, they cannot resist the temptation to plant a rest area with some bright colored exotic flowering trees, or to plant a few clumps of such trees off in the distance. If kept within reason, this may be alright, but any planting of conspicuously flowered trees tends to divert the driver's attention.

Billboards are being removed or restricted so travelers can better appreciate the wealth of plants we still have; old car "cemeteries" are being screened from the public view to aid esthetic values we see in the landscape. "Green belts"—connecting areas of natural woods and planted lands—are being bought and put together by private citizens, then presented to the town in which they live so that future generations will be assured of natural beauty in their community. Groups of determined citizens the country over are becoming energetically active in doing these things now. For nowhere are growing trees and green grass needed more for beauty, our health, and the health of future generations than in the modern urban areas where so many of us work and live.

For further reading:

U.S. Department of Agriculture, *Making Land Produce Useful Wildlife.* Farmers' Bulletin 2035, Washington, D.C. 20250, 1969.

—————, *Sericea Lespedeza, Its Use and Management.* Farmers Bulletin 2245, Washington, D.C. 20250, 1970.

landscaping to enhance business, industry

JOHN DAWSON enjoyed working at his company's new plant. Each day he and his coworkers took their lunch and coffee breaks amid the green trees and colorful flowers of the company's new patio-garden—part of the extensive landscaping installed by XYZ Manufacturing during a recent renovation project.

John, if he took the time to check, would find that he is only one of thousands of workers in the United States who are benefiting from an increasing trend in commercial and industrial landscaping. In fact, a 1967 survey of 200 top industrial companies by the American Association of Nurserymen turned up the fact that over 90 percent of the responding executives felt that attractive landscaping was "very important" to their companies.

One executive commented, "an attractive working environment attracts good employees, and well-landscaped industrial plants are assets to any community. We believe this is part of our 'good citizen' responsibility and it is our policy to build and maintain plant sites that are a source of pride to everyone."

In this age of environmental pollution, the use of plants to enhance industry is really an encouraging sign. But special problems need to be met. Tainted air and polluted water around "hard" industrial sites, the everyday processes and procedures of business and industry, inadequate maintenance programs, litter, compacted soils—all take their toll of trees and shrubs expected to thrive in what is at best a hostile environment. However, certain plants and planting designs can do well under these conditions.

Which varieties of plants will be used

and what the final landscape design will look like depends on a careful analysis of needs. This is the point to consult a landscape architect and qualified nurseryman who can plan the landscaping for greatest effectiveness.

Many questions need to be answered and chief among these will be the question of maintenance. An industrial plant or business should be prepared to spend money to maintain its investment, for any landscape planting goes rapidly downhill unless cared for properly. There are firms which specialize in landscape maintenance on a contract basis. Or the company's own maintenance department can, with some training, undertake to keep up the plantings. If this means no more than mowing, fertilizing, and pruning, it will not be difficult. Professionals can then be called in to cope with unusual problems.

Landscape designers use a number of techniques to insure that maintenance of landscape plantings is kept to a minimum. A big part of this will be proper selection of plants—using only the "tried and true" materials which they are sure will do well in the particular environment.

For instance, trees like Norway maple, honeylocust, ginkgo, Austrian and scotch pine, London planetree, and Washington hawthorn do fairly well in smoky and dusty atmospheric conditions—conditions which are likely to exist in a highly-developed industrial area. Among the shrubs which might be used in this same situation would be Japanese barberry, snowberry, privet

Author PHILIP E. BACON is an administrator with the American Association of Nurserymen Inc., Washington, D.C.

Plantings in a variety of settings.

Curbed planting areas in parking lots protect trees and shrubs.

varieties, Van Hout spirea, and forsythia. There are many others, and these may not be the plants for a particular locality, but designers and nurserymen will select the ones most suitable for the area.

Much of the effectiveness of using plants to enhance industrial and commercial sites is achieved through the use of construction materials. These are materials such as wood, stone, gravel, paving, brick, and concrete. They are used both to enhance and protect areas for pedestrian traffic, screening, and other uses.

Planters constructed of concrete, brick, or wood are particularly effective for accenting plants. Raised high enough and with broad edges, planters are particularly useful in "people" areas where they may serve as informal seating. Again, the fact that the plants are raised above ground level protects them from abuse and makes them easy to care for. Flowers installed in planters may also be changed seasonally for variety.

Industrial and commercial sites always involve automobile parking and it is here that trees and shrubs can help tremendously with the overall appearance. Parking lots can be completely screened from view by planting a hedge of buckthorn or, in subtropic climes, Cuban laurel. Both of these plants make fine, tall, dense hedges. Within the parking lot, trees like American linden,

pin oak, and white ash, among others, cast shade and help cool and soften the effect.

I strongly recommend that all plant materials used in parking lots be confined to planting areas with protective curbs about them. Keep trees 4 to 5 feet within these areas so as to avoid injury from possible bumping by careless parking manuevers. It is also a wise idea to select trees which have a "high trunk"—that is, trees whose branches do not start until the 6- or 7-foot level.

Trees and shrubs which drop messy fruit should be avoided in traffic areas. Although its bloom is beautiful in the spring, crabapple is a particular offender in this respect.

The landscape plan will undoubtedly have areas devoted to lawn—the particular grass variety depending upon the area of the country. Lawn areas are fine, but try to stay away from small patches of grass in hard-to-get-at locations. The bulk of the maintenance program will be involved in taking care of lawn areas—mowing, fertilizing, trimming, watering, so a business or manufacturing plant should be sure lawn areas are easy to take care of. Curves and slopes should be gentle to facilitate use of a power mower. Any slope which is too steep to handle with a mower should be devoted to shrub plantings or another ground cover. Nowadays, underground sprinklers are almost a must.

Brick or concrete mowing strips reduce lawn edging problems.

Mowing strips—borders of brick or decorative concrete set flush with the lawn and used to separate the planting areas from grass, will cut down on trimming enormously. One wheel of the mower simply rides on the strip and the grass is sheared flush at the edge of the brick or concrete. I have seen wide mowing strips (2 or 3 feet) used adjacent to structures where there is no foundation planting. These have the added advantage of keeping mechanical equipment away from buildings.

Smaller Businesses

Even small retail businesses with limited space can be made more attractive through planting. And, the improvement can have a tremendous effect because these businesses meet the public everyday.

Planting in decorative containers is one of the easiest ways to dress up small businesses. Decorative planters come in a wide range of shapes, sizes, and materials. Installation costs are minimal. Properly selected trees and shrubs will do just as well in a planter as they will planted in the ground, and they have the extra advantage of portability. Plants can be changed seasonally.

Informal groupings of potted, flowering plants around the entrance—chrysanthemums, azaleas, Floribunda roses —are all good. In warmer climes, bougainvillea or camellia can be used. The added color will make the entrance more important and appealing.

Plants in containers can draw attention to a business entrance.

Signs offer opportunities for plantings.

Long blank walls can be softened and made more interesting by silhouetting small trees or large shrubs against them. Here again, they can be planted in the ground or in decorative planters.

Many small businesses have a free-standing sign in front of the establishment. This provides a marvelous opportunity to combine the sign with an easy-to-care-for planting. Trees, shrubs, and ground covers grouped with a tasteful sign will draw attention—and at the same time tell the world that this business is concerned about its public appearance. Of course, shrubs should be selected which do not grow rapidly and obscure the sign.

Boulders set partially in the ground and washed river gravel are becoming often-used design features of this type of planting, for they help to reduce maintenance.

Trees and shrubs may also be used to hide unsightly areas of businesses. This is far and away the most effective use of plant material to enhance a business appearance. Loading docks, warehouse activities, storage facilities, employee parking, and other workaday activities which are carried on outdoors can all be neatly hidden from public view by plantings. Hedges or combinations of trees and shrubs will do an effective job of blocking out noises, dust and dirt, and objectionable sights.

Cost is an important part of every businessman's daily life and any investment must be gaged against its dollars and cents return. Using plants to improve the appearance of a business site —purchasing, installing, maintaining— costs money, anywhere from 1 or 2 hundred dollars up to many thousands of dollars. What is the return?

The John Dawsons could tell you— the employees work harder, are happier, take greater pride in their jobs, respect their employer as progressive, and are absent less often. The business executives mentioned at the beginning of this chapter were unanimous about the effect good landscaping had on employee morale.

The public could also give an answer very possibly through increased traffic and sales. Landscaping creates friends, and rather than an intruding eyesore, a business may become a welcome neighbor and a source of pride for the community. Industrial companies that have gone further—created parks, ballfields, and playgrounds which can be used by the community—become civic leaders and find their working relationships with local municipalities greatly improved. A good public relations policy like this cannot be measured in dollars and cents.

Many businessmen have become interested in improving their firm's appearance through the effort of community groups. Examples of how women's clubs, service clubs, school

Garden club planting enhances approach to a bank in Tennessee.

children, churches, and other civic groups have provided the impetus for improving the neighborhood can be found in almost every community. In fact, one such effort started in 1912 became so successful that it is now a national program—The National Clean-up, Paint-up, Fix-up Bureau!

Advice on how to go about landscaping a business site is easily ob-tained. Landscape architects and nurs-erymen are located in most parts of the country. Another good source of in-formation is the county extension agent —he can tell about special problems and needs for the area. Businessmen who already have landscaped their sites make another good source. And the local garden club will probably be de-lighted to help with ideas.

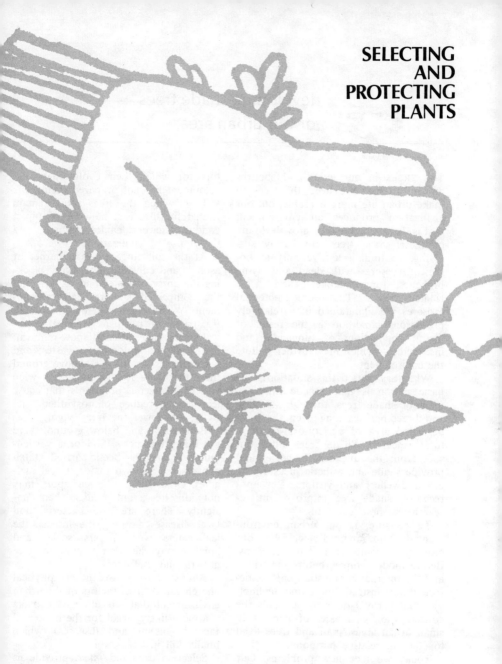

developing shade trees
for our urban areas

THE TREES in our cities and suburbs are in trouble. We need the trees to make urban life more bearable, but our civilization produces an environment that is detrimental to tree growth. Many of these shade trees are barely surviving, continuing to live only as botanical eyesores with dead and dying branches, fungal cankers, and insect riddled leaves. That some potential eyesores are maintained in a relatively prosperous condition is the result of liberal applications of fungicides and insecticides—which may further pollute the environment.

What has caused this situation? The basic reason is that genetic improvement of shade trees, through selection and breeding, has long been the most neglected area of agricultural-horticultural research. Shade trees filter out soot from the air, absorb noise, and provide shade and esthetic pleasure for urban dwellers and visitors. Yet until recently, shade tree improvement research was practically nil.

To be sure, if our urban environments had not changed since 1900, our city trees would have few problems. Before modern times, before electricity and the internal combustion engine, before the industrialization and technology that permits or even demands the concentration of masses of persons in small urban areas, man and trees lived together in relative harmony.

Today we face new problems. Our cities and suburbs are becoming inhospitable for the survival of trees— and man. But trees have a major role to play in humanizing our urban environment and making it a better place to live and work.

Trees in the city must survive a multitude of environmental stress factors for which their evolutionary development has not prepared them. The soil, in which the trees must remain rooted for life, is a network of pipes, conduits, sewers, cables, tunnels, and the refuse of civilization.

At the soil surface lies a carpet of asphalt and concrete, effectively blocking the entry of water and oxygen into the compacted subterranean environment. Where water can enter the soil, it carries with it a heavy load of chemical pollutants: salt from snow removal; industrial and automotive wastes; and —sometimes—pesticides. Above ground the atmosphere is choked with a wide variety of gaseous pollutants that cause leaf injury, reduce photosynthetic activity, and lower the trees' vigor.

Both above and below ground, there are many tree pests. Soilborne verticillium wilt and the beetle-carried Dutch elm disease are two major fungal maladies. Other fungi, like leaf spots, may not kill trees, but render them unsightly. There are also bacterial and viral diseases. Among the insects, the leaf eaters, wood borers, scales, and aphids may be detrimental to tree growth and usefulness.

Almost without exception, physical and chemical stress factors of the urban environment that weaken a tree make it a more likely target for the biological factors (insects and diseases) which finally kill it.

Selection can, and *must,* provide us with superior trees that will not only

Author FRANK S. SANTAMOUR, JR., is a Research Geneticist in charge of shade-tree research at the U.S. National Arboretum, Plant Science Research Division, Agricultural Research Service.

endure, but prosper, in our urban environments.

How many tree species have been grown in our cities over the years? Probably most of those that were reasonably acclimated to a particular region have been tried at one time or another. Trees live a long time, and we can look at the survivors.

Of the trees that were widely planted in the early 1900's and remain today, American elm, sycamore and London plane, pin oak, and silver maple stand out as native species grown from seed.

In their native habitat, these trees often grew in areas subject to periodic flooding. When the root systems of a tree are covered with water, very little of that water can be used by the tree. The lack of oxygen in the root zone prevents active water absorption. The capacity to survive periods of low soil oxygen levels allowed these species to survive in the oxygen-deficient, compacted, asphalt-covered soil of the city.

Of course these trees have other troubles: Dutch elm disease, sycamore anthracnose disease, the obscure scale insect on pin oak, and the susceptibility to storm damage of silver maple.

The time has probably passed when we can recommend a certain native tree *species* for use in city planting.

Furthermore, it is unlikely that the introduction of any exotic species will solve our problems. First of all, most species have already been tried. Secondly, and most importantly, the extreme variability in growth rate, growth habit, and pest susceptibility found in all seedling progenies may often result in a low percentage of acceptable trees.

The best trees for any area of the country are those, either native or exotic, which have proved capacities to prosper under the area's prevailing climatic conditions. In wide-ranging species like red maple or red oak, it is best to select from more northern populations for cold hardiness.

Trees that are "borderline" cases are not worth the time and money. For instance, the lovely streets of live oaks in Mobile cannot be duplicated in Washington, D.C., even if seedlings from the northernmost outpost of that species in Virginia are used.

Even when trees have climatic survival potential, however, the variability among seedlings argues against their use in city planting.

We demand much from our city trees. We want uniform and high survival. After all, the young trees planted on our streets cost more than a mature tree of the same species is worth as timber. We want uniform and maximum resistance to pests and to urban stress factors. We usually want uniformity of growth rate and tree form for esthetic reasons. The only way to achieve these goals is clonal selection.

A clone is a group of plants derived asexually from a single individual. The members of a clone are reproduced from the original tree through grafting, budding, or the rooting of cuttings and are all genetically identical; like identical twins. In current horticultural practice selected clones are called 'cultivars' and they are given fancy (non-Latin) names. The 'Bradford' pear, selected and introduced by the U.S. Department of Agriculture, is an example of a new and useful shade-tree cultivar.

The clone or cultivar thus gives us the maximum in uniformity for desirable characteristics. The clone is also uniform in undesirable traits. If, for example, a well-shaped, fast-growing clone of honeylocust has not been tested and selected for resistance to the mimosa webworm, the steady spread of this introduced insect pest might decimate large-scale plantings of this clone and make chemical spraying the only chance for survival.

There are many cultivars of shade trees currently in the nursery trade— maples, ashes, lindens, and others. But almost without exception, these cultivars have been selected only for their growth and form characteristics. Their resistance or susceptibility to major insect and disease pests is unknown. Their tolerance of urban stress factors such as air pollution and salt is likewise undetermined. The only way to select the best possible trees is through an adequate testing program.

Selection may be both the first and last process necessary to insure that a tree is definitely superior to the average individual of a species or to the best tree available in the nursery trade. Between the first and final selection lies a long period of testing.

Initially, selection may be made among young trees in a nursery, trees growing in forest stands, or mature trees on the streets in urban areas.

This type of selection is based primarily on the tree's shape and general vigor, and in the case of mature trees, there should be some assurance that vegetative propagation will result in a clone with a very similar growth habit.

Vegetative propagation by cuttings or grafting, the building of clonal population, is the first step in the testing program. Frequently this is a crucial point, for if a tree cannot be propagated in sufficient numbers at a reasonable cost, it is unlikely that it will find a lasting place in the commercial nursery trade.

Following vegetative propagation, the tree should be tested in a variety of climatic zones to determine the limits of hardiness. A tree selected in California or Washington, D.C., may not prove adaptable to the climate in St. Paul or even Boston. Testing in different geographic areas will help to eliminate the costly mistakes that occur when large numbers of trees are planted in areas not suited for their optimum survival.

Members of the clone should also be tested for insect and disease resistance. The fact that an American elm or an American chestnut has survived more than 40 years of natural exposure to their major diseases is no assurance that the trees are disease resistant. In fact, trees of these species, selected from natural or planted stands, have invariably succumbed to artificial inoculation with the disease pathogen. Insect resistance may be more difficult to determine, but certainly the enhancement of the insect population can be practiced in test areas and, over the years, a fair measure of insect resistance may be obtained.

It would also be desirable to test the clone for tolerance to air pollution and salt in the soil. Artificial fumigation with pollutant gases requires special equipment and facilities, but these are becoming more common at government and university research centers. Testing of salt tolerance may likewise be a somewhat complicated process and require specialized procedures.

The major point to be remembered is that testing should precede the introduction and release of a new and potentially superior shade tree cultivar.

If there is no testing program, the buyers of the new cultivars will become the testers, and possibly at their great expense.

The best that Nature has to offer is frequently not good enough. We can improve upon Nature by creating new patterns of variation through selective breeding.

In any genus of shade trees—elms, maples, oaks—we find some species that are quite acceptable with regard to growth characteristics and general adaptability to city conditions. Other species may possess an undesirable growth habit or grow too slowly for urban use. If, as frequently happens, the generally acceptable species is susceptible to one or more insect or disease pests, genes for pest resistance are often available in the less desirable species. Through artificial hybridization, we can combine the genes and traits of two or more species to develop a truly superior tree.

This is not to say that the first-generation hybrids will have all the virtues we would like in a shade tree. The hybrids will vary among themselves and we would be fortunate, indeed, to discover a really outstanding tree within this hybrid group. Perhaps disease resistance is a recessive character, and all the hybrid progeny prove to be susceptible to artificial inoculation. In such a case, a second generation of breeding would be required before the right combination of genes is attained.

Selective breeding involves selection of the best available individual trees as parents, rigorous testing of the seedling progenies, and further selection of the

Geneticist examines leaves of an unusual Siberian elm used in U.S. National Arboretum's breeding program for resistance to Dutch elm disease.

best hybrids for use as cultivars or parents in the second breeding cycle. Artificial hybridization—between species or between individuals within a species—is the only practical way to create a new pool of variability from which genetically superior trees may be selected.

Within the U.S. Department of Agriculture two new projects have recently been initiated for the express purpose of developing better trees for use in tomorrow's cities and suburbs. Shade-tree genetics research at the U.S. National Arboretum in Washington, D.C., was begun in 1967 and at the Shade Tree and Ornamental Plants Laboratory in Delaware, Ohio, in 1970. These two projects encompass a wide range of tree genera and problems including air pollution, disease resistance, and salt tolerance.

In addition, several State and university research units are attempting breeding and selection work for resistance to Dutch elm disease. Other institutions are concerned with critical evaluation of the shade tree cultivars that are presently available.

In short, the need for better shade trees has been recognized, and research is underway. With time, and increased effort, the city and suburban trees of tomorrow will be superior to today's.

For further reading:

U.S. Department of Agriculture, *How a Tree Grows.* Forest Service pamphlet 32, Washington, D.C. 20250, 1970.

those distinctive durables: shrubs for your landscape

SHRUBS have many functions. Second only to trees, they comprise the most durable and distinctive element of the living landscape. They provide esthetic structure and background interest to the home garden, the field, and wood-lot. They are useful in many ways. They serve as soil stabilizers, as visual, wind, or noise barriers, and as providers of food and shelter for animal wildlife.

Shrubs, for the most part, are easy to grow. The great majority can be transplanted with bare roots and are not fussy with respect to either soils or growing conditions. As a class, they are relatively pest resistant and they can be very durable. From New England to the Carolinas, the site of many a hillside farmstead, long gone, remains identifiable by a gnarled, yet still vigorous, clump of purple or white lilac.

Shrubs are needed, and can be grown, in every garden and in almost every landscape. They are capable of providing a wealth of bloom and of exhibiting a broad variety of forms, heights, colors, and textures.

Climatically adaptable varieties of shrubs are available for use in every State of the Union and for filling every major design or functional need—up to a point. The list of selections is not always as long as it could be, nor have environmental and cultural problems been fully surmounted. But before exploring these facets of the problem, let's first look at some of the principal or most useful purposes which shrubs serve, and at the kinds of plants which reliably meet these needs.

To avoid any misconceptions, it should perhaps be stated that the term "shrub," in general understanding, encompasses all classes of woody-stemmed plants which fall within a normal height range of a few inches to about 15 feet. As distinguished from a tree with its single main stem or trunk, a shrub is usually many-branched from beneath or close to ground level. To be sure, there are areas of overlap. Some trees may be quite small in stature and some kinds of shrubs may eventually attain tree form, especially if you use a pair of pruning shears.

Using height and branching structure as the main guidelines, it becomes obvious that our shrub definition includes the large group of leaf-shedding, or deciduous, bushes such as forsythia, lilac, and spirea. It also includes evergreen kinds such as rhododendron, mountain-laurel, or camellia which are characterized by persistent broad leaves, together with those, such as the yews and bush junipers, which bear the much smaller or narrower leaves of the pine or conifer relatives.

Shrubs and small flowering trees (such as dogwood, shadbush, and redbud) exist as the main background and interest feature of the natural landscape. They provide the understory of our richest forests. They edge our roadsides, bound our pastures, paint California hillsides with the blue of ceanothus, blanket high shoulders of the Smoky Mountains in seas of pink-purple rhododendrons, and soften the desert scene with the green dots and patches of ocotillo, brittlebush, and mesquite.

So, too, do shrubs provide structure, background, and decorative interest to the home garden, at minimum expense

Author HENRY T. SKINNER is Director of the U.S. National Arboretum, Plant Science Research Division, Agricultural Research Service.

and with minimal problems of upkeep. The only need is for an understanding of the kinds which may be best adapted for use in a given situation, and of the space and planting requirements for the varieties chosen. Fortunately, there are a number of good texts which provide such information.

Well-chosen shrubs can do much to enhance the appearance of a house, to accent a door or window, soften a sharp corner, add interest to a blank wall, or supply color in spring or summer. But please keep in mind that word "enhance." Only the most poorly designed houses may repay smothering; even with these, the windows, at least, should remain visible. This is where the plant choice counts for so much, in avoiding either crowding or spottiness of appearance, and in maintenance of scale with minimal need for continuous trimming or training.

Away from the house, it may be that some wind protection would be helpful or that a less-than-exciting view needs blocking out. The answer could be found in a trimmed hedge derived from such plants as yew, holly, buckthorn, or privet. But it could also be an informal, untrimmed screen or windbreak for which a wide range of evergreen or flowering shrubs might easily include a double-planted row of beautybush, forsythia, spirea, viburnum, yaupon holly, or camellia, according to climate.

Steep banks present problems of maintenance which can often be satisfactorily and permanently solved by the use of shrubs. Candidates might include wintercreeper, myrtle, English ivy, or jasmine if a low or neat effect is needed (Waukegan juniper if the soil is dry, hot, or poor) or some taller, thicket-forming selection, such as weeping forsythia, Scotch-broom, sweetfern, ceanothus, or rugosa rose, if the bank area is extensive.

But shrubs are usable in many ways. Rhododendrons, azaleas, and camellias are unsurpassable for semi-shady places or for open woodland, if the soil is reasonably acid. Together with a gamut of accessory materials, these same plants can be combined into groupings or "shrub borders" of almost any size or length. With judicious varietal selection, with suitable spacing, and with development of a pleasing arrangement pattern, the shrub border is capable of providing interest throughout the year, besides as many cut flowers as the lady of the house may wish to use.

Your success with shrubs will depend on good planting and maintenance techniques. It is equally dependent upon the selection of varieties of likely adaptability to the local situation—to the local soil, the planting exposure, and the climate where you live.

The majority of shrubs, fortunately, are not too fussy about soils. They respond, to be sure, to addition of manure or other organic matter, but they care little whether the soil is of limestone origin or is mildly acid.

A minority of shrubs, however, will grow only in reasonably acid soils with a fairly high content of acid peatmoss or other humus material. It is important to be aware of these, for they comprise some of the very showiest for landscape planting: all the azaleas, both evergreen and deciduous, rhododendrons, mountain-laurel, the camellias, blueberries, heathers, and even the Scotch-brooms, although the last will succeed with much less humus provided their normally sandy situation is both acid and well drained. Some work is involved, but there are a number of ways of developing acid-soil planting sites within a generally neutral to alkaline area.

Planting exposure relates both to the direction of principal light source (as west- or east-facing exposure) and to the amount of overhead shade and wind protection.

Some shrubs can withstand much more shade than others and can thus be used in semi-woodland or on the north or east side of the house. But always remember that a variety of borderline hardiness may be subject to two kinds of winter injury: the damage occasioned by warm sunlight while the roots are in a heavily frozen condition, and the potentially more severe damage that can occur during periods of buffeting by strong, cold winds. Provision of partial shade may alleviate the first situation, natural or artificial wind shelter may minimize the second.

The east side of your house normally affords maximum protection in winter, and is a preferred site for survival of camellias, rhododendrons, and other evergreen shrubs at the northern edge of their climatic range.

Hardiness has become an alternative term for a plant's climatic adaptability —its ability to satisfactorily perform in a given geographic locality. Performance is actually regulated by a number of factors including air and soil moisture, day length, summer temperatures, wind velocity (particularly at low temperatures), and winter cold. The last factor is especially important, since it tends to be the principal determiner of survival.

A combination of the effects of these factors can be expressed geographically, the product being a hardiness map. Using the hardiness map, you can determine the geographic zone or range of zones in which a particular shrub will survive and perform.

Common sense dictates that, for best results, you select those shrubs known to be the best adapted for the particular climatic or geographic location, and most of the best have been zone rated for their adaptability. But a gardener, being human, quite often prefers to treat common sense as a stretchable commodity and at least "try" a beautiful camellia or azalea well beyond its northern range of performance.

He discovers the result but has only partially learned his lesson. For a few years later he retires to Florida or California, and subsequently develops a hankering for a favorite lilac or Exbury azalea which he has sent to him at considerable expense. This time the plants may survive for a year or two but, from a performance standpoint, the original lesson will have been relearned.

The adaptability range for every plant is relatively fixed. Only by introducing new genes through the hybridization process can a parental line be changed with respect to its basic temperature or adaptability tolerances.

Many thousands of shrubs and shrub varieties are available for the improvement and the enhancement of home grounds and of farmsteads, parks, golf courses, and highways throughout the length and breadth of this land. Each one of these may well have something special to contribute by way of serviceability for a given utilitarian purpose or for the seasonal or year-long interest values of its habit, foliage, flowers, or fruit.

Much information has been compiled in this area so that the garden or park planner has a series of listings available for consultation—of shrubs with upright, horizontally branched, or weeping habit; of those with particular colors of flowers or foliage, fall foliage coloration, with interesting fruit, and so on.

The sample listing on page 95 has been arbitrarily limited to shrubs which can be relied upon to survive and perform with minimum care. They are good, they are tough, and they have few or no pest problems. Hardiness zones are keyed to the USDA Plant Hardiness Zone Map, Misc. Pub. No. 814. The map is reproduced inside the front cover of this Yearbook.

Of the many good shrubs which thrive and perform on a basis of modest cultural requirements, even the best are subject to one or several kinds of use limitation. They may require dry or wet soils and full sun or shade—in addition to having an adaptability range which is climatically limited.

Other shrubs, excellent in themselves, can be the victims of insects or diseases that add to maintenance problems; still others, as we are beginning to discover, may be susceptible to air pollutants of the urban or manufacturing environment. An atmospheric buildup of ozone or fluorides has been shown, for example, to adversely affect the performance of such shrubs as bridalwreath, lilac, privet, snowberry, and blueberries.

All these factors of soil or light preference, climatic adaptability, and the degrees of susceptibility to pests and pollution are, for the most part, fixed for each vegetatively propagated shrub variety.

Forty Shrubs for Survival

Abelia grandiflora .... Glossy abelia—Z 6b–10a, M, 1, 3
Acanthopanax sieboldianus ...... Aralia—Z 5b–8a, T, 3, 5
Arbutus unedo .... Strawberry tree—Z 8–10, T, 2, 3
Aronia arbutifolia .... Red chokeberry—Z 4–9a, T, 1, 2, 4
Berberis thunbergii .... Japanese barberry—Z 3–10a, M, 2, 4
Buxus microphylla japonica ..... Japanese boxwood—Z 6–10a, M, 3, 5
Camellia japonica (in variety) .. Camellia—Z 7–10a, T, 1, 3, 5
Chionanthus virginicus .... Fringe tree—Z 5–10a, T, 1, 2, 4
Clethra alnifolia .... Summersweet—Z 3b–9, T, 1, 4
Deutzia gracilis .... Slender deutzia—Z 5–8, D, 1
Elaeagnus angustifolia .... Russian olive—Z 3–9, T, 2, 3
Euonymus alatus .... Burningbush—Z 3b–10a, T, 2, 3, 4
Forsythia intermedia .... Forsythia—Z 5b–8, T, 1
Fothergilla monticola .... Alabama fothergilla—Z 5–9, M, 1, 4
Hamamelis mollis .... Chinese witch-hazel—Z 6–9, T, 1, 4
Hibiscus rosa-sinensis .... Chinese hibiscus—Z 9–10, T, 1, 3
Hibiscus syriacus .... Shrub althea—Z 5b–10a, T, 1
Hypericum patulum henryi ..... Henry St. Johnswort—Z 7b–10, D, 1, 3
Ilex crenata .... Japanese holly—Z 6b–9, T, 3, 5
Juniperus chinensis 'Pfitzeriana'. Pfitzer juniper—Z 4–10, M, 3
Kalmia latifolia .... Mountain-laurel—Z 5–9a, 1, 3, 5
Kolkwitzia amabilis .... Beautybush—Z 5–9, T, 1, 2
Lagerstroemia indica .... Crapemyrtle—Z 7–9, T or M, 1, 3, 4
Lonicera tatarica .... Tatarian honeysuckle—Z 3–8, T, 1, 2
Nerium oleander .... Oleander—Z 8b–10, T, 1, 3
Philadelphus coronarius .... Mock-orange—Z 4b–9a, T, 1
Pieris japonica .... Japanese andromeda—Z 6–9, M, 1, 3
Pittosporum tobira .... Japanese pittosporum—Z 8–10, T, 1, 3
Potentilla fruticosa .... Bush cinquefoil—Z 2b–9, M, 1, 3
Raphiolepis indica .... India hawthorn—Z 8–10, M, 1, 2, 3
Rhododendron (in variety) ..... Rhododendron and azalea—Z 4–9, T, M, D, 1, 3, 4, 5
Rhodotypos scandens .... Jetbead—Z 5–9a, M, 1, 3
Rhus copallina .... Shining sumac—Z 5–9, T, 2, 3, 4
Rosa rugosa .... Rugosa rose—Z 3–8, M, 1, 2, 3, 4
Spiraea bumalda .... Bumalda spirea—Z 4–9a, D, 1, 3
Spiraea vanhouttei .... Vanhoutte spirea—Z 4–10a, M, 1, 4
Taxus cuspidata .... Japanese yew—Z 5–8, T or M, 2, 3, 5
Viburnum carcephalum .... Fragrant snowball—Z 5b–10a, T, 1, 2, 3
Viburnum plicatum 'Mariesii' .... Maries doublefile viburnum—Z 5b–8, T, 1, 2, 3, 4
Xanthorhiza simplicissima ...... Yellowroot—Z 5–9, D, 3, 5

Key to Symbols

Hardiness

Z—Zone range adaptability
Height at Maturity
T—Tall, above 6 ft.
M—Medium, 3–6 ft.
D—Dwarf, below 3 ft.

Decorative or Other Values
1—Showy flowers
2—Ornamental fruits
3—Evergreen or interesting foliage
4—Fall foliage color
5—Suitable for light shade

Within the species, there is a chance of variability with respect to pest susceptibility or temperature tolerance. However, it happens that named selections within most of our important woody plant genera have derived from relatively few representatives of the wild species and these, often, have come from but one portion of the full climatic range of the species. If plants from the colder and warmer parts of the species' geographic range can be obtained for hybridization with them, we have set the stage for creating new kinds or new races of shrubs embodying new combinations of decorative serviceability with additional hardiness, pest resistance, etc. This is happening.

Plant exploration and scientific plant breeding are the linked phases of research forming the basis of an assembly line from which our shrubs of the future are already being produced. Through the cooperatively sponsored explorations of the U.S. Department of Agriculture and Longwood Gardens, Kennett Square, Pa., and through the efforts of other semi-public and private collectors of the United States and foreign countries, new species and new representatives of formerly tried species are being constantly introduced for testing and evaluation.

exception of two or three genera such as *Rhododendron,* the efforts of amateurs have been generally confined to the isolation of chance seedlings and spontaneous variants, that industry has been largely disinterested, and that progress has necessarily become dependent upon the commitments of Federal- or State-supported institutions.

Space precludes any detailed coverage, or even listing, of new shrub introductions of recent years. However, a few examples illustrate research and improvement trends in certain classes of largely decorative shrubs.

Left, pink buds provide striking contrast to white, waxy flowers of Viburnum *'Cayuga.' Foliage of this new variety is disease resistant. Right,* Ilex *'Oriole,' a new shrub holly for the small property. Berries are a brilliant red.*

Using the best of the older materials and combining them with these newer introductions, plant breeders of some 20 U.S. institutions are engaged in improvement programs within 25 or more shrub genera. This does not include the research efforts of commercial growers, notably with roses, nor those of a host of amateurs which have been, and continue to be, enormously productive.

In comparison with annuals or herbaceous plants, the breeding of woody plants is a slow and costly process. Parents and hybrid progenies may take from 5 to 10 or more years to attain flowering size. There may be difficulties in seed germination in addition to the cost of extensive space occupancy.

It is little wonder that, with the

In the process of introduction by the University of Illinois, and for use where space is a limiting factor, is a new, compact, and upright form of fringe tree called *Chionanthus virginicus* 'Floyd'. The same institution has been engaged in the improvement of Japanese quinces and has previously introduced such selections as *Chaenomeles* x *californica* 'Arthur Colby', and *C. superba* 'Spring Fashion', both with glossy, disease-resistant foliage, a more bud-hardy selection called *C. speciosa* 'Starlight', and another, notable for its late-flowering quality, *C. speciosa* 'Echo'.

Canada-hardy *Weigela* 'Centennial' is a product of hybridization with a new and more tolerant form of *W.*

florida which was brought from Manchuria by workers at the Experimental Farm, Morden, Manitoba. From the same station, and notable for their hardiness, clear colors, disease resistance, and pleasing, compact habit, have come such newer lilacs as *Syringa* 'Hiawatha', 'Red Wine', and 'Miss Canada'.

Fragrance has finally been brought to the Japanese camellias by way of *Camellia* 'Fragrant Pink', a *C. japonica* hybrid produced at the U.S. Plant Introduction Station at Glenn Dale, Md., in which the fragrance derives from the second parental species, *C. lutchuensis*.

And improvements of several kinds are incorporated in the products of breeding programs of the National Arboretum, operated by the U.S. Department of Agriculture in Washington, D.C. Either introduced or in process, these include such items as a heavily-foliaged hibiscus with brilliant red, long-lasting flowers, and a shrub althea with unbalanced chromosome complement which is nonseed-producing and which blossoms for an exceptionally long time.

A series of viburnums are notable for their improved flower quality, fragrance, or foliage disease resistance. Improved hollies have been distributed. New crapemyrtles combine large, colorful inflorescences with mildew-resistant foliage. Azaleas and rhododendrons show promise of being both easier to propagate and more tolerant of summer heat. A yellow-fruited firethorn, resistant to apple scab and fireblight, has been introduced for northern cultivation, and so on.

The quality of the shrubs is being maintained, pest resistance strengthened, and their adaptability ranges increased. These, or ones like them, are the shrubs of the future.

mainstays of a garden—
the popular perennials

A PERENNIAL may be defined as a plant that lasts for 3 years or longer in a given locality. Generally this excludes annuals (plants that live for 1 year) and biennials that complete their life span within 2 years. However, certain plants can be annuals, biennials, or perennials depending on the locality or purpose for which they are grown.

While most trees and woody shrubs are long lived, to gardeners and horticulturists the term "perennial" means the herbaceous group including the bulbs. These plants normally die down to the ground each winter and then renew themselves in the springtime and flower during the growing season. But some perennials such as the evergreen daylilies keep their foliage in winter.

Perennials are popular because they live for many years once established in the flower garden.

To plan a new perennial garden or to improve one that is in existence, you should first find out as much as you can about garden plants and their culture. You can learn a lot from reading popular gardening magazines, library books, and newspaper articles dealing with current gardening problems. For detailed information you can turn to books, periodicals, or the Home and Garden Bulletins of the U.S. Department of Agriculture dealing with specific plants.

Other good sources of information are your fellow gardeners, members of garden societies, the county extension agents, State and Federal experiment stations, and commercial nurseries.

Your perennial garden should be planned to satisfy your individual tastes and objectives. You may be interested in a display garden or in growing plants just for your own enjoyment. Or you can seek a compromise between these two objectives. If you decide to specialize in a single genus or group of plants such as lilies, daylilies, or iris, then you face the difficult task of achieving balance and continuous interest in the garden from spring to winter using only a limited number of species.

Plan your perennial garden with paper and pencil. Graph paper is excellent for this purpose. On graph paper you can outline to scale the shape and size of the flower border, and the placement of plants within this border.

Plants should be arranged so that the short ones are in the front and tall ones are in the back. In selecting plants for the border, consider (1) whether these plants will contribute to the overall effect or objectives of your garden; (2) if the plants are reliably hardy in the given locality; and (3) whether the plants are available.

Let's take up the first consideration, relating to your objectives. You might be interested in the display of certain floral colors or a variety of colors throughout the growing season, or you might prefer different forms, colors, and textures of foliage. Some gardeners prefer fragrant plants.

In general, a larger garden offers greater flexibility in the choice of plants to achieve various garden effects. To select plants for special purposes you need to consult garden books for lists of plants classified according to use such as edging plants, background plants, rock garden plants, plants for dry areas, plants for wet areas, plants for sunny areas, or plants for the shade. Some of that information is contained in this Yearbook.

The second consideration deals with limitations imposed by the environment. Prevailing winter temperatures determine to a great extent the type of plants that can be grown. Some plants will survive with minimum protection.

_____

Author TORU ARISUMI is a Research Plant Geneticist in the Ornamentals Investigations Unit, Plant Science Research Division, Agricultural Research Service.

Some need no protection. Some may require protection only during the first winter in the garden.

Plants that are otherwise hardy in the area may be killed by poor exposure or poor drainage during the winter months. Some hardy plants may not be able to survive the hot summers of your region.

A plant struggling for existence in one corner of your garden may thrive in a different spot. You can learn much by trial-and-error experimentation with different sites in the garden.

The third consideration is availability. If the plants are not available in commercial nurseries, you must grow them from seed or obtain cuttings or divisions from your friends and fellow gardeners.

Plant propagation by seed or by vegetative means usually requires precise timing and methods of handling. You need to determine when to sow seed and how to care for the seedlings until they are ready for your garden. For vegetative propagation you should know when to take cuttings or divisions, how to root cuttings and grow them until they are established in the garden. USDA's Home and Garden Bulletin 114, _Growing Flowering Perennials,_ will be helpful.

Now let's get back to your garden plan. Besides outlining the bed or border, and placing of plants, your plan should include notes on the operations required before planting, and a work schedule or calendar for planting, fertilizing, spraying, dividing, and digging plants.

No garden plan is final. As you gain in experience and knowledge your garden is likely to become progressively better. Plants that die or prove unsatisfactory must be replaced each year. Your objectives may change, and you may want to redesign the garden accordingly.

The garden soil should be prepared to a depth of about 12 to 18 inches. If the soil lacks organic matter, peat moss or composted soil should be added. Well-rotted horse or cow manure is excellent but not readily available in

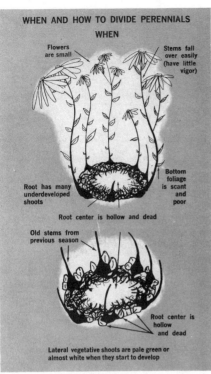

WHEN AND HOW TO DIVIDE PERENNIALS
WHEN

Flowers are small

Stems fall over easily (have little vigor)

Root has many underdeveloped shoots

Bottom foliage is scant and poor

Root center is hollow and dead

Old stems from previous season

Root center is hollow and dead

Lateral vegetative shoots are pale green or almost white when they start to develop

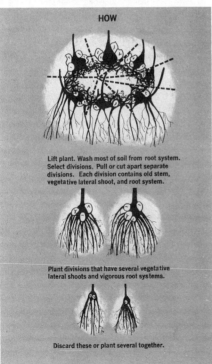

HOW

Lift plant. Wash most of soil from root system. Select divisions. Pull or cut apart separate divisions. Each division contains old stem, vegetative lateral shoot, and root system.

Plant divisions that have several vegetative lateral shoots and vigorous root systems.

Discard these or plant several together.

many places. If there is a hardpan near the surface, it should be broken by digging through it, or if this is impossible, drain tiles should be laid for proper drainage, to prevent plants from drowning.

If your garden is close to large trees or shrubs, the garden plants must be protected from invading roots of the trees and shrubs. Metal or concrete barriers placed between garden borders and the trees or shrubs will keep out most unwanted roots.

All of these operations should be completed before the plants are set out in the garden.

The best time for planting varies with the species and the locality. Transplanting in the fall in colder regions should be done at least 6 to 8 weeks before freezing weather to allow sufficient time for roots to get established. Some plants such as monarda and the late flowering chrysanthemums may not survive in Northern States if they are transplanted in the fall.

Water requirements of a garden depend on the kind of plants, soil, and rainfall. In many places you need to water only during periods of severe drought, if the soil has been properly prepared. As a rule it is better to water thoroughly or not at all because light watering promotes root growth close to the surface of the soil where roots are easily killed by the hot sun.

Unless the soil is very fertile, most garden plants will respond to fertilizers during the growing season. There are many different types of plant food in the market. For most purposes an ordinary garden mixture such as the 5–10–5 fertilizer should be adequate.

Weeds can be controlled by hoeing, pre-emergence herbicides, or by mulch. Young weeds are easily removed by hoeing. Before applying herbicides, you should read the directions and make sure your plants are not susceptible to damage from the herbicides.

Mulching has the added advantages of conserving soil moisture and protecting the surface roots of shallow-rooted plants. For winter protection it is best to apply mulch after the ground is

99

frozen. Mulch may be loosened in the spring, but it should be left to protect the plants until the last killing frost is over.

Some plants and varieties are more resistant or tolerant to insects and diseases than others, and require little or no protection. You would be wise to select resistant varieties whenever this is possible.

There are many insecticides and fungicides on the market, to help protect your plants. Because these chemicals can be toxic to man and animals, you should take proper precautions and follow directions on the label.

Finally, to help you select plants for your garden, brief descriptions of some well-known perennials are provided in the following paragraphs.

The list represents only a small fraction of the perennials that do well in most areas of the United States.

Achillea (Yarrow). Yarrows grow 6 to 24 inches high, and have white, pink, or golden flowers frequently combined with silvery foliage. Dwarf types can be used for rock gardens. Yarrows are also good for cut flowers. *Achilleas* will grow in most soils. Propagation is by seed or division of clumps. Seed germinates in 7 to 14 days.

Aquilegia (Columbine). Columbines are useful for rock gardens or the herbaceous border, and for cut flowers. They have a wide range of flower colors, and grow 12 to 18 inches high. They prefer sunny areas but will tolerate some shade. Propagation is by seed planted any time from spring to September. Germination is irregular.

Aster (Hardy aster). Hardy asters are easy to grow in the shade or full sun. They are also used for cut flowers. Propagation is by seed or division of clumps. Seed germinates in 14 to 21 days. They grow 12 to 60 inches high.

Chrysanthemum (Hardy chrysanthemum). Hardy chrysanthemums will grow well in most garden soils. They grow 6 to 24 inches high. Chrysanthemums are usually cut back early in the season to promote branching and compact growth. They are easy to propagate by division of clumps in the spring.

To prevent overcrowding, older clumps should be dug in the springtime and replanted.

Convallaria (Lily-of-the-valley). This is an easy plant to grow in the shade. It will do well on heavily fertilized, rich soil. It grows about 12 inches high. Propagation is by the division of old clumps. The clumps should be dug and replanted every 3 or 4 years to insure good blossoms.

Crocus. Crocus varieties are grown in the rock garden, border, or in many bare spots in the garden or in front of woody shrubs. They grow 4 to 5 inches high. The bulbs are planted in October or early November, about 3 inches deep and some 3 to 6 inches apart. They will grow in the same place for many years.

Delphinium (Larkspur). Delphiniums provide a variety of colors over long periods in the summer. They need well-drained soil and sunny locations for best results. They grow 18 to 60 inches high, and can be used for the border, for background plantings, or for cut flowers. The plants will rebloom if the old flowers are removed. Propagation is by seed or cuttings. Plant seed any time from spring to September in a sunny, well-drained spot. Seed germinates in about 20 days. Take cuttings in the spring.

Dianthus (Hardy pinks, Sweetwilliam, Carnation). Species and varieties of this group are useful for the border, rock garden, and for edging. They are also used as cut flowers. Propagation is by seed or cuttings. Some hardy pinks are best grown as biennials since they winterkill in wet locations and have a tendency to rot at the soil line. Seed germinates in about 5 to 20 days.

Dicentra (Bleedingheart, Dutchmans-breeches). Species of this group grow from 12 to 48 inches high. They are easy to grow in the shade or sun, but they prefer the shade. They can be propagated from seed, stem cuttings, or root cuttings. Plant seed in late autumn. Seed takes 50 days or longer to germinate. The foliage of *Dicentra* dies down soon after bloom, leaving a bare spot in the garden.

100

Gaillardia (Blanketflower). Gaillardia grows 12 to 15 inches high, and will do well in the garden for show or for cutting. It prefers sunny locations and sandy soil. It should be dug and divided when the clumps become old and produce no flowers. It can be propagated from seed or from root cuttings. Sow seed in early spring or late summer. Germination takes 20 days.

Gypsophila (Babysbreath). Gypsophila is useful for the border or for cut flowers and for drying. It grows about 24 to 48 inches high. It prefers soil that is alkaline. It can be propagated from seed or cuttings. Plant seed any time from early spring to September in a sunny location. Seed germinates in about 10 days.

Hemerocallis (Daylily). Modern hybrids of this genus are far superior to the species. They grow 18 to 48 inches high, and are useful in the border as background plants or for massed plantings. Daylilies do best in the sun, but will tolerate shade. Evergreen types are suited for warmer climates while the dormant ones do best in colder regions. Semi-evergreen types do well in many areas of the South. Daylilies will grow in most soils. They can be propagated from seed, but should be grown from the division of older clumps to obtain plants that are true to type.

Hibiscus (Rosemallow). Hibiscus hybrids have large white to crimson flowers that are quite colorful. They bloom from July to September. They grow up to 8 feet tall, and may spread over large areas. The smaller ones can be used in the garden or as background plants. They will grow in most soils. They prefer sunny locations but will tolerate some shade. To obtain plants that are true to type, it is best to propagate hibiscus from division of the roots.

Iris. German, Japanese, and Siberian types are commonly grown in the garden. They are grown for cut flowers also. Plant blubs or rhizomes (specialized underground stems) in late fall. Dwarf iris grows 3 to 12 inches high, while tall iris grows 24 to 30 inches.

Lilium (Lily). When well grown, a group of species and varieties of this genus provides much color and fragrance from late spring to midsummer. Lilies require well-drained, loose soil, preferably in full sun for best results. The bulbs are planted in late fall. Most lilies are stem rooting, and these should be planted about 5 to 6 inches deep. The nonstem-rooting lily, such as the madonna lily, should be slightly covered with soil. The plants grow from 30 to 60 inches high.

Lupinus (Lupine). Lupines do well in partial shade and wooded areas. They grow 24 to 36 inches high. They prefer well-drained soil with plenty of moisture and plant food. Propagation is by seed, cuttings, and side shoots. Because lupines do not transplant well, seed should be planted where you want them to grow. Seed germinates in about 20 days.

Monarda (Beebalm, Horsemint). Monardas grow 24 to 36 inches high. They are good for masses of color in borders or island beds. They can be raised from seed or division of clumps in the spring. Plant seed in the spring or summer. Seed germinates in about 15 days.

Narcissus (Daffodil). Useful for spring flowers, the Narcissus family grows 3 to 20 inches high. Plant bulbs 4 to 6 inches deep and 4 to 8 inches apart in September and October. They should be dug and replanted every 3 to 4 years to prevent overcrowding.

Paeonia (Peony). Peonies have beautiful flowers and foliage. They grow about 24 to 48 inches high and about equally wide. They can be grown by themselves or with other perennials in the border. They require rich, heavy soil that is well drained. Peonies should not be moved except for dividing and replanting. They are usually propagated by division of the clumps.

Papaver (Poppy). The Iceland poppy grows about 15 to 18 inches high, and the Oriental poppy about 36 inches. They are both useful in border plantings and for cut flowers. The Oriental poppy requires some winter protection, while the Iceland poppy is very hardy. Propagation is by seed, division of the

Tulip bulb planting patterns.

Tulips in blossom.

clumps, or by root cuttings. Plant seed in early spring, in a sunny spot where you want them to grow because poppies are difficult to transplant. Seed germinates in about 10 days.

Phlox (Hardy phlox, Moss phlox). The tall hardy phlox blooms in the summer and grows about 36 inches high. It is useful for the border and for cut flowers. Moss phlox is a spring bloomer and grows 4 to 5 inches high. It is drought resistant and widely used in rockeries, over dry banks, and as edging for borders. Both types of phlox are propagated by division of clumps, stem cuttings, or seed. Chill seed for a month in the refrigerator before planting. Germination requires about 25 days and is very irregular. Seed-grown plants are highly variable in color and form.

Primula (Primrose). Primroses are good for rock gardens, edging a border, and along streams. They are also useful for cut flowers. They grow 6 to 9 inches high. They need rich, well-drained soil in shaded spots. Propagation is by division immediately after flowering in the spring or later in the fall, or by seed. Seed germinates in

about 25 days, but germination is very irregular.

Chrysanthemum (Painted daisy). It is useful for the borders and for cut flowers. It grows about 24 inches high. It does best in sunny locations with well-drained soil. This plant winter-kills in wet spots. Propagation is by seed or by division of plants. Seed planted any time from spring to September germinates in about 20 days.

Sedum (Stonecrop). Sedums grow 1 to 18 inches high depending on the species. They are useful for rocky areas in the garden or for edging. They prefer sandy soil and sunny locations. Sedums are easily propagated by rooting pieces of the plant.

Tulipa (Tulip). Species and varieties of tulips grow 3 to 40 inches high. They bloom from early to late spring. Tulips are useful for landscaping and for cut flowers. The bulbs are planted 4 to 6 inches deep in late October or early November. The flowers get smaller each year so the old bulbs should be replaced with new bulbs after about 3 years.

For further reading:

Bloom, Alan, *Hardy Plants of Distinction.* W. H. & L. Colingridge Limited, London, 1965.

Cumming, Roderick W. and Lee, Robert E., *Contemporary Perennials.* The Macmillan Co., New York, 1960.

Hottes, Alfred C., *The Book of Perennials.* A. T. De La Mare Company, Inc., New York, 1950.

Potter, Charles H., *Perennials in the Garden for Lasting Beauty.* Criterion Books, New York, 1959.

U.S. Department of Agriculture, *Growing Flowering Perennials.* Home and Garden Bulletin 114, Washington, D.C. 20250, 1970.

——————, *Growing Iris in the Home Garden.* Home and Garden Bulletin 66, Washington, D.C. 20250, 1971.

——————, *Spring Flowering Bulbs.* Home and Garden Bulletin 136, Washington, D.C. 20250, 1968.

——————, *Growing Peonies.* Home and Garden Bulletin 126, Washington, D.C. 20250, 1971.

——————, *Summer Flowering Bulbs.* Home and Garden Bulletin 151, Washington, D.C. 20250, 1971.

for dazzling garden color— the flowering annuals

IT IS DIFFICULT to envision any home garden or other landscape planting that couldn't include flowering annuals to good advantage. The wealth of kinds available today allows you to choose varieties for every taste and situation. In addition, most are easily grown and provide continuous color over a long season.

Annuals can truly contribute to a better environment through beautification—both urban and rural.

What makes up this large group of colorful ornamentals we call "annuals"? It's a diverse collection of plants used for garden effect in a single season. Some are true annuals—plants that complete their life cycles in a few months. A few are first-year blooming biennials. Many others are frost-tender perennials; these would survive indefinitely in milder climates, but are killed by freezing temperatures in colder areas.

The versatility of flowering annuals is noteworthy. Not only do annuals provide a vast array of colors, but also many flower forms, plant heights, growth habits, and foliage textures. Moreover, nearly all provide garden color from spring or early summer until late fall. And they are as much at home in formal groupings as in informal settings, as effective in mass plantings as in small intimate beds.

Annuals are ideal in beds and borders, for neat edgings, interplanted with biennials and perennials, or set among newly-planted shrubs. Try them also in window boxes, outdoor planters, patio tubs, and hanging baskets. Others are good for fast-growing screens or temporary hedges. Some are satisfactory as winter house plants, too.

New varieties are continually being developed by plant breeders around the world. Their diligence brings improved types: new colors, better plant forms, earlier and fuller flowering, enhanced disease resistance, and sometimes even wholly unique types.

Selecting the varieties to grow from among the hundreds on the market is partly a matter of personal preference. You would, of course, pick ones that are attractive to you and which fit your needs. But it is also wise to choose those that have proven dependable in your area in previous years.

Catalog descriptions are helpful, but you should rely more on the advice of your greenhouse or garden center manager. Local gardening experts can be consulted. And in larger cities, call your park district for the location of beds planted with annuals. Find out what has done well for your neighbors, or in plantings around public buildings, industrial installations, shopping centers and similar landscaped areas in your locality.

Some State experiment stations and other organizations publish annual lists of currently recommended varieties. Plan to visit any trialing plots in your area; these are usually maintained by seed companies, experiment stations, or botanic gardens.

It is wise to depend on newer improved varieties of annuals, even though they may be a bit more expensive. Some of our best annuals are F_1 hybrid seed strains. Professional plant breeders produce F_1 hybrid seed

Author G. M. FOSLER is an Assistant Professor of Ornamental Horticulture at the University of Illinois, Urbana-Champaign.

by crossing two different true-breeding parental lines, combining some of the best characteristics of each. This is an expensive and delicate operation, usually done by hand.

Hybrids continue to increase in importance, giving us many of our finest varieties—notably in ageratums, geraniums, marigolds, pansies, petunias, snapdragons, sultanas, wax begonias, and zinnias. They can be counted on for vigor and uniformity of color, size, and growth habit. And F_1 hybrids nearly always outclass standard inbred varieties in the abundance of blooms produced.

Among the best of the new offerings each year are the "All-America Selections." These award-winning varieties have demonstrated superior performance in unbiased trialing tests conducted in widely separated parts of both the United States and Canada.

Survival is all-important. And the kinds of plants you grow should be chosen with this in mind. Following is a group of unusually tough, durable annuals that give a good account of themselves, even under highly adverse conditions: cosmos, four-o'clock, Madagascar periwinkle, marigold, sultana, moonflower, spiderflower, and summer-cypress.

Choosing varieties for a particular purpose or effect is one thing. But you must also consider such important environmental factors as light. Plants obviously require light to grow. And the amount of light you have in different spots in your garden determines the kinds of plants to select for them.

An inexpensive light meter, measuring in foot candles (FC), can be borrowed or purchased to help you assess the light situation in your garden. Do this on a bright, sunny day.

As a guide, *full sunlight* is regarded as 3000 FC or more through the day, with no shade falling on the plants. *Partial sunlight* indicates shade or dense shadows for a portion of the day, or roughly 1200 to 3000 FC of light. *Light shade* (500 to 1200 FC) is a light shadow from distant buildings, or reduced illumination due to filtering of sunlight through foliage or screens. Where deep shadows exist all day with no direct sunlight (100 to 500 FC), the situation is termed *dense shade.*

Few flowering or foliage plants will flourish in dense shade, unless they are first grown in sunlight and then moved there when well developed. With less than 100 FC of light, plants generally fail to survive.

Most flowering annuals perform best in full sunlight.

Fortunately, some are fairly shade-tolerant, too. Included in this group are browallia, coleus, exacum, lobelia, pansy, sultana, wax begonia, and wishbone flower. Very few of these, however, will thrive in continuous dense shade.

Still other kinds bloom satisfactorily in partial sunlight, or even light shade, but not as well as in full sunlight. In this grouping are ageratum, balsam, calendula, Chinese forget-me-not, cosmos, flowering tobacco, gloriosa daisy, Madagascar periwinkle, mealycup sage, petunia, scarlet sage, summer forget-me-not, and sweet alyssum.

Aside from adequate light and choosing kinds adapted to your climate, annuals are rather undemanding in their general requirements. Seldom are they plagued by serious diseases or insects. Most soils, even poor ones, can be modified or improved to grow fine flowers.

Good drainage is essential. In many areas, natural rainfall won't be adequate and should be supplemented by watering, particularly during drought periods. And several light applications of fertilizer are usually needed.

Raising good flowering annuals is becoming more of a challenge because our environment is changing, often for the worse. The resulting stresses have a definite effect upon the plants we grow.

Crowded conditions exist, especially in urban areas, with serious pollution of the air, water, and even soil. The environment in city gardens may also be particularly abnormal because of unique situations that occur there.

For example, many surfaces (streets,

Above, Carefree Deep Salmon geranium, All-America Selections award winner for 1968. This is an F₁ hybrid seed-grown strain. Below left, tall-growing American marigold. Below right, super tetra snapdragons.

sidewalks, roofs, walls) absorb and reradiate heat in the summertime. Thus, it's easy to see how the walls of buildings in close proximity can cause rapid changes in air circulation. Veritable "wind tunnels" of torrid air are set up. Plants growing in such places are quickly damaged, particularly those receiving full sunlight.

Air pollution can be very distressing, for the damage to many ornamentals is often serious. Furthermore, the symptoms may be mistaken for those caused

sunlight by the chemical combination of nitrogen oxides with hydrocarbons in the atmosphere.

General symptoms of ozone and PAN injury are spotted, streaked, and bleached leaves. Plant growth is also retarded, and early leaf drop sometimes occurs.

Among the annuals most sensitive to ozone are geranium, petunia, and wax begonia. On the other hand coleus, sultana, and garden verbena show only intermediate sensitivity. Kinds suscep-

Penthouse terrace in New York City. Plantings are changed with the seasons.

by diseases or insects. Pollution problems are covered in detail by another chapter in this book.

Sources of air pollution are many. They include factories and power plants, vehicle engines, refuse burning, heating plants and home heating units, and forest fires. Among the most serious gaseous pollutants are sulfur dioxide, ethylene, fluorides, peroxyacetyl nitrate (PAN), chlorides, nitrogen dioxide, ozone, and various hydrocarbons. But there are many others.

Two of the most pernicious pollutants are ozone and PAN, sometimes called photochemical pollutants. Oxides of nitrogen in the air, in the presence of sunlight, react with oxygen to form ozone. Similarly, PAN is formed in

tible to PAN injury include China aster, petunia, and sultana; while relatively resistant to it are balsam, calendula, coleus, Madagascar periwinkle, and wax begonia.

Note, however, that some varieties or cultivars within a species may be more susceptible to injury than others. For example, white-flowered petunias are extremely sensitive to photochemical pollutants while purples, blues, and reds are more resistant. Furthermore, the F_1 hybrid multiflora type of petunia (small leaves and flowers) is generally less prone to injury than the robust, larger-flowered F_1 grandifloras.

As a rule, the small-leaved types of plants are more resistant to air pollutants than large-leaved types. Stage

107

of plant development has a bearing too, for young and old leaves are often less affected than recently matured foliage. You may also note that slow-growing plants are more resistant than rapidly growing ones with soft tissues.

Air pollution is a real problem in many urban areas, with severity affected by prevailing weather conditions. But if you live in a high-pollution zone, carefully note what kinds of annuals have done well in other plantings nearby before you choose ones for your own garden.

There are no deep dark secrets in how to grow good annuals—just common sense and time-proven procedures. Proper soil preparation can't be over-stressed. A loose, porous soil with adequate aeration and moisture-holding capacity gives best results.

Deep spading is advised, working in several inches of organic matter (such as peat moss, compost, or well-rotted manure) annually. And if the soil is unusually heavy, sand or perlite should be added, too. Fertilizer and lime are

Top, Pink Snow, an early-flowering, single grandiflora petunia. Left, petunia Sunburst, a light yellow single grandiflora. Below, verbenas in a border planting.

incorporated shortly before planting time.

A 5–10–5 dry fertilizer applied at the rate of 1½ to 2 pounds per 100 square feet should be adequate. But follow up at 6-week intervals with a light sprinkling around each plant. Spread evenly and work into the soil shallowly.

If you prefer, liquid fertilizers can be used instead. Dissolve in water and apply as directed on the container.

When soil tests indicate the need for lime, add only enough to bring the pH up to the 6.0 to 6.8 level (just slightly acid).

Once the bed has been prepared and raked down smoothly, it is ready for planting.

If you plan to use seeds, be sure you have fresh viable supplies that will germinate well. Some flowering annuals can be sown in late fall or as early in spring as you can work the soil. Examples are calendula, cornflower, larkspur, portulaca, and spiderflower.

Seeds of certain robust and rather large-seeded annuals germinate reliably when planted directly in the ground. Good examples are balsam, cockscomb, cosmos, dahlia, four-o'clock, marigold, nasturtium, and zinnia. Wait, however, until the soil is warm and danger of frost is largely past.

Many other annuals are either small-seeded or rather touchy in their germination requirements. Unless you have proper facilities for starting them indoors, or in a hotbed or greenhouse, it is probably best to buy started plants. These also will give you earlier blooms than from seed.

If you start your own plants indoors, don't sow the seed more than 4 to 8 weeks before the average date of the last killing frost. Otherwise, the plants will become overgrown and leggy before they can be set out.

You will need to thin the seedlings from seeds sown in outdoor beds. Many gardening references provide help on how far apart different kinds of annuals should be spaced. This information is equally important for the plants you buy. Overcrowding gives poor results.

Giant cactus-flowered zinnias.

When buying plants, look for the healthy, clean, well-branched specimens—rather than merely being sure they are in bloom. Nearly all annuals, whether home grown or purchased, should be tipped or "pinched back" when a few inches tall. In other words, break or cut off the tips of the stems, leaving 3 to 5 leaves (or sets of leaves). The first flower is sacrificed, but greatly enhanced branching develops.

Petunias are a prime example of an annual that often remains stringy and sparsely branched unless pinched. Several annuals that shouldn't be pinched back are balsam, cockscomb, and poppy.

You may want to start a few kinds of plants for your garden from cuttings taken from winter house plants. It's easy to root "slips" of such things as bloodleaf, coleus, geranium, sultana, and wax begonia. Set out the well-started plants when frost danger is past.

About 1 inch of moisture per week is usually adequate for flowering annuals. If rainfall is deficient, supplementary watering will be needed. When the soil is dry to the touch, apply water gently and slowly with a sprinkler or soaker hose until the soil is moistened down through the root zone (7 to 10 inches). Then don't irrigate again until the soil is fairly dry.

Avoid light superficial waterings which do more harm than good. If you use a sprinkler, then water early enough in the day so the foliage has a chance to dry off before nightfall.

Automatic watering systems are on the market for the avid and affluent gardener. You can also purchase injectors that pump nutrient solutions into the water lines, allowing you to fertilize as you water.

Removing old flower heads helps tidy up the garden but also promotes further blooming. This is particularly important on such annuals as ageratum, calendula, pansy, snapdragon, and zinnia. Pruning back long, ungainly stems (on petunia, for example) helps retain good plant form.

Plan to protect your garden plantings in every way possible to ensure success—regardless of how trying the environment in which they are growing may be. First of all, watch for insects and diseases, and if necessary, seek expert advice on their control.

To keep your flowerbeds free of weeds, pull as many as you can by hand. If you use a hoe, merely shave off the weeds and gently break up the surface crust. Deeper cultivation damages the shallow root systems of annuals, and also brings a whole new crop of weed seeds to the surface.

Proper drainage has already been emphasized. Annuals don't like "wet feet." Sometimes tiling or regrading must be resorted to, in order to carry off excess water. Another approach is to mound up the bed, raising its level a few inches above that of the surrounding area. This can be done by bringing in soil, or by digging furrows along the sides and adding this soil to the bed. With this elevation, surplus water seeps down into the furrows.

Mulching is desirable. One or 2 inches of a good organic mulch (coarse peat moss, shredded hardwood bark, cocoa hulls, etc.) not only improves the appearance of your flowerbeds but has many other benefits. A mulch retards water loss, practically eliminates weeds, prevents soil compaction and crusting, and adds organic matter to the soil. Apply summer mulches when the plants are well started and the ground is warm.

Certain kinds of upright or tall-growing annuals will need staking to support the stems, particularly where drafts or winds buffet the plants. Use strong stakes (wood, bamboo, heavy wire, or rigid plastic) that are a bit shorter than the plants themselves, and drive them into the soil behind each plant. Loosely tie each one to its stake with plastic-coated twistems, using care not to damage the stem or to pull the wire so tight that girdling results.

To protect your garden against heat and wind damage in summer, screens of wood, cloth, plastic, reeds, or even taller plants can be effective. Screen off those areas where drafts and full sunlight result in rapid wilting. Arrange the screens so air circulation remains good; otherwise, overheating and excess humidity levels may occur.

Also use some of the easily-grown taller annuals for barriers or temporary hedges—to block out unsightly views or to help hide litter in the vicinity. In addition, they make pleasing foils for the lower-growing annuals. Some examples of taller annuals are amaranthus, castor bean, hollyhock, spider-flower, summer-cypress, sunflower, and tithonia. Climbers such as black-eyed Susan vine, gourds, moonflower, and morning-glory can be useful, too.

A minor but important side benefit from this technique is to help control noise pollution, by dampening or deflecting the sounds of passing traffic, for instance.

Use night lighting in portions of your garden to extend enjoyment of it and to illuminate the surroundings—a protection feature in itself for your home.

White-frosted incandescent lamps, the most commonly used light source for this purpose, shouldn't be left on later than about 10 p.m. because they alter the growth of certain ornamentals. Amber-coated incandescents aren't recommended. Ordinary mercury and high-pressure sodium lamps are satisfactory, but require special installation. A lighting engineer can help you with your garden lighting plans.

Other than selecting annuals that are resistant to air pollution damage, there is little that can be done to protect them from this menace. It does pay, however, to reduce the amount of nitrogen fertilizer applied and the frequency of watering. High soil moisture and nitrogen levels cause soft, succulent growth which is particularly susceptible to air pollutants. Moderate applications will retard growth and make the plants better able to survive.

Although no practical antipollutant chemical treatments are available, antitranspirant sprays may be of some benefit. These are latex, wax, or plastic waterproofing materials that are sprayed on the foliage and stems in spring and summer when growth is rapid. Antitranspirant products are sold by garden supply dealers. Apply according to directions on the container.

Dust, soot, fly ash, and other solid residues—another form of pollution— also settle on plants in the garden.

These are unsightly, and interfere with plant growth. Syringing with water sometimes is sufficient. But you may have to resort to soapy water, heated to a little above air temperature.

Use only a very mild soap (not a laundry powder or liquids). Apply the solution to the foliage with a laundry sprinkler, avoiding excessive runoff or drip. In 5 or 10 minutes, flush off the grime with a fine nozzle on the hose.

Many a gardener becomes discouraged when summer heat, wind, drought, pollution, and other hazards take their toll. But growing annuals can be fun. Avoid overextending yourself—plant what you can take care of properly. Above all, don't be a "scratch and plant" gardener.

Good gardening practices improve your chances of success, and help you reap the rewards and satisfactions of beautifying the environment—at least your little corner of the world—with flowering annuals.

For further reading:
U.S. Department of Agriculture, *Growing Flowering Annuals.* Home and Garden Bulletin 91, Wash., D.C. 20250, 1970.

selecting lawn grasses, from bahia to zoysia

GRASSES constitute one of the most appealing parts of our outdoor environment. They provide recreational and beautification areas for children and grownups in the form of lawns, athletic fields, golf links, parks, and roadsides.

Most people may fail to realize that grasses are important in pollution control. They prevent wind and water erosion and they supply vital organic matter to the soil. They also absorb carbon dioxide and enrich the atmosphere with oxygen through plant photosynthesis.

Selection of turfgrasses depends in

large part on climatic conditions. Cool-season grasses grow best in the North and warm-season grasses in the South. The growth cycle of grasses varies with temperature.

Seedbed preparations are similar for establishing nearly all grasses. First you should plow, disk, or rototill to loosen the subsoil.

Lime is generally required for soils east of the Mississippi River. Apply 50 to 80 pounds of ground limestone per 1,000 square feet every 5 to 6 years. When there is uncertainty about the need for lime, the soil should be tested.

RELATION OF TEMPERATURE TO GROWTH RATE IN COOL AND WARM SEASON GRASSES

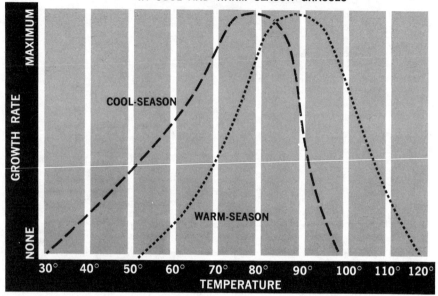

If lime is needed, it should be incorporated into the soil, along with 30 to 40 pounds of phosphorus 0–20–0 per 1,000 square feet. On established lawns, apply lime on the surface.

Before planting seed, sprigs, or sod pieces, apply a complete fertilizer containing nitrogen, phosphorus, and potash. The analyses on the bag are always listed in the order mentioned. For example, a 10–6–4 fertilizer contains 10 percent nitrogen, 6 percent phosphorus, and 4 percent potash.

Apply 10 pounds of a fertilizer containing 10 percent nitrogen per 1,000 square feet and rake into the soil. Apply with a 20–10–10 fertilizer, 5 pounds per 1,000 square feet.

Fertilizer is seldom required on western soils where blue grama and buffalograsses are used for turf.

Plant the seed adapted to your region

Author FELIX V. JUSKA is a Turf-Research Agronomist in the Forage and Range Research Branch, Plant Science Research Division, Agricultural Research Service.

Coauthor KERMIT W. KREITLOW was Assistant Chief of the Forage and Range Research Branch. He died in 1971.

evenly over the seedbed with a spreader or by hand. If the seed is applied by hand, mix it with sand or soil to provide bulk. Half of the seed should be sown in one direction and the other half at a right angle to the first seeding. Lightly rake the seed into the soil to a depth of a quarter of an inch.

Scatter weed-free straw, hay, pine needles, or other mulch material over the seeded area. Mulch reduces erosion and provides shade and favorable moisture conditions for the emerging seedlings. One 60- to 80-pound bale of mulch is about enough per 1,000 square feet. About half of the soil should be visible after the mulch is laid.

Water the area lightly two or three times daily until the seedlings become established. Mulching materials need not be removed if you use them in moderate amounts and distribute them well.

Most southern grasses such as bermudagrass, St. Augustinegrass, and zoysia are established from sprigs (individual plants or runners) or pieces of sod. The sod or sprigs can be planted at 1-foot intervals. However, the closer together the sprigs, plugs (round cores of grass and soil), or sod pieces are planted, the more rapidly your lawn will become established.

If your lawn has thinned out so only half of the perennial grasses remain, you can still restore it without plowing and reseeding the entire area.

For cool-season grasses (Kentucky bluegrass, red fescue, bentgrass, etc.) rake dead areas to remove the thatch and loosen up the soil. The seed must come in contact with the soil in order to germinate.

After seeding, raking, and mulching, spread fertilizer over the lawn at recommended rates. Water the newly seeded areas two or three times daily. Continue to mow the lawn at the recommended height for the species.

Late August and September are the best times for renovating cool-season lawns, although seeding bare areas in early spring is frequently successful.

Southern grasses that spread by runners (stolons) may be sprigged or sodded into dead areas without much soil preparation. Make a slit in the soil with a spade, insert the sprig, and firm the soil with your foot. Soil can be stripped with a spade and sod pieces laid and firmed into the soil the same way as with sprigs. Water the replanted areas and apply fertilizer over the entire lawn. Continue to mow as usual.

Cool-season grasses make their best growth in the fall and spring—Kentucky bluegrass, red fescue, Colonial bentgrass, crested wheatgrass, ryegrass,

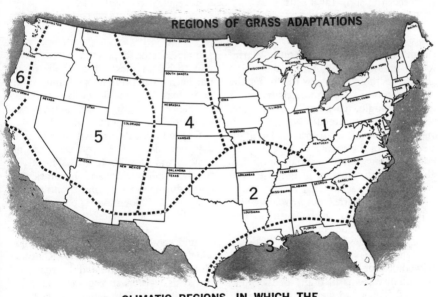

REGIONS OF GRASS ADAPTATIONS

CLIMATIC REGIONS, IN WHICH THE FOLLOWING GRASSES ARE SUITABLE FOR LAWNS:

1. Kentucky bluegrass, red fescue, and Colonial bentgrass. Tall fescue, bermuda, and zoysiagrasses in the southern part.

2. Bermuda and zoysiagrasses. Centipede, carpet, and St. Augustinegrasses in the southern part; tall fescue and Kentucky bluegrass in some northern areas.

3. St. Augustine, bermuda, zoysia, carpet, and bahiagrasses.

4. Nonirrigated areas: Crested wheat, buffalo, and blue gramagrasses. Irrigated areas: Kentucky bluegrass and red fescue.

5. Nonirrigated areas: Crested wheatgrass. Irrigated areas: Kentucky bluegrass and red fescue.

6. Colonial bent, Kentucky bluegrass, and red fescue.

Grass	Best planting time	Seed (lbs. per 1,000 sq. ft.)	Sod (sq. ft.)[1]	Fertilizer (lbs. of nitrogen 1,000 sq. ft.)	Height of mowing (in.)
Bahia	Spring	2–3		4	2
Bentgrass, Colonial	Fall	1–2		4–6	½–1
Bermuda (hulled)	Spring	1–1½	5–10	5–10	¾–1
Blue grama	"	1–1½		[2]	1–2
Buffalo (treated)	"	½–1½	25–30	[2]	1–2
Carpet	"	3–4	8–10	2–3	2–2½
Centipede	"	¼–½	8–10	2–3	1–1½
Crested wheat	Fall	1–2		0–1	2
Ky. bluegrass	"	1½–2		3–6	1½–2
Red fescue	"	3–4		2–3	1½–2
Rough bluegrass	"	1½–2		2–4	1½–2
Ryegrass	"	3–4		3–4	1½–2
St. Augustine	Spring	None	8–10	4–5	2–2½
Tall fescue	Fall	5–6		3–5	2
Zoysia	Spring	None	8–10	4–6	¾–1½

[1] Needed to sprig 1,000 sq. ft.   [2] Seldom required on most soils.

rough bluegrass, and tall fescue. Warm-season grasses are planted in the spring and make their best growth during the summer months—bermuda, bahia, blue grama, buffalo, carpet, St. Augustine, zoysia, and centipede grasses. Climatic regions of lawn grass adaptation are shown in the map with this chapter. For planting times, propagation, fertilization, and mowing height, see the table on this page.

Colonial bentgrass (*Agrostis tenuis*) is a fine-textured grass with a few creeping stems and underground rootstocks (rhizomes). It forms a dense turf when heavily seeded and closely mowed. Colonial bentgrass is used for high-quality lawns in many of the New England States and west of the Cascade Mountains in Washington and Oregon (regions 1 and 6 on the map that appears on page 113).

Colonial bentgrass requires fertile soil and frequent fertilizing. It must be watered during dry periods and it is susceptible to a wide variety of diseases.

Two strains of Colonial bentgrass are generally planted for lawns, Astoria and Highland.

Crested wheatgrass (*Agropyron cris-*

tatum), a seeded perennial bunchgrass, will thrive in most of the soils of the northern Great Plains and intermountain areas (regions 4 and 5). It is recommended for dry, cool areas where irrigation water is not available.

Crested wheatgrass withstands long, dry periods and heavy wear if not mowed too closely. It grows mostly in the fall and spring and becomes dormant during hot summer months.

Kentucky bluegrass (*Poa pratensis*) is a hardy, long-lived, perennial, sod-forming grass that spreads by underground rootstocks. It is one of our most widely used lawn grasses. Kentucky bluegrass is well adapted to regions 1 and 6 and grows in regions 4 and 5 if irrigated. It is propagated by seed.

Kentucky bluegrass will not grow well on poorly drained sites or in acid soils (below pH 6.0). Soil testing will indicate whether your soil is acid or alkaline in terms of pH. A pH of 4 is very acid and a pH of 7 is neutral. Merion was one of the first improved varieties to be released but others such as Fylking, Pennstar, Windsor, Prato, Sodco, and Park are now marketed.

Red fescue (*Festuca rubra*) and

Kentucky 31 fescue lawn on new home site in Tennessee.

Chewings fescue (*Festuca rubra* var. *commutata*) rate next to Kentucky bluegrass in importance for northern humid regions. Red fescue will spread slowly from underground rootstocks. Chewings fescue is an upright, bunch-type grass.

Both fescues are established by seeding, and both are used extensively in mixtures with Kentucky bluegrass. They grow well in medium-shaded areas and on poor, droughty soils.

Improved varieties of red fescue are Pennlawn, Illahee, Golfrood, and Ruby. Jamestown is the only available improved strain of Chewings fescue.

Rough bluegrass (*Poa trivialis*) is a shade-tolerant perennial that is useful for lawns only in the North. It is established by seeding. Rough bluegrass prefers moist sites. It is seriously injured by hot, dry weather.

The leaves are similar in texture to Kentucky bluegrass but are shiny. Stems and leaves lie flat and are lighter green than most Kentucky bluegrasses.

Italian or annual ryegrass (*Lolium multiflorum*) and the perennial ryegrass (*Lolium perenne*) are propagated by seed. Much ryegrass lawn seed is a mixture of both annual and perennial ryegrasses.

Many commercial lawn seed mixtures contain too much ryegrass; the ryegrass competes with the slower growing Kentucky bluegrass and red fescue. For a late spring seeding and on slopes, it is advisable to include some ryegrass for green color and to avoid erosion.

Perennial ryegrass varieties include Pennfine, NK-100, Pelo, Manhattan, and Norlea. Varieties of annual ryegrass include Astor, Gulf, Magnolia, and Tifton 1.

Tall fescue (*Festuca arundinacea*) is a tall-growing, perennial bunchgrass that has coarse, dense, basal leaves and a strong fibrous root system. It is vigorous, grows well on both wet and dry sites, but does best on heavy soils.

Because of their wear-resistant qualities, two varieties of tall fescue—Kentucky 31 and Alta—are seeded in lawns, play areas, athletic fields, airfields, and other areas where a tough turf rather than a fine-textured turf is needed.

Kentucky 31 tall fescue forms a tough, durable turf throughout much of the transition zone where neither cool-season grasses nor warm-season grasses are especially well adapted. Tall fescue is seldom seriously injured by insects or diseases.

When seeded at heavy rates (see table with this chapter), tall fescue produces finer leaves, the plants do not clump as readily, and a quite respectable lawn results.

Bahiagrass (*Paspalum notatum*) is a low-growing perennial that spreads slowly by short, stout underground rootstocks. It grows best in the South Central Plains, and is established by seeding. Several varieties are adapted to sandy soils from central North Carolina to eastern Texas. This grass is primarily for pastures and roadsides but the varieties Paraguay and Pensacola are used for lawns.

Bermudagrass (*Cynodon* spp.) is adapted to regions 2 and 3, where many varieties are sold. Each variety generally is for a specific use.

Common bermudagrass is coarse textured and propagated from seed. Other varieties are established vegetatively because the seed is sterile or is nearly so.

Bermudagrass grows on a wide range of soils from heavy clays to deep sands, provided they are fertile. It grows satisfactorily on both acid and alkaline soils and has a high tolerance to saline conditions. It persists on relatively infertile soils yet high nitrogen fertilizing is required for good-quality turf. While rated drought tolerant in humid regions, it cannot grow in arid regions without supplementary irrigation.

Bermudagrasses are not shade tolerant; however, there are slight differences among varieties.

Bermudagrass will grow vigorously, spreading by runners and underground rootstocks. It often becomes a pest in flowerbeds and other cultivated areas. Once established, it is hard to eradicate.

This grass turns brown following the first frost and does not become green again until warm weather occurs in the spring. But even with its shortcomings, bermudagrass is one of our most widely used turfgrasses.

Varieties of bermudagrass that are used in high-quality lawns receiving maximum maintenance and on golf course greens, tees, and fairways are Tifgreen, Tiffine, Tifway, Bayshore, and Tifdwarf.

The bermudagrasses require frequent, heavy applications of nitrogen fertilizer in water soluble form. Bermudagrasses also require dethatching once or twice a year to remove dead runners, roots, and leaves that accumulate.

Blue gramagrass (*Bouteloua gracilis*) is a low-growing, perennial bunchgrass adapted to parts of the Great Plains. As a turfgrass it is limited to cool, dry sites where there is little or no irrigation available.

This grass is highly drought resistant and is established from seed. It becomes semidormant and turns brown during excessively dry periods.

Buffalograss (*Buchloe dactyloides*) is a fine-leaved, warm-season, sodforming perennial that spreads by runners. It grows on the Great Plains from western Minnesota to central Montana, south to northwestern Iowa, Texas, and Arizona. It is drought resistant, tolerant of alkaline soils, and adapted to clay soils.

USDA agronomist discusses turfgrass research at a Beltsville, Md., field day.

Buffalograss can be established from sod pieces or by seeding.

Carpetgrass (*Axonopus affinis*) is a rapid spreading, perennial grass. It spreads by runners and produces a dense, compact turf when mowed, but is coarse textured. It can be established by seed or sodding. Carpetgrass is most abundant in lowland areas from coastal North Carolina to Florida and westward to Texas. It grows best in moist, sandy loam soils or those which have a relatively high content of moisture throughout the year. It sometimes invades infertile, upland sites but does not grow well in dry soils or in regions which remain dry during part of the growing season.

Carpetgrass produces tall seedheads that are difficult to mow and make the lawn look ragged. Mowing frequently with a rotary mower is recommended. No improved varieties are available.

Centipedegrass (*Eremochloa ophiuroides*) will spread rapidly from short, creeping runners that form plants at each node or joint. It forms a dense, weedfree turf. Centipedegrass is usually planted vegetatively, but some seed is available.

This is considered the best low-maintenance grass for the South. It has survived winter conditions as far North as northern Alabama and central areas of North Carolina.

Centipedegrass requires less mowing, less watering, and less fertilizing than other southern grasses. Applications of iron compounds correct yellowing.

Centipedegrass should not be planted on farm lawns—it may escape and contaminate cropland. Common centipedegrass is most extensively planted.

Oklawn is a variety selected for tolerance to drought and high temperatures; it grows in shade as well as in full sunlight.

St. Augustinegrass (*Stenotaphrum secundatum*) is the best shade-tolerating grass for the South. It is a creeping perennial and spreads by long runners that produce short, leafy branches. It is restricted to the Gulf Coast States and milder parts of California. It is established vegetatively.

This grass can withstand salt water spray. It grows best in soils of high fertility.

St. Augustinegrass is very susceptible to chinch bug injury and to brown patch disease. Varieties available for lawns are Bitter Blue and Floratine.

Three species of zoysiagrass are recognized and used for turf. These are *Zoysia japonica*, *Z. matrella*, and *Z. tenuifolia*. They are distinguished primarily on the basis of size, vigor, and winter hardiness.

Common zoysia, *Zoysia japonica*, also known as Japanese lawngrass, can be propagated vegetatively or from seed. It is rather coarse leaved and is used to some extent for lawns.

Meyer zoysia, a selection from common zoysia, is intermediate in leaf width between common and *Zoysia matrella*. It is well adapted to the mid-Atlantic area. Meyer zoysia is more desirable for home lawns because of its finer textured leaves. It must be propagated vegetatively by sprigs, sod pieces, or plugs.

Although Meyer zoysia survives in soils of low fertility, it makes best growth when given liberal applications of complete fertilizers high in nitrogen. Meyer zoysia is relatively drought tolerant in humid regions. This grass is highly resistant to wear and withstands close clipping.

Emerald zoysia is a hybrid variety superior to Meyer zoysia in the South. The grass is fine leaved, dense growing, and dark green.

Manilagrass (*Zoysia matrella*) has about the same leaf texture as emerald but is a lighter green. Manilagrass is adapted to the South. It produces a dense carpetlike turf that resists weeds and wears well. Manilagrass is sensitive to highly acid soils. It responds well to liberal applications of nitrogen fertilizer and is established by sprigging or spot sodding.

Mascarenegrass (*Zoysia tenuifolia*) is a stoloniferous grass that is the least winter hardy of the zoysiagrasses. It is adapted to a very few locations in Florida and California. It ultimately becomes sod bound and humps up.

All zoysiagrasses turn offcolor during cool weather and become brown with the first killing frost. Zoysias do not become green until the warm weather in spring.

Points to remember: A lawn is not difficult to establish and maintain if a few cardinal principles are followed. Preparing a good seedbed is a start toward obtaining a good lawn. Select and plant lawn seed or lawn mixtures adapted to your region and location.

Fertilize your lawn according to the needs of the lawn grass species or mixture in your lawn. Do not overstimulate the lawn with nitrogen fertilizer. Succulent grass requires more frequent mowing, and may be more readily infected by fungus diseases. Too much nitrogen causes shallow rooting.

Do not water established lawns frequently and lightly. When the lawn shows need for water (slight wilting and footprinting), water the soil deeply to at least 6 inches, and do not water again until the symptoms reappear.

Mow at the recommended height for the dominant species in the lawn. Mowing frequencies will vary with the grass species in the lawn. The bermudagrasses and bentgrasses require more frequent mowing than do most upright-growing grasses.

Where shade is a problem, use grass species that are more shade tolerant, and remove lower branches of trees.

 # protecting lawn grasses against pests, wear

LAWN GRASSES, like people and pets, respond to the attention or abuse they receive. Unlike man and animals they can't complain when a disease attacks or an insect bites nor can they depart the scene when the environment becomes unfavorable. The user and the enjoyer of grass must watch for symptoms of attacks by pests or signs of abuse in order to speedily correct the trouble and maintain an esthetically appealing carpet of green.

Most diseases of lawn grasses are caused by fungi. They occur as microscopically small filaments (called mycelia) that are parasitic within or on plant parts. Masses of these cobwebby or cottony fungus filaments are sometimes visible on grass blades.

Many fungi attacking grasses reproduce by means of microscopic fruiting structures called spores. They are most noticeable when grasses infected with rust or smut fungi are being mowed and the spores are released like dust into the air.

Some fungi, such as mushrooms and slime molds, are not true disease organisms. They do not attack lawn grasses directly but are discussed with disease organisms because they commonly occur in lawns.

You can avoid or reduce damage from some fungus-caused diseases by following recommended cultural practices, growing disease-resistant varieties, or applying fungicides according to the manufacturer's or the turf specialist's instructions.

Helminthosporium leaf spot and foot rot gets its name from the *Helminthosporium* fungi that are among the most widely distributed and destructive lawn grass diseases. On Kentucky bluegrass, one of the species most severely damaged, the disease occurs mainly during cool, moist weather of spring and fall. The foot rot stage generally occurs during warm, dry summer months.

Infection in lawn grasses is most conspicuous on the leaves where reddish-brown spots develop. The leaf spots are often characterized by lighter-colored centers. Diseased leaves usually shrivel and die prematurely. When the grass crown becomes diseased, the entire plant dies.

The fungus responsible for brown patch disease attacks most species of the lawn grasses during warm, humid weather. Grasses which are growing rapidly following excessive application of nitrogen fertilizer are most severely damaged. Brown patch also develops if a heavy swath of grass clippings is left on the lawn following mowing.

Brown patch occurs in irregular, circular areas varying from a few inches to several feet in diameter. If the grass is wet and the disease is spreading, dead brown grass may be bordered by a narrow ring of dark-colored, recently infected grass. Sometimes only the leaves are affected and the turf recovers within 2 or 3 weeks.

A disease called dollar spot is most destructive on many species of grasses during spring and fall, especially during seasons of low rainfall. Damage is usually greatest if nitrogen fertility is low. The disease is characterized by development of bleached spots about the size of a silver dollar. Sometimes the individual spots become so numerous that they merge and form large irregular patches of dead grass. Lesions that are light tan with a reddish-brown border often extend across the entire grass blade.

Fusarium blight occurs on several grasses but is most damaging to Kentucky bluegrass. The disease occurs throughout the growing season although it is most noticeable in late spring and summer when the temperatures exceed 75°F. and humidity is high.

Patches of diseased grass first become

Author KERMIT W. KREITLOW was Assistant Chief of the Forage and Range Research Branch, Plant Science Research Division, Agricultural Research Service (ARS). He died in the fall of 1971.

Coauthor BERNARD A. APP is a retired Assistant Chief of the Grain and Forage Insects Research Branch, Entomology Research Division, ARS.

Coauthor RALPH E. ENGEL is Research Professor in Turfgrass Management, Rutgers University, New Brunswick, N.J.

light green, then rapidly fade to tan and light straw color. Dead areas may be circular, crescent-shaped, streaked, or in circles. A patch of live grass often occurs in the center of a dead area.

This disease is most severe where turf has been heavily fertilized with nitrogen and a layer of thatch has accumulated. (Thatch consists of dead but undecomposed stems and leaves at the soil surface.) Removing the thatch and treating with recommended fungicides help to control the disease.

Several rust fungi attack lawn grasses. The earliest rust pustules appear in spring but infection does not become noticeable until after the fungus multiplies and reaches its infection peak in midsummer and autumn.

Diseased grass blades are usually covered with powdery-yellow to orange-brown pustules. When abundant, the brownish-orange spores coat mowing equipment and shoes. Frequent mowing helps to remove diseased leaves so that newly emerging leaves are not so readily exposed to heavy spore concentration.

Rust injury is more severe on Merion Kentucky bluegrass and zoysia than on other grasses. The Kentucky bluegrass varieties Fylking and Pennstar are rust resistant.

Smut fungi attack the leaves and heads of grasses. One of the most widely distributed diseases is stripe smut. It produces narrow gray or black stripes that may be continuous or discontinuous lengthwise in leaf blades.

The gray stripes are unruptured smut lesions. The black stripes result when the smut lesions rupture and liberate a mass of black, powdery spores. Following rupture of the stripes, diseased leaves wither, curl, and shred from the tip downward.

Diseased plants often are pale green to slightly yellow and shorter than neighboring healthy plants. You can see them more readily during cool weather of spring and fall.

Many smutted plants die during hot, dry weather of midsummer. Since smutted plants are internally infected by the fungus, they will stay diseased until they die.

Smut damage is less severe if Merion Kentucky bluegrass is mixed with common Kentucky bluegrass, or if smut-tolerant varieties like Fylking, Park, or Pennstar are grown.

Lawn grasses are sometimes attacked during the winter months by snow mold fungi. Some of the fungi are active at or near freezing temperatures in the absence of snow; others attack grasses beneath melting snow.

Bentgrasses are usually the most severely damaged by snow mold fungi. Damaged areas may be a few inches to several feet in diameter. Grass blades often turn light brown or gray and tend to cling together and mat down. The diseased areas are sometimes discolored dirty white to pink.

To prevent snow mold, use grasses adapted to your area and avoid over-stimulating growth with high nitrogen fertilizers in fall. Keep the lawn mowed as long as the grass grows so that it will not mat down over winter.

Mushrooms that grow singly or in clumps often develop from buried organic matter such as pieces of construction lumber, logs, or stumps. Such mushroom fruiting bodies may be unsightly, but they are usually harmless to grass.

Another group of fungi produce mushroom-like fruiting bodies in circles or arcs of dark-green grass surrounded by light-colored or dead grass. These are known as fairy rings. The fungi that cause fairy rings spread outward from an initial infection point at the rate of 6 to 24 inches annually. Fairy rings are usually more noticeable in large lawns and seldom occur in lawns that are adequately fertilized and maintained.

Slime molds are fungi that cover grass blades with a dusty, bluish-gray, black, or yellow mass. Slime molds are not parasitic on grass. They occur during wet weather and disappear when it becomes dry. The discolored masses can be broken up by sweeping with a broom or by spraying with a strong stream of water.

About 60 species of insects injure lawn grasses by feeding on roots, stems, and leaves. This insect feeding weakens plants, causing patches of grass to turn yellow or brown and die. A few insects damage lawns by their burrowing or nesting habits.

It is virtually impossible to predict insect infestations, as populations fluctuate seasonally and locally depending upon climate, prevalence of natural enemies, abundance of food plants, and other factors. Fortunately only a few species are sufficiently abundant in any one year or any one place to justify control measures. You should examine your lawn frequently to detect insect infestation so that it can be properly treated before serious damage occurs.

Grubs are the most destructive soil inhabiting pests. They are the larvae of several species of beetles and in general are similar in appearance. They are whitish, soft bodied, usually with brown heads, and generally found in a curled position. These pests feed on the roots an inch or two below the surface, often destroying the turf.

The grubs hatch from eggs. They usually spend about 10 months in the soil, although some species require 2 to 3 years to reach maturity and emerge as adults. Birds, skunks, and moles feed on the grubs and often damage the lawn as they search for them.

Adult beetles of most species feed on the leaves of trees and shrubs and do not damage lawns.

White grubs are the most widely distributed in the United States. They are the larvae of the familiar yellow-brown to blackish May beetles or June bugs that are attracted to lights.

Grubs of Japanese beetles are very damaging in some eastern areas. The adults are shiny metallic green with coppery-brown wing covers and six patches of white hairs along the sides and back of the body. The beetles are active during the day and feed on many flowers and fruits.

Grubs of the Asiatic garden beetle, masked chafers, European chafer, and the Oriental beetle are other important species that damage lawns.

The nest-building habits of several species of ants and a few species of bees and wasps sometimes will damage lawns. They mound up the soil around their nests and may smother the grass.

Since 1960, billbugs have been destructive to lawns. One species called the hunting billbug has severely damaged zoysiagrass lawns in the East.

Billbugs are hard-shelled beetles ⅕- to ¾-inch long with a long snout. The larvae are legless, as much as ⅝-inch long, white with a reddish or yellowish-brown head. The adults burrow in the grass stems near the soil surface and the larvae feed upon the roots, often cutting them off so the grass can be easily pulled out.

In the Southeast, mole crickets often damage lawns by feeding on the grass roots. Their burrowing also uproots plants and allows the soil to dry out. Newly seeded lawns may be severely damaged. Adult mole crickets are about 1½ inches long, velvety brown with large, shovel-shaped front feet well suited for digging.

Caterpillars of several species damage lawns. Sod webworms are the most important. These are the larvae of small, whitish or grayish moths called lawn moths that are seen flying over the grass in early spring evenings. They can be easily recognized by their habit of folding their wings closely around their bodies when at rest. There are many species and one or more can be found in all parts of the United States. Sod webworms may have several generations per year depending on the species and location.

Larvae are about ¾-inch long when mature, and are brown or gray and usually spotted. They feed on grass leaves and are most active at night. The injury is first noticed as irregular brown spots and later as patches of uneven growth.

The fall armyworm is commonly found on lawns. This insect overwinters only in the extreme South and migrates north as the season advances.

When fully grown, the caterpillars are about 1½ inches long and vary from green to almost black. They feed on leaves and during outbreaks may devour the grass to the ground. The adults are ash-gray moths with mottled forewings.

When the wings are opened they measure about 1½ inches across. The insect produces several generations per year on the southern part of its range.

The armyworm is somewhat similar to the fall armyworm in size and appearance but much less common in lawns. Moths of this species are brown with a small white spot near the center of each front wing. There are usually three generations per year.

Chinch bugs are the most important sap-sucking pests of grasses, particularly in the East and the South. The hairy chinch bug is common in lawns in the Northeast and the southern chinch bug is a major pest, especially of St. Augustinegrass, in Florida and along the Gulf Coast.

The adults are about ⅙-inch long and black with white wings folded over their backs. The nymphs are bright red when very small but turn gray as they grow older. They have a white band across their backs.

Both the nymphs and the adults suck plant juices, causing the grass to turn yellow in irregular patches. If feeding continues, the grass turns brown and dies.

The hairy chinch bug has two to three generations per year and the southern chinch bug three to five.

Scale insects also suck plant juices. Some species attack the roots while others damage the aboveground parts. Newly born scales, called crawlers, are active and move about over the plant. In a few days they settle down, insert their mouthparts into the plant, lose their legs, and begin an attached existence. The Rhodesgrass scale, bermudagrass scale, and ground pearls are common species.

Several species of leafhoppers are found in lawns. They are small wedge-shaped insects about ⅕-inch long, ranging from yellow to green and gray. Both nymphs and adults retard grass growth by sucking sap from the leaves and stems. Injury appears as whitened areas often mistaken for drought or disease damage.

The damage which insects cause to lawns can be reduced by following recommended cultural and maintenance practices. A healthy, vigorous turf can support greater insect populations without serious harm better than one in poor condition.

Biological control of insect pests helps to reduce damage. Birds seek out and destroy many insects in lawns. Insect parasites, predators, and diseases reduce populations but their impact on lawn insects has not been thoroughly studied. None of the grass varieties we commonly use for lawns is resistant to insects. When lawn insects become numerous they can be controlled with insecticides.

Lawn grasses tolerate a wide assortment of natural and manmade contamination hazards. Surprisingly few of these prevent grass growth, but they often do make growing good turf more difficult.

Annual bluegrass was found sensitive to California smog 20 years ago. Annual bluegrass and bentgrass have shown injury from ozone while red fescue and bentgrass are sensitive to sulfur dioxide. Red fescue is intolerant of industrial fumes in some parts of New Jersey.

Grass tolerates a wide range of water quality. Water with heavy metals and/or high salt content can cause serious trouble, but is seldom encountered. Of course, some man-prepared chemicals can be harmful. An example is highly chlorinated water; yet such injury is observed infrequently. Few soils fail to grow grass if the soil acidity is properly adjusted and management practices are favorable.

When all the natural and manmade excesses of the environment are totaled, they are but a minor cause of turfgrass failure.

Rather than turfgrass existence becoming seriously threatened by the overused environment, grass is a plant type that may become more abundant. Its potential value for maintaining a good environment in populous areas is legendary with those folks who know its ways.

Some of the contributions of grass to a purer environment are: controlling erosion from wind or water, consuming carbon dioxide and releasing oxygen, trapping noise and dust, cooling areas through transpiration, providing a living surface for recreation, and serving as the greatest soil conditioner throughout mankind's history of environmental manipulation.

Turfgrasses stand alone as the most wear tolerant of the living ground covers. This tolerance is possible through their renewable leaf cushion above the soil and their abundance of renewable roots beneath the surface. While most professional and amateur turf growers know that grass is easier to grow without traffic, they realize that turf is grown to be used. Use problems become more intense with increasing population density.

Research on traffic and wear problems of turf is sparse. However, some basic guides have been developed. A key consideration is restricting traffic to permit the grass to survive and to grow the cover desired. Wear that destroys established turf necessitates non-use periods when turf is being re-established.

Experience and limited research have provided us with a few practices that permit better utilization of turf. Rotation practice or spreading wear to prevent loss of grass is helpful. This not only avoids concentrated damage in small areas, but it enables the grass to renew its vigor which is necessary for survival. Attractive and easily moved barriers can be employed to spread or rotate traffic on excessively used turf areas.

Keeping off turf at times when grass may be unusually susceptible to injury can provide more total use throughout the rest of the year. A very wet turf can be destroyed within a short time and the soil may become severely compacted.

When the weather is hot and dry, traffic on the cool-climate grasses is very damaging. Conversely, the warm-weather grasses, bermudagrass and zoysia, are more intolerant of traffic in winter.

Seedling turf must be protected from traffic for several mowings; and only a limited traffic should be permitted during the first year.

With very weak grass growth, where stand failure could result from various causes, use of the turf should be avoided to increase its chance for survival.

Where a choice of grass exists, use the most wear-tolerant species. In warm, sunny, subtropical areas such as the Southern United States or in tropical areas, bermudagrass is excellent for the heavy wear areas. In the Northern United States and similar cool, temperate areas, Kentucky bluegrass is most desirable because of its vigor and rhizome (underground stem) development. Grasses such as tall fescue, zoysia, and ryegrass have tougher leaves and they may be the best grass where local conditions permit.

When it is necessary to restrict traffic on turf, a small adjacent area of all-weather concrete, asphalt, paving block, or plastic mats may be provided.

In the future, we can anticipate obtaining more days of use from natural turf. This can be done by avoiding overstimulation of grass growth from high nitrogen fertilizer or water, by developing and utilizing more wear-tolerant grass varieties, by learning to modify soils to reduce their susceptibility to compaction and to insure good drainage, and by devising mechanical methods of relieving soil compaction.

Weeds can destroy desirable turf cover. Crabgrass (*Digitaria ischaemum* and *D. sanguinalis*), chickweed, annual bluegrass (*Poa annua*), dandelion, and to some extent white clover are examples of weeds that destroy turf cover, where they develop vigorously, or cause unsightly contrasts.

Some weeds make sports turf unusable. They include goosegrass, the sedges (*Carex* spp.), and white clover. The latter is undesirable on various types of sports fields and it attracts bees to home lawn sites.

In mixtures, otherwise useful turfgrasses such as bermudagrass, tall fescue, and bentgrasses are sometimes unwanted species and assume the role of weeds.

While control of turf weeds varies with the species involved, the single, most used and best weed control method is growing a dense and persistent cover of turfgrasses. Even when other methods such as hand-weeding or herbicides are used, these treatments become far more effective and less frequently required when a good turf cover is growing. Good cultural practices help to develop such a turf.

Once weeds threaten a turfgrass area, it is important to avoid cultural practices which increase the weed at the expense of the turfgrass. In case of crabgrass encroachment, avoid watering, fertilization, and close mowing. These treatments help to keep the weed from making increasingly dense growth which smothers grasses like Kentucky bluegrass when it is growing slowly in summer.

A good technique for the control of crabgrass in Kentucky bluegrass turf involves shading-out the crabgrass seedlings before they become established. Generous fertilization in late summer and early fall, plus a high cut of 3 to 4 inches the following spring, gives a tall, dense canopy that prevents crabgrass seedlings from germinating in spring. Once crabgrass is under control, the mowing height can be lowered to approximately 1½ to 2 inches.

The best control for some turf weeds is complete elimination. Dandelions and crabgrass are common examples. Once weeds of this type cease to exist in turf, their control can be easy and inexpensive. Each year the few plants starting from the occasional invading weed seed should be removed; this involves little work and less herbicide. You must persist in obtaining complete control of the weed. Failure to make the small effort each year will nullify the weedfree condition.

While growing good turf is by far the most universal, single antidote for weeds, there is almost no hope of controlling some weeds without the use of herbicides. Various chemicals have been used as herbicides to control turf weeds for more than 40 years.

The early chemicals were often lacking in effectiveness and safety to the turf. Occasionally they were dangerous to the user and left unwanted residues. But modern herbicides are a boon to the homeowner and to the turf grower.

Proper choice of herbicides and observance of instruction will help to control most common weeds of turf. The herbicide 2,4–D has been used for 25 years. Earlier, vapors of this chemical readily damaged adjacent desirable plants. However, low volatility forms now available have largely eliminated this problem. Combining some herbicides controls most broadleaved weeds in turf, although the chemicals can damage some trees and shrubs if applied carelessly or at excessive rates. The main concern with the preemergence crabgrass herbicides is overdosage which can temporarily thin the turf.

Efficient weed control with herbicides reduces the need for nitrogen fertilizer. Prior to the development of effective herbicides, heavy nitrogen application was the only alternative for controlling some serious weeds.

Several turf weeds such as annual bluegrass, sedges, goosegrass, and torpedograss have not responded to the currently useful management practices or herbicides.

For further reading:
U.S. Department of Agriculture, *Better Lawns.* Home and Garden Bulletin 51, Washington, D.C. 20250, 1971.
———, *Lawn Weed Control With Herbicides.* Home and Garden Bulletin 123, Washington, D.C. 20250, 1971.

ground covers can cure headaches such as problem sites, bare spots

THE BUILDER, in siting your house to your lot, makes deep cuts in the ground to fit house, walks, and driveways to the main road. The exposed soil slowly washes away with each rain . . .

A hard, foot-beaten path through your yard is used as a shortcut by everyone in the neighborhood while that expensive stone and gravel path you put in remains unused . . .

The spreading and upright shrubs you planted near the foundation of your house are finally beginning to grow. But the view from the street is something less than the photo in the garden magazine—the one you blew $75 at the nursery to duplicate. Your plants look dreadfully haphazard and helterskelter . . .

You're spending a lot of time clipping between the individual trees and shrubs and the grass underneath isn't growing very well, either, because of the dense shade . . .

Blowing your top isn't the solution to these problems. There's a better way.

Try planting ground covers, which include any low growing plants. You can use most vines, prostrate forms of conifers, broad- and narrow-leaf evergreens, and some annual and perennial herbaceous plants.

Low-growing plants can do a lot of things. They can cover bare spots in the yard, prevent soil erosion, regulate foot traffic, and tie together unrelated plants into a composition. In addition, they may serve as a fire-retarding screen in arid regions, filter out dust particles from the air, and hide litter that might blow into your yard.

Ground covers can be used in areas where no other kind of plant or artificial cover can be used. Installed with careful attention to the requirements of plants and site, ground covers can solve such site problems as a steeply

Author HENRY M. CATHEY is Leader of Ornamental Investigations in the Plant Science Research Division, Agricultural Research Service.

sloping bank, the inner courtyard of a shopping mall or building, and areas of dense shade.

Once established, ground covers require yearly maintenance at the most to keep them attractive.

The establishment of ground covers always takes a lot of time. Regardless of the site selected for the ground covers, the soil must be modified to support root growth of the plants.

You should make certain that water is available at all times to prevent the soil and the roots from drying out.

And, you'll have to keep the bed clear of weeds until the plants cover the area. You'll find that it's a good idea to keep the growing areas carefully defined, both for the sake of looks and to keep the plants within bounds.

Regardless of what plant you select, you will find that they are all handled very much alike for site, soil preparation, planting procedures, watering and fertilizing, over-winter care, and yearly management.

The site itself should be prepared thoroughly before setting out the plants. Dig the soil at least 6 inches deep.

Spring flowering bulbs were planted in ground cover, Euonymus, for extra color.

Spread 2 to 3 inches of organic material such as peat, well-rotted manure, or leaf mold over the ground and spade it into the soil.

On uneven ground where the entire area cannot be worked, dig individual planting holes. Dig these deep enough so you can backfill partially with soil mixed with organic material before you set out the plants. Use topsoil for the rest of the refill.

You can plant most slopes and banks in ground covers. Low banks 2 to 4 feet high can be planted without any additional preparation, but you should build retaining walls at the foot of steep slopes to reduce the slope and help prevent erosion. Sloping areas are usually dry so you must select plants which will tolerate periodic drought. Large, vigorous plants such as junipers or cotoneasters usually are grown on slopes.

Use a fertilizer on the planting site when you prepare the soil. Spade the fertilizer into the soil. Follow recommendations for fertilizer for your area. Fertilizer needs vary according to soil types and area of the country.

Although you can plant ground covers anytime during the growing season, early spring is the best time in most places. This allows the plants to become well established during a long growing period before winter.

When you plant ground covers, space the plants so they will cover the site as quickly as possible. You may put small plants like bugleweed as close as 4 to 6 inches apart. Set such large plants as juniper or cotoneaster as much as 4 feet apart. Closer planting will cover the ground more rapidly but the cost of additional plants may be prohibitive.

The table shows the area that approximately 100 plants will cover when set at various distances apart. For example, if you set the plants 4 inches apart, 100 plants will cover around 11 square feet.

A well-established ground cover planting usually needs little maintenance. Occasional fertilizing, mulching, weeding, and watering are the main requirements.

Areas Covered by 100 Plants at Different Planting Distances

Planting distance (inches)	Area covered (square feet)
4	11
6	25
8	44
10	70
12	100
18	225
24	400
36	900
48	1,600

Fertilize the plants during winter and again in early spring. To avoid burning the foliage, scatter a pelleted form of commercial fertilizer over the planting when the foliage is dry.

Ground covers are slow in covering bare ground. Consequently, weeds are likely to grow, especially the first year. You can control most weeds with a mulch of wood chips, straw, or other organic refuse. The mulch will also retain moisture in the soil. If weeds break through the mulch, pull them by hand. The selection and uses of mulches are discussed in the chapter that begins on page 241.

Do not dig around the plants. Digging breaks the surface roots and promotes germination of weed seeds.

Do not rely on summer rainfall to keep your ground cover watered. Water on a regular schedule throughout the growing season, particularly during dry weather. Methods to automate watering are discussed on pages 66 and 67.

Allow the water to penetrate deeply into the soil, but do not water so heavily that the soil becomes soggy. Water again when the soil is dry to the touch and the tips of the plants wilt slightly at midday. One inch of water every 10 to 14 days is satisfactory for rapid establishment of the plants. During winter months, water the plants thoroughly when the weather is dry and the temperature above freezing.

In cold climates with no permanent snow cover, plantings in direct sunlight may need protection during the winter months to prevent the thawing out of plant tissues. Direct sunlight can cause permanent damage. You can protect the plants by laying conifer branches or burlap over the beds. If the plants heave out of the soil in cold weather, push them back immediately. Do not wait until spring.

Ground covers usually need pruning only to remove dead wood and keep the planting in bounds. You can mow some plants that are grown on level ground.

Ground covers will show winter injury just as do other plants. Evergreen plants, for example, suffer considerable damage when the foliage has been windburned following an extremely dry winter. You can shear such plantings or individually prune out damaged branches in early spring.

Plantings of juniper may be so badly winter damaged that soil areas become bare. When this happens, you should replant bare areas rather than wait until the old planting fills in the gaps.

You can reduce winter damage by covering the plants with an anti-transpirant spray. These sprays cut down moisture loss. They are available at garden supply stores. If you spray plants in the fall, they will retain the waterproof cover for most of the winter months. You also should spray plants when you transplant them. How to make cuttings and divide ground cover plants are discussed in the chapter that begins on page 195.

From the list, you can select a ground cover for any hardiness zone, height, and site. It gives the common and Latin name, height at maturity, type of growth, hardiness zones, soil and light requirements, and comments on leaf, flower, or fruit color or other characteristics.

Plants are keyed to the numbered hardiness zones shown on the map inside the front cover of this book. The temperatures shown for each zone are based on average minimum temperatures taken from long-term weather records. Soil type, rainfall, summer temperatures, and daylength also determine whether a plant can thrive in a given location.

Guide to Selecting Groundcovers

Common name	Height (Inches)	Hardiness (Zone)	Type	Soil and light	Comments
Barrenwort .... *Epimedium alpinum; E. grandiflorum; E. pinnatum*	12	4–8	Woody herb	Tolerates almost any soil	Dense foliage; lasts into winter; white, yellow, lavender flowers
Bearberry .... *Arctostaphylos uvursi*	6–10	2–9	Evergreen shrub	Excellent in stony, sandy, acid soils	Low; hard to transplant; bright red fruit
Bergenia, heartleaf ...... *Bergenia cordifolia*	12	5–10	Creeping, clumpy perennial; thick rootstocks	Sun or partial shade	Pink flowers; thick, heavy foliage
Broom .... *Genista pilosa; G. sagittalis*	6–12	5–9	Deciduous shrub	Well-drained soil; sun	Flowers are pea shaped
Bugleweed .... *Ajuga reptans*	4–8	5–9	Perennial herb	Tolerates most soils	Densely packed plants; blue-purple flowers; rapid grower
Capeweed .... *Phyla nodiflora*	2–4	9–10	Creeping perennial herb	Sand and waste areas	Low-growing; spreads rapidly; cut like grass; light pink flowers
Coralberry .... *Symphoricarpos orbiculatus*	to 36	3–9	Deciduous shrub	Thrives in poor soils	Rapid growth by underground stems; requires yearly pruning
Cotoneaster .... *Cotoneaster adpressa* *C. apiculata* .... *C. dammeri* .... *C. horizontalis* .... *C. microphylla*	6–30	5–10 5–9 6–10 7–10	Semi-evergreen herb	Full sun, reseed	Stems will layer subject to fire blight
Cowberry .... *Vaccinium vitis-idaea*	to 12	5–9	Small evergreen shrub	Acid soil	Small pink flowers, dark-red berries
Creeping lilyturf ...... *Liriope spicata*	to 12	5–10	Matted herb	Extreme heat, dry soil, stands salt spray	Dense mat, dark green leaves, purple flowers
Creeping lippia ...... *Phyla nodiflora* var. *canescens*	2–4	5–10	Creeping perennial	Any soil, sun	White, lilac flowers

127

Guide to Selecting Groundcovers—Continued

Common name	Height (Inches)	Hardiness (Zone)	Type	Soil and light	Comments
Creeping thyme .... *Thymus serpyllum*	to 3	5–10	Subshrubby with creeping stems	Tolerates dry soils, sun	Substitute for grass, extremely variable
Crownvetch .... *Coronilla varia*	12–24	3–7	Herb	Dry, steep banks, sun	Small pink flowers
Daylily .... *Hemerocallis*	18–60	3–10	Root, fleshy and tuberous parts	Sun, dry to boggy soils	Few problems; summer flowers
Dichondra .... *Dichondra repens*	1–2	9 and 10	Evergreen perennial	Sunny or shady locations	Poor drought resistance; rarely needs clipping; spreads rapidly
Dwarf bamboo .... *Sasa pumila, S. veitchii, and Shibataea kumasaca*		6–10	Low shrub	Sun; sandy soil	Foliage brown in winter; fire hazard; grass substitute
English ivy .... *Hedera helix*	6–8	5–9	Evergreen vine	Sun or shade	Clip leaves to control leaf spots
Forsythia species .... *Forsythia* spp.	Trim to 18	5–9	Deciduous shrub	Sun, well-drained soil	Stems root easily; yellow flowers in spring
Galax .... *Galax aphylla*	6	5–7	Evergreen, stemless perennial herb	Moist, rich, acid soil, shade	White flowers in spring; leaves turn bronze in fall
Germander .... *Teucrium chamaedrys*	to 10	6–10	Small woody perennial	Sun or partial shade	Winter damage without protection
Ground-ivy .... *Glechoma hederacea*	3	3–9	Trailing perennial	Sun or shade; any soil	Becomes a pest in lawn if not trimmed; forms a low mat
Heath .... *Erica carnea*	6–12	5–8	Evergreen shrub	Poor, acid soils, sun	Pink, purple, red, white varieties
Heather .... *Calluna vulgaris*	6–24	4–7	Evergreen shrub	Acid soil, well-drained, low fertility, sun	Shear plants each spring
Holly, Japanese .... *Ilex crenata*	Keep to 24	6–10	Evergreen shrub	Sun or semi-shade	Slow growing; small bank plantings
Hollygrape, dwarf .... *Mahonia repens*	to 10	6–9	Evergreen shrub	Sun or shade, any type soil	Yellow flowers

128

Name	Height	Zone	Type	Conditions	Remarks
Honeysuckle, Japanese .... *Lonicera japonica*	to 10	5–9	Twisting, trailing vine	Sun or partial shade	Prune yearly to keep in bounds; a semi-evergreen with white turning to yellow flowers
Iceplant .... *Cephalophyllum, Carpobrotus,* *Delosperma, Drosanthemum,* *Malephora, Lampranthus*	4–6	10	Low succulent	Sun; well-drained soil	Temporary ground cover in cold climates; brilliant colored flowers open in full sunlight
Japanese spurge .... *Pachysandra terminalis*	to 6	5–8	Evergreen herb	Semi-shade under tree	Spreads by underground stems
Juniper .... *Juniperus horizontalis* *J. sabina* *J. procumbens* *J. chinensis* *J. conferta*	12–18 trim to 36	3–10	Evergreen conifer	Sun; dry areas	Yearly pruning of upright forms; wide range of foliage colors; some turn purple in winter
Lantana .... *Lantana sellowiana;* *L. montevidensis*	6–10	8–10	Trailing shrub	Sun, high salt tolerance	Wide range of flower colors
Lily-of-the-valley .... *Convallaria majalis*	6–10	4–9	Rootstock	Rich, moist, high organic soil; partial shade	Fragrant white bell-shaped flowers
Lilyturf dwarf (Mondograss) .... *Ophiopogon japonicus*	to 10	7–10	Matted herb	Any soil, sun or shade	Spikes of pale lilac flowers
Moss sandwort .... *Arenaria verna*	3	2–9	Perennial herb	Fertile soil, moist; partial shade	Requires some winter protection
Moss, pink .... *Phlox subulata*	6	4–10	Evergreen perennial	Porous soil; sun	Flowers are shade of pink and white
Periwinkle .... *Vinca minor* (small leaves) *V. major* (large leaves)	6–8	5–10	Trailing herb	Avoid high nitrogen fertilizer, poorly drained soils	Purple, blue, and white flowers

Guide to Selecting Groundcovers—Continued

Common name	Height (Inches)	Hardiness (Zone)	Type	Soil and light	Comments
Plantain lily .... *Hosta* spp.	12–16	4–10	Tufted plant with broad leaves	Moist, well-drained soils; shade	Needs frequent division
Polygonum, dwarf .... *Polygonum cuspidatum* var. *compactum*	12–24	4–10	Stout perennial	Rocky or gravelly soil; sun	Foliage turns red in fall
Rose, memorial .... *Rosa wichuraiana*	6–12	5–9	Semi-evergreen low-growing shrub	Banks and sand dunes	2-inch white flowers
St.-Johns-wort .... *Hypericum calycinum*	9–12	6–10	Semi-evergreen shrub	Semi-shade; sandy soil	Yellow flowers in summer; red foliage in autumn
Sand Strawberry .... *Fragaria chiloensis*	10–12	6–10	Perennial herb	Suitable for most soils	Spreads rapidly
Sarcococca .... *Sarcococca hookeriana*	to 72	6–10	Evergreen shrub	Shade	Shear for height control; small white flowers, large leaves
South African daisy .... *Gazania rigens*	6–9	9–10	Evergreen perennial	Avoid high nitrogen fertilizers; poorly drained soils	Light green foliage; orange flowers
Stonecrop, goldmoss .... *Sedum acre*	4	4–10	Evergreen perennial	Dry areas	Forms mats of tiny foliage
Strawberry geranium .... *Saxifraga sarmentosa*	15	7–9	Perennial herb	Partial shade; rock gardens, heavy clay soils	Spreads by runners
Thrift .... *Armeria maritima*	6	5–9	Perennial herb	Sandy soil; full sun	Small pink flowers in spring
Wandering-Jew .... *Zebrina pendula*	6–9	10	Tender herb	Shade, acid or alkaline soils	Roots easily
Wintercreeper .... *Euonymus fortunei*	2–4	5–10	Clinging evergreen vine	Sun; shade; ordinary soil	Rapid, flat growth; subject to scale insects
Wintergreen .... *Gaultheria procumbens*	4	5–7	Creeping evergreen	Acid soil; moist shady areas	Creeps over area
Yarrow .... *Achillea millefolium*	2–3	5–9	Fern-like perennial herb	Adapted to poor, dry soil; full sun	Remains green even during drought

vegetables, fruits, and herbs:
how to grow food cheaply

A HOME GARDEN can provide a family with an abundant supply of high-quality vegetables, fruits, and herbs at low cost. Gardening is also an excellent form of relaxation and can give you the satisfaction of having grown your own produce.

To help ensure success and to derive maximum yields, the entire garden should be planned in detail before anything is planted. In planning you should consider the location of the garden, the crops and varieties of each to be grown, when and where each crop will be planted, and the amount of each crop to plant.

Ideally, the garden soil should be deep, granular or easily pulverized, well drained, high in organic matter such as compost and humus, and slightly acid. However, it is not always possible to have such a soil and it may be beneficial to improve your soil by adding fertilizer, lime, and organic matter.

The garden should receive direct sunlight all day. In addition, it should be far enough from trees so they don't compete with the crops for water.

If you have only a small site available for a garden, we suggest you grow crops that will yield the heaviest over the longest period of time. Vegetables suitable for a small garden include tomatoes, peppers, cucumbers, bush summer squash, bush lima and snap beans, and onions.

Vegetables that require much space and yield a small return include muskmelons, sweet corn, watermelons, winter squash, and pumpkins. These crops are adapted to a large garden.

Vegetables vary greatly in their response to temperature. Some make their best growth in the spring and fall,

or winter in the South, when cool temperatures prevail. Other vegetables are very sensitive to cool temperatures and thrive only during warm weather. Temperature requirements of the common vegetables are given on page 132.

Although lettuce, spinach, collards, cabbage, mustard, kale, and turnips are cool-hardy plants, there are varieties of each that are more tolerant of warm temperatures than others. The heat-tolerant varieties are slower to bolt or produce a seed stalk.

Because of different climatic requirements and different maturity rates for various vegetables, it is wise to use successive cropping in the garden. This conserves space and enables you to grow a variety of crops.

Examples of successive cropping systems are: spinach, lettuce, green onions, or endive, followed by beans, tomatoes, peppers, or eggplant; cabbage, cauliflower, carrots, beets, or peas, followed by snap beans, cowpeas, or corn; beans followed by late cabbage, cauliflower, or corn; or corn followed by beans, beets, lettuce, turnips, carrots, or by spinach.

After deciding on the vegetables to be included in your garden, you must make the important decision of what varieties to grow. Vegetable varieties differ in their adaptation to different

Author ALLAN K. STONER is a Horticulturist in the Vegetables and Ornamentals Research Branch, Plant Science Research Division, Agricultural Research Service.

Coauthor HOWARD J. BROOKS is Chief of the division's Fruit and Nut Crops Research Branch.

Coauthor LLEWELYN WILLIAMS is a Botanist in the division's New Crops Research Branch.

Some Common Vegetables With Approximate Times They Can Be Planted and Their Relative Requirements for Cool and Warm Weather

Cold-hardy plants for early spring planting		Cold-tender or heat-hardy plants for late spring or early summer planting			Hardy plants for late summer or fall planting except in the North
Very hardy (plant 4 to 6 weeks before frost-free date)	Hardy (plant 2 to 4 weeks before frost-free date)	Not cold-hardy (plant on frost-free date)	Requiring hot weather (plant 1 week or more after frost-free date)	Medium heat-tolerant (good for summer planting)	(Plant 6 to 8 weeks before first fall freeze)
Broccoli	Beets	Beans, snap	Beans, lima	Beans, all	Beets
Cabbage	Carrots	Corn, sweet	Cucumber	Chard	Collards
Lettuce	Chard	Okra	Eggplant	Corn, sweet	Kale
Onions	Mustard	Squash	Melons	Soybeans	Lettuce
Peas	Parsnips	Tomato	Peppers	Squash	Mustard
Potato	Radish		Sweetpotato		Spinach
Spinach					Turnips
Turnips					

areas of the country and soil types; resistance to diseases and nematodes; quality for fresh use, canning, or for freezing; and days from planting to maturity.

Names of vegetable varieties adapted to your local area can be obtained from your State agricultural experiment station or county extension agent. Experienced local gardeners may also be good sources of information on the locally adapted varieties.

To insure a steady supply of crops such as sweet corn or snap beans, you can make successive plantings several days apart. Harvests can also be spread out by planting varieties that mature

Above, mini-vegetable garden on balcony of suburban Washington, D.C., apartment. Growing in laundry pails and plastic pots, plants are all in small wagons or wheelbarrows so they can be easily moved to sunny areas or indoors on cool nights. Left, a Maryland gardener.

Vegetable	Early variety	Late variety
Beans—green pod (bush).	45	65
Beans—green pod (pole).	56	72
Beans, lima	65	78
Beets	55	80
Broccoli [1]	70	150
Brussels sprouts [1]	90	100
Cabbage [1]	65	110
Chinese cabbage	70	80
Carrots	60	85
Cauliflower [1]	55	75
Celery	90	115
Collards	70	80
Corn, sweet	65	90
Cucumber	55	75
Eggplant [1]	70	85
Kale	55	70
Kohlrabi	55	62
Lettuce (head)	45	76
Lettuce (leaf)	45	50
Muskmelon	75	110
Okra	55	60
Onions	90	130
Parsnips	110	130
Peas	58	75
Peppers (bell or sweet) [1]	62	80
Potato	90	120
Pumpkin	100	115
Radish	23	30
Rutabaga	80	90
Southern peas (cowpeas) .	65	105
Spinach	35	45
Squash (summer)	50	60
Squash (winter)	95	110
Sweetpotato	120	150
Tomato [1]	65	90
Turnips	42	55
Watermelon	80	95

[1] Days from transplanting. Additional time needed from seeding to transplanting.

at different times. Ranges in maturity of different varieties of the common vegetables are given above.

Growing a variety resistant to diseases and nematodes often means the difference between obtaining a crop or having a total crop failure. This is especially true with plant diseases that cannot be controlled by spraying or dusting with chemicals. Examples of such diseases are fusarium and verticillium wilts of tomato, Stewart's wilt of sweet corn, tobacco mosaic virus of peppers, and cucumber mosaic virus of cucumbers and muskmelons.

Even though a disease can be controlled by chemicals, growing a resistant variety may eliminate the need for repeated applications of pesticides. Diseases that can be controlled by spraying, but to which resistant varieties are available, include downy and powdery mildew of cucumbers and muskmelons, and gray leaf spot and late blight of tomatoes.

It is not always necessary to grow resistant varieties since not all diseases occur in all areas of the country. For example, nematodes are most prevalent in warm climates, so it is not necessary to grow a nematode resistant tomato variety in the northern areas. Likewise, curly top virus is only a problem in certain western areas, so resistant beans and tomatoes are necessary only in these areas.

If vegetables are grown primarily for fresh consumption, we generally suggest you avoid growing varieties that have been bred for machine harvesting. Such varieties are developed to have their entire crop ripen at one time, whereas the home gardener usually prefers to spread the harvest over a long period of time. For canning or freezing, however, the machine harvest varieties may be desirable.

The quality (color, taste, texture, etc.) and the intended use (fresh, canning, or freezing) of the produce should be considered in the selection of varieties. Differences in quality include yellow vs. green podded beans, white vs. red radishes, and hot or pungent vs. mild-tasting onions. Some varieties are especially suited for fresh consumption, while others are suited for canning or freezing.

A partial list of vegetable varieties for home garden use begins on the next page. Additional information on varieties can be obtained from catalogs published annually by seed companies, newspaper gardening columns, and the garden or horticultural magazines.

Fruits take more space in the garden than vegetables but they can be equally rewarding. Once established, adapted

Some Vegetable Varieties Suited for Home Gardens

Variety	Remarks
Asparagus	
Mary Washington	Widely adapted, tolerant to rust
Beans (bush)	
Topcrop	Widely adapted, resistant to bean mosaic
Contender	Resistant to bean mosaic and powdery mildew
Bush Blue Lake 274	Heavy yield, resistant to bean mosaic
Resistant Cherokee Wax	Yellow pods, resistant to bean mosaic
Resistant Kinghorn Wax	Yellow pods, resistant to bean mosaic
Beans (pole)	
Kentucky Wonder	Widely adapted, excellent for freezing
Dade	Adapted to South, resistant to rust, common and Southern bean mosaic
Romano	Widely adapted, good for freezing
Beans, lima	
Fordhook 242	Widely adapted
Henderson's Bush	"Baby" or small seeded
Jackson Wonder	Widely adapted
Beets	
Detroit Dark Red	Widely adapted
Ruby Queen	Widely adapted, good for canning
Broccoli	
Waltham 29	Widely adapted, good for freezing
Green Comet	Widely adapted
Brussels sprouts	
Jade Cross	Widely adapted
Long Island Improved	Heavy yield over extended period
Cabbage	
Golden Acre	Resistant to cabbage yellows
Early Jersey Wakefield	Slow bolting, resistant to cabbage yellows
Copenhagen Market	Widely adapted, early maturity
Red Acre	Red color
Chinese cabbage	
Michihli	Widely adapted
Carrots	
Danvers 126	Widely adapted, heavy yield of long tapered roots
Royal Chantenay	Widely adapted, broad-shouldered roots with little taper
Imperator Long Type	Widely adapted, long slender roots
Cauliflower	
Snowball Y	Widely adapted, produces over a long period
Early Snowball A	Early maturing
Celery	
Utah 52–70	Widely adapted, tolerant to celery mosaic, resistant to boron deficiency
Collards	
Vates	Slow bolting
Georgia	Widely adapted
Corn, sweet	
Iochief	Resistant to Stewart's wilt
Seneca Chief	Resistant to Stewart's wilt
Butter and Sugar	Mixture of white and yellow kernels, excellent quality
Golden Security	Resistant to Stewart's wilt

135

Variety	*Remarks*

Cucumber (slicing)
Ashley . . . . Resistant to downy mildew
Saticoy Hybrid . . . . Tolerant to downy mildew and mosaic
Marketer . . . . Resistant to downy mildew

Cucumber (pickling)
Pioneer . . . . Tolerant to scab, mosaic, downy and powdery mildew, anthracnose, and angular leaf spot
Wisconsin SMR–18 . . . . Resistant to scab and mosaic

Eggplant
Jersey King . . . . Elongated fruit, widely adapted
Black Beauty . . . . Oval globe fruit, widely adapted
Mission Bell . . . . Early high yield

Kale
Vates . . . . Slow bolting
Siberian (sprouts) . . . . Very vigorous

Kohlrabi
Early White Vienna . . . . Widely adapted

Lettuce (leaf)
Salad Bowl . . . . Slow bolting, high quality
Grand Rapids . . . . Tip burn resistant

Lettuce (butterhead)
Buttercrunch . . . . Slow bolting, high quality

Lettuce (crisp head)
Great Lakes . . . . Slow bolting, widely adapted

Muskmelon
Supermarket . . . . Resistant to fusarium and downy mildew
Hales Best Jumbo . . . . Large fruit
Saticoy Hybrid . . . . Resistant to fusarium, tolerant to powdery mildew

Mustard
Green Wave . . . . Slow bolting
Southern Giant Curled . . . . . . Slow bolting
Florida Broad Leaf . . . . Slow bolting

Okra
Dwarf Green Long Pod . . . . . . Dwarf vine
Clemson Spineless . . . . Spineless
Emerald . . . . High quality

Onions
Yellow Sweet Spanish . . . . Large globe shape
Ebenezer . . . . Yellow, quite pungent
Downing Yellow Globe . . . . . . Good storage

Parsnips
Hollow Crown . . . . Widely adapted

Peas
Alaska . . . . Resistant to fusarium wilt
Little Marvel . . . . Good quality, good for freezing
Progress No. 9 . . . . Large early peas

Peppers
Calwonder . . . . Sweet, widely adapted
Yolo Wonder . . . . Sweet, resistant to tobacco mosaic virus
Keystone Resistant Giant . . . . Sweet, resistant to tobacco mosaic virus
Hungarian Yellow Wax . . . . . . Hot

Variety	Remarks

Potato
Irish Cobbler .... Early, widely adapted
Sebago .... Widely adapted
Kennebec .... Widely adapted

Pumpkin
Connecticut Field .... Large smooth orange fruit
Cinderella .... Bush vine, 10-inch fruit
Jack O'Lantern .... Large uniform yellow fruit

Radish
Cherry Belle .... Red color
Champion .... Red color
Icicle .... White color

Southern Peas (cowpeas)
California Blackeye No. 5 .... Good for freezing, large seed with black eye
Pink Eye Purple Hull .... Elongated seed, light color
Mississippi Silver .... Early maturing, large seed, light green to cream in
color

Spinach
Early Hybrid No. 7 .... Resistant to downy mildew and cucumber mosaic virus
Long Standing Bloomsdale .... Widely adapted, slow bolting

Squash (summer)
Zucchini .... Bush plant, cylindrical
Early Prolific Straightneck .... Bush plant, tapered cylindrical fruit
Yellow Summer Crookneck ... Bush plant, fruit tapered cylinder with curved neck
Early White Bush Scallop ..... Bush plant, flat round fruit

Squash (winter)
Waltham Butternut .... High quality, elongated pear-shaped fruit
Table Queen .... High quality, heart-shaped fruit
Hubbard .... Large globular fruit tapered at ends
Golden Delicious .... Large, somewhat oval-shaped fruit

Sweetpotato
Centennial .... Widely adapted
Puerto Rico .... Widely adapted

Tomato
Ace VF .... Adapted to West, resistant to fusarium and verticil-
lium
Fireball VF .... Adapted to East and North, resistant to fusarium and
verticillium
Manapal .... Widely adapted, resistant to fusarium, gray leaf spot,
and blossom end rot
H1350 .... Adapted East and Midwest, resistant to fusarium and
verticillium
Better Boy .... Resistant to fusarium, verticillium, and nematodes
Supersonic .... Resistant to fusarium and verticillium
Small Fry .... Small fruit, resistant to fusarium, verticillium, and
nematodes

Turnips
Purple Top White Globe ...... Widely adapted
Shogoin .... Quick growing, primarily for greens

Watermelon
Sugar Baby .... Small round, early
Crimson Sweet .... Blocky oval, resistant to fusarium and anthracnose
Charleston Gray .... Oblong, resistant to fusarium and anthracnose

varieties of fruits will bear year after year. Considerable care must be taken, however, to select those fruits and varieties most suited to each growing area. Like vegetables, fruits require full sunlight.

Here we will discuss strawberries, raspberries, blackberries, blueberries, grapes, cherries, peaches, plums, apples, and pears. These all require a well-drained soil. Blueberries require a soil pH of 4.5 to 5.0. Soil pH of other fruits should be between 5.5 to 6.5. (The pH of a soil is a measure of its acidity. Soil analyses can be arranged by the county agricultural extension agent.)

Since all fruits blossom early in the spring, frost pockets should be avoided. Even when your garden has good air drainage, the blossoms may have to be protected against cold. Temperatures of 30° F. will often kill blossoms and young developing fruit.

Apples, pears, and plums require cross-pollination. Thus, more than one variety of these fruits should be planted. Wild bees and other insects will pollinate the blossoms. Insecticides should not be applied in the garden during the period of blossoming and pollination.

The strawberry is probably the best fruit for use in the home garden. It takes but little space and fruits will be produced one year after planting. Strawberries are very productive. You can expect 1 quart of fruit for each foot of row. Plants should be set 1½ feet apart in the row with rows spaced 4 feet apart. Water strawberry plants frequently to develop good vigorous growth. The plants should be mulched with straw or hay in the late fall.

Only varieties resistant to the red stele fungus should be planted in most areas of the East and Central States. The following varieties are recommended: East—Midway, Surecrop, Raritan, Catskill, Guardian; West— Marshall, Northwest; South—Albritton, Florida 90, Dabreak, and Tioga.

Red raspberries grow best in regions where summers are cool and moist. Plants should be spaced 3 feet apart in the row with 5 feet between rows. The plants will bear fruit in the second year. Old fruiting canes should be removed each fall. In some areas, fruit canes may have to be covered to protect them during the winter months. Following are the varieties recommended: East— Latham, September, Taylor; West— Willamette, Meeker; South—Southland.

Black raspberries are less hardy than red raspberries. The Bristol and Black Hawk varieties are recommended in the East; Munger and Plum Farmer in the West.

Blackberries are generally less hardy than raspberries. They can, however, be grown over a large portion of the country. They should be planted at the same distance as raspberries. The plants will tolerate poor soil and drought conditions. Good soil moisture, however, is required for best growth and berry size. The Darrow, Raven, and Thornfree varieties are recommended for the East; the Boysen, Cascade, and Olallie for the West; and the Brazos, Raven, and Oklawaha for the South.

Blueberries require an acid soil and protection from birds. They will, however, provide an attractive bush and fruit to follow the strawberry season. Plants should not be planted closer than 5 feet. Blueberries have a very shallow root system. Mulch should be used around the plants to help retain moisture and suppress weeds.

The following highbush blueberry varieties are recommended: East— Bluetta, Blueray, Bluecrop, Berkeley, Darrow; South—Morrow and Croaton. Tifblue, Woodard, and Delite are rabbiteye blueberry varieties recommended for the South.

Grapes should also be considered for the home garden. The vines can be used effectively as a screen during summer months. One vine will cover 8 to 10 feet of the trellis each year. For good fruit production, however, vines must be pruned each winter.

The European grape can be grown in most of the sections of the United States. The Concord, Caco, and Niagara are recommended varieties. The Vinifera grape is grown mostly on the West

Coast. Cardinal, Perlette, and Blackrose are suggested varieties.

Muscadine grapes are recommended for the South. The Magoon and Magnolia varieties are self-fertile and so do not require cross-pollination. The Scuppernong variety requires a second variety for pollination.

Sour cherries can be recommended for the home garden. They do not require cross-pollination and only one tree is required. Once established, the tree requires very little attention. The Montmorency, English Morello, and Early Richmond varieties are hardy over most of the United States. Because of the very serious problem with birds, sweet cherries cannot be recommended for the home garden.

The peach is an excellent fruit for the home garden. With the selection of early, midseason, and late varieties, the peach fruiting season can be extended to 6 or 8 weeks in most parts of the country. The tree will have to be pruned each winter. Developing fruit have to be hand thinned to about 5 inches apart. Peaches do not require cross-pollination and a single tree will bear fruit. You should plant trees no closer than 15 feet apart.

There are many peach varieties to choose from. Most varieties will grow satisfactorily in all regions. Freestone varieties are recommended for fresh fruit; clingstone varieties for canning. Nectarines are almost identical with the peach except that nectarines have no fuzz or hairiness on the fruit.

Plums also are excellent for the home garden. Care must be taken, however, to select only those varieties recommended for each growing area.

Japanese plums can be considered for most southeastern and western areas. Because of disease problems, however, they are not recommended for the Southeast. Trees and fruit buds will be injured in northern areas. Santa Rosa, Casselman, Laroda, and Beauty are recommended varieties for the West. Methley and Ozark Premier are suggested for eastern areas.

European type plums are more hardy and are suggested for northern areas.

The Fellenburg, Stanley, and Shropshire varieties are recommended.

Plums require little pruning. Trees should not be planted closer than 15 feet apart.

Apricots are not recommended for the home garden. They bloom very early in the spring and their flowers are often killed by spring frosts.

Apples have to be sprayed for disease and insect control more than other fruits. If you are willing to go to this expense and trouble, you may wish to consider apples for the home garden.

Apples can be grown in all parts of the country. The standard tree grows well on all soils but it may grow too large for home gardens. Dwarfing rootstocks are used to reduce tree size but they are not adapted to poor soils. Different rootstocks cause different degrees of dwarfing. You must fertilize and water your trees if dwarfing rootstocks are used. Prune your trees each winter. All apples require cross-pollination.

The Red Delicious variety is the most common variety grown in this country. It is not a cooking apple. Golden Delicious, another popular variety, can be used both for fresh fruit and cooking. The Stayman and Jonathan varieties are also dual purpose varieties. The McIntosh variety is recommended for northern areas. McIntosh does not color well in the South.

Pears require less care than apples. Fire blight disease, however, is a serious problem in all parts of the country. This disease is most severe in the Central and Southeastern States where there are periods of warm moist conditions during the flowering period. Dwarfing rootstocks should not be used on poor soils.

The Bartlett pear is the most common variety. It is used for both eating out of hand and canning. It is, however, very susceptible to fire blight. Magness and Moonglow varieties have a degree of resistance. The Kieffer variety is quite resistant but lacks quality.

No matter what fruits are selected for the home garden, a fertilization program must be followed. Grass and weeds should be removed from around all trees. When trees are watered, sufficient water should be applied to penetrate the top 5 inches of soil. Apply fertilizer in the early spring.

Fruit trees will have to be sprayed to control insects and diseases. Caution should be used in selecting and applying pesticides.

You must also anticipate that birds and squirrels will be major pests in the home fruit garden.

Many people include herbs along with vegetables and fruits in their garden. The word "herb" is applied to low plants, some of which emit a particular fragrance. Others possess medicinal virtues. A number of herbs are used to season, enrich, or otherwise to impart a flavor and aroma to certain foods, and thus make them more pleasing to the taste. Fragrant or savory leaves, seeds, buds, bark, and roots have been used for such purposes since ancient times, and many have long figured in folklore and tradition.

Many useful herbs, introduced and long cultivated in the United States, originated on the warm shores of the Mediterranean and the region eastward to India. In their natural environment they generally grow in sunny sites, or granular, or easily pulverized, alkaline soil. Under propagated conditions, the majority of herbs may be grown successfully under a wide range of soil conditions, but thrive best in a fertile, well-prepared soil, mixed with humus and fertilizer. Barnyard manure, compost, and wood ashes are especially beneficial.

Annuals, or herbs that have to be planted each year, are usually grown from seed and are sown directly in the garden in the early spring when the soil is sufficiently dry and there is no danger of frost. These annuals include: anise, sweet basil, borage, chervil, coriander, dill, fennel, marjoram or sweet marjoram, parsley, and savory.

Biennials or perennials may be purchased as seedlings, or started in a coldframe or window box from seeds or cuttings and the plants reset in the garden at the proper time. Among these herbs (or mints) are: angelica, lemon balm, caraway, catnip, chives, geranium, lavender, lovage, peppermint and spearmint, wild marjoram, rosemary, sage, tarragon, lemon-verbena and thyme.

Consideration should be given to the location of the herbs in your garden. For example, sage, thyme, and rosemary are sensitive to moist conditions and require a well-drained, moderately humid situation. Chervil, parsley, and the mints, on the other hand, grow best on soils that retain moisture but have good drainage.

Such plants as sage, lemon balm, and rosemary may be propagated by stem cuttings. Stems from the latest growth or the upper part of the older stems make the best cuttings and root readily in the summer or fall. To start cuttings, use a shallow box with 4 or 5 inches of clean sand and fitted with a glass cover. This makes a good rooting bed. Insert the cuttings to a depth of one-half to two-thirds their length in moist sand, pack firmly, and saturate with water. The glass cover should have a ½- to 1-inch opening on one side to permit ventilation.

Place the box in a protected sunny place and keep moist, but not wet, at all times. To prevent wilting, protect the cuttings from direct sunlight during the first week or two by shading with paper or cheesecloth. On hot sunny days, increase the ventilation by raising the glass cover on one side. Roots should develop in about 2 weeks. In 4 to 6 weeks, the cuttings should be ready to pot or to set in a coldframe for protection during winter. The plants may be transplanted to a permanent site in early spring.

Some herbs—such as thyme, savory, and marjoram—can be easily propagated by layering. This method consists of covering the side branches with soil, and leaving the top exposed. When the covered branches have rooted, they are nipped from the parent and set out.

Other herbs, such as chives and tarragon, may be propagated by dividing the crown clumps, after 1 or 2 seasons of growth, into individual plants. These subdivisions may be planted directly in permanent sites if removed in the early spring, or set in a coldframe for winter protection when removed in the fall.

Mints spread rapidly by means of runners that may grow several feet from the parent plant and usually at a depth of 1 to 2 inches beneath the surface. New plants spring up at the nodes of the runners during summer. These plants, with roots attached, can be removed and transplanted in the spring or early summer or the runners alone may be planted in rows and covered to a depth of 2 inches.

Whenever possible, herbs should be used when fresh, as some plants when dried lose their fragrance or flavor after about 1 year. They should be harvested on a clear morning, when the leaves are free of dew.

The leaves usually have the best flavor or fragrance when gathered immediately before the flowers open. Flowers or leaves should be cut with a sharp knife or scissors, leaving enough foliage for new growth.

Leaves should be washed, the excess water shaken off, and then dried on a wire or cheesecloth frame, or tied in bunches and hung up to dry in a dark place.

Seeds, also, should be thoroughly dried before storing to prevent mold and loss of viability. After curing for several days in an airy room, exposure to the sun for a day or two before storing will insure safe storage.

As soon as the leaves or seeds of herbs are dry they should be cleaned of stems and foreign matter. Then place them in airtight glass, metal, or cardboard containers, to preserve their delicate fragrance and flavor. Glass jars make satisfactory containers, but they should be painted black or stored in a dark room to prevent bleaching of the green leaves by light.

For further reading:
A Primer for Herb Growing, Herb Society of America, 300 Massachusetts Avenue, Boston, Mass. 02115, 35 cents.

U.S. Department of Agriculture, *Minigardens for Vegetables.* Home and Garden Bulletin 163, Washington, D.C. 20250, 1970.

——————, *Growing Tomatoes in the Home Garden.* Home and Garden Bulletin 180, Washington, D.C. 20250, 1970.

pests that plague our plants; what you can do about them

AS A GARDENER, you will compete with insects and mites, diseases, nematodes, and weeds for use of the plants you grow. The complex and competitive garden environment must be considered and efficiently managed to successfully grow productive food plants or plants of esthetic and ornamental value.

Entomologists say that more than 750,000 insect species have been identified. About 10,000 of these are known noxious pests. They cause losses estimated at more than $4 billion annually. In addition, 50,000 species of fungi cause 1,500 plant diseases; over 1,800 weed species annually cause serious economic losses; and about 15,000 species of nematodes attack crop plants with about 1,500 of them causing serious damage.

Don't be discouraged, though. As a home gardener, you will never be plagued with all of these pests. However, to understand the problems of pest control, it is important that you recognize and appreciate the competitive nature of the garden environment.

Insects and mite pests damage plants in different ways. There are insects that feed on leaves. There are insects that suck plant juices. These latter produce damaged and dead plant tissues. They also serve as disease vectors (carriers). There are insects that bore; they attack the woody parts of plants. Finally, there are insects that live in the soil and feed on roots and other plant parts.

Insects and mites only become garden pests when they do sufficient damage to result in loss. The insect population at the damage state reaches high enough levels to kill the plant or prevent its development. Many factors affect the ability of pests to develop large populations. The reproductive potential of most insects is tremendous.

Adult insects may lay several hundred eggs, increasing populations as much as five-fold or more in a generation. And a generation may be only 2 to 3 weeks. The numbers of insects present fluctuate greatly for many reasons. They are affected by seasonal and weather conditions, food supply, and natural enemies.

Assuming that an insect or mite species is adapted to an area, the most important factor regulating populations and preventing them from developing to damaging proportions is the presence of natural enemies (parasites, predators, and pathogens).

Less than 2 percent of the known insects are pests. Many others (parasites and predators) are vital factors regulating pest insect populations. These insects are among the best friends of the gardener. In addition, more than 1,100 viruses, bacteria, fungi, rickettsia, and nematodes attack insects in their environment.

These natural enemies of pest insects

regulate the fluctuations of pest populations and keep them within bounds. In other words, they stabilize the pest population. Scientists call this the species equilibrium position.

When a species is stabilized at equilibrium where the numbers present are causing economic damage to the plant life in the garden, they are called pests; conversely if the equilibrium is established where the numbers present do not cause economic damage, they are of little concern and there is no need to further reduce their numbers.

Many of the insects that the home gardener sees are beneficial and destroy insects and mites injurious to the food crops or ornamental plants.

In home vegetable and ornamental gardens, very few pests will cause appreciable plant damage if parasites and predators are protected. The commonly observed aphid lion, assassin bug, lady beetle, praying mantis, and a variety of wasps are only a few of the beneficial insects which are continually working in the garden environment feeding on aphids, scale insects, mites, and a number of other pest species.

Spider mites, cabbage caterpillars, Colorado potato beetles, and aphids are common pests that attack vegetables in the home garden. If you find any of these, treat them promptly to reduce populations. Some pests of ornamental plants are spider mites, aphids, beetles, lacebugs, thrips, and scale insects.

Chemicals remain the number one weapon for immediate control of pest insects in the home garden. They probably will remain essential for the foreseeable future. However, chemicals used unwisely not only kill the target pest; they kill beneficial insects, too. Recognition of the pest-beneficial insect relationship is necessary if you are to take advantage of the best control features of both chemical and biological control.

Before selecting and applying any chemical, be sure you can accurately identify the insect. And don't apply chemicals unless they are absolutely necessary to prevent damage to your plants.

Author T. J. HENNEBERRY is Branch Chief, Vegetable, Ornamental, and Specialty Crops Insects Research Branch, Entomology Research Division, Agricultural Research Service (ARS).

Coauthor J. H. GRAHAM is Assistant Chief, Vegetables and Ornamentals Research Branch, Plant Science Research Division, ARS.

Coauthor L. L. DANIELSON is Leader, Weed Investigations—Horticultural Crops, Plant Science Research Division.

Coauthor J. M. GOOD is Leader, Nematology Investigations, Plant Science Research Division.

SOME BENEFICIAL GARDEN INSECTS

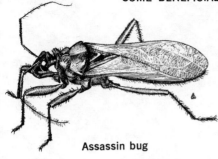

Assassin bug

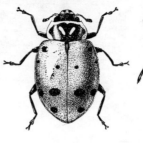

Adult and larva of lady beetle

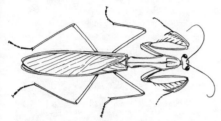

Praying mantis

Tiny wasp depositing egg in an aphid

SOME GARDEN INSECT PESTS

Cabbage looper

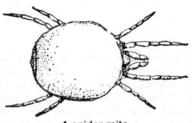

A spider mite

Aphids on underside of leaf

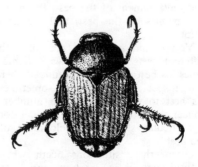

Japanese beetle

143

Spraying a broad-leaved plant with lukewarm water is one way to remove aphids, mealybugs, thrips, and spider mites.

The time when chemicals are applied is important. You will want to eliminate the pest without killing the pest's natural enemies. You will have better control if your application of chemicals is based on a sound knowledge of the life cycle, seasonal occurrences, habits, and development of the pest, the natural enemies of the pest, and the host plant.

You obtain maximum control with different pests in different ways. Sometimes it's best to apply a chemical when a pest species first appears; sometimes it's best to wait until certain numbers appear; sometimes it's best to wait for a particular stage of development of the pest.

Often, these situations occur when natural enemies are least susceptible to the effects of the chemical. For example, aphids, scales, and mites generally first appear and become active in early spring. If you apply chemicals for scale control before the plants begin to grow and early in the season for mite and aphid control, your application may have minimum effect on natural enemies.

Generally speaking, you shouldn't treat for pests when the pest's natural enemies are active.

Other ways to kill the pest without harming the pest's natural enemies include making sure you mix the chemicals according to the manufacturer's instructions, being careful to use the proper dose, and putting the chemicals on the right part of the plant.

For example, some chemicals have been developed which are taken up by plant roots or through the leaves. These chemicals only kill insects which feed on the plant; natural enemies of the

144

culprit insect are spared. Hopefully, more of these chemicals will be developed in the future.

You should be especially careful to protect bees and other insect pollinators. They are essential for producing many garden crops. You can minimize the effects of chemicals on them by following a few simple rules:

- Use the lowest effective dose of the least hazardous chemical.
- Apply the chemical only when necessary.
- Use granular formulations when possible (generally, they are less hazardous).
- Apply the chemical in the evening when bees are not active.

There are a number of other ways to control or help control injurious insects. Many species of insects and mites overwinter on plant parts and debris left in the garden from the previous year. These species emerge early in the spring to develop populations on weeds and newly planted garden material. You should clean up all plant beds in the fall. This will prevent or reduce overwintering insect and mite populations and minimize their effect. During the growing season, weeds provide another host material for many insects. Try to keep your plant beds free of weeds.

One of the best ways to combat insects in the garden is to use plants that are resistant to attack. Plants are resistant for several reasons. They may not be attractive to the insect as food, shelter, or for egg-laying; they may adversely affect the biology of the insect; they may be able to survive despite the insects' attack, sustaining a number of insects that would stunt or kill the more susceptible plant types. Resistant plant types are present in nature and scientists are placing greater emphasis on identifying them and incorporating their resistance into desirable horticultural types for use of the gardener.

Garden plants are subject to many diseases. Symptoms of some of these diseases are damping-off (dying of seedlings), leaf spots, mildew, blight, leaf mosaic, stunting, fruit rots, galls (woody growths), twig dieback, yellowing, bulb rot, wilt, and root rot. These diseases may be caused by fungi, bacteria, or viruses.

If you are going to prevent or effectively control a disease, you need to know the cause, the symptom, and the way that whatever caused the disease survives and spreads.

Many garden plants grow and thrive despite certain diseases. During some seasons they may completely escape any damage. But other plants—garden roses, for example—are damaged quite severely by black spot and powdery mildew almost every year. If you want beautiful roses, you have to treat them with fungicides. Some plant diseases can be held in check by good cultural practices, such as removal of old infected plants in the fall.

Wilts and root rots are often fatal, and prevention is the best and often only control. Scientists have made much progress in developing plants that are genetically resistant to one or more of the major diseases. This type of biological control is more desirable and often more reliable than chemical control. Your county agent or extension specialist can supply you with a list of recommended varieties and plants for your garden. Look for those that are resistant to the destructive diseases in your area.

Here are some general tips for controlling diseases on your garden plants:

Use fertile, well-drained soil and a good grade fertilizer.

Buy seed that has been treated with chemicals to protect against decay and damping-off.

Purchase disease-free plants; make sure they do not have swellings on the roots, cankers on the stems, or spots on the leaves.

Purchase disease-free certified seed.

Plant crops that are suited to the soil location and climate.

Grow disease-resistant varieties, if available. Resistant varieties are available for only a few diseases of certain crops. No variety is resistant to all diseases.

Keep down weeds and grass.

Keep your garden plants growing

well with proper soil enrichment and watering.

Use chemical sprays carefully, READ THE LABEL, follow directions, and heed all precautions.

Destroy diseased plants of each annual crop as soon as harvest is complete.

Destroy leaves and flowers of infected woody plants as they fall.

Stake up plants so the fruit does not touch the soil. This will decrease fruit rots.

Prune out infected plant parts well below the infection area (cankers or galls).

Disinfect pruning tools to avoid virus spread.

Paint pruning wounds.

Here are some of the commonly occurring garden diseases. Young seedlings of all crops may be killed by damping-off fungi (molds) that persist in the soil. Seedlings topple over soon after coming up or die before breaking through the soil. If possible, you should buy seed treated with a protectant. To treat seed yourself, read the label on cans of seed protectants in the garden shop, find one that lists the seed you have, and follow directions for its use.

Soil fumigation before planting will also control damping-off fungi as well as insects and weeds. Get specific directions from your county agent or extension specialist before you attempt to fumigate the soil.

Leaf diseases are common in the home garden. The leaf may show irregular to rounded spots, rust-colored raised blisters, blighting, browning of margins, and other discolorations. In most instances the agent causing the disease survives between crops (overwinters) on residues of infected crops or on the seed. To minimize the chance of a disease being carried over from year to year on annual plants, remove the infected plants after harvest or in the fall.

Sometimes you can use fungicides to protect the leaves. To be effective, a film of the fungicide must be on the leaf before the fungus spores are blown or splashed onto the plant. Fungicides that are effective against many leaf-spotting fungi include: zineb, folpet, ferbam, and maneb. Read the label to be sure that the chemical is registered for use for both the plant and the disease.

For the control of seedborne diseases such as bean and pea blights, plant fresh, healthy seed grown in the arid West. It is usually not advisable to save your own seed if you live in humid areas of the country.

Powdery mildew, common on many vegetables and ornamentals, is a powdery white growth on the upper leaf surfaces. Although normally occurring late in the season, powdery mildew may kill many of the leaves. You will decrease disease losses if you dust the leaves with sulfur. Resistant varieties of cucumbers, melons, beans, lilacs, crabapple, and some other plants are available. Once again, to reduce the disease the following year, clean up fallen, infected leaves.

Downy mildew, a frequent disease of vegetables, may be severe on many crops. A downy growth develops primarily on the undersides of leaves and on the stems. Leaves turn yellow and shrivel. The fungus spores live overwinter in most tissue or are spread by the wind from south to north as the season develops. Resistant varieties of some crops are available, for example —cucumbers, muskmelons, spinach, lima beans, and onions. Zineb spray is effective against downy mildew on several crops.

Root rots and wilts are common to vegetables, flowers, shrubs, and trees. Tips of branches wilt or gradually dieback; leaves turn yellow and wither or drop off; and roots are discolored and finally killed. Organisms causing these diseases usually persist in the soil and in old plant parts in the soil.

There are very few ways to control root rots and wilts. Some varieties of tomatoes are resistant to two of the most common wilts. In vegetable gardens, plant peas, beans, sweet corn, and melons in different sections of the garden each year. Change garden locations at intervals, if you have room.

Shrubs with root rot or wilt should

be discarded; replace soil before replanting, or plant in another location; provide good soil drainage.

Viruses of vegetables and ornamentals (flowers and shrubs) will cause colored spot and blotches on leaves and fruits, or moderate to severe dwarfing or distortion of plants. The virus may survive between seasons on weeds and be carried to crop plants by insects. Therefore, effective programs to control weeds and insects will also aid in reducing losses from such diseases. The best control is to start with virus-free planting stock or seed purchased from a reliable seed company, and use resistant varieties when available.

A common malady of woody plants is winter injury. If the plants have been winter injured, the leaves will have a bronze or brownish cast or will have irregular-shaped dead areas, particularly along margins. Ends of twigs dry out and die. Evergreens may loose their needles; deciduous plants may not leaf-out properly in the spring. The cause of dying is often not just low temperatures, but freezing and thawing, and excessive drying out.

Practices you can use to reduce damage include: watering the plants during late fall; mulching your plants; and fertilizing them well in the spring. Fertilizing in the fall may start new tender growth that is easily winter damaged.

To protect valuable plants during the winter, you can build windbreaks. You can also experiment with anti-transpirant sprays for the leaves.

Woody plants are, in general, damaged by twig diebacks, galls, and canker diseases. These are often controlled simply, but effectively, by pruning. However, deep cankers on the main trunk of large plants, such as trees, are difficult to remove by surgery.

Leaves of plants, particularly perennial shrubs and trees, may turn yellow if they are deficient in a single minor element—iron. The addition of chelate iron directly on the leaves or around the plant will make the leaves green-up.

Organic matter is extremely valuable in the garden. Besides its gradual release of the nutrients needed for plant growth, it is valuable for several other reasons:

- It improves soil aeration.
- It improves the water-holding capacity of the soil.
- It reduces soil crusting.
- It stimulates the growth of beneficial micro-organisms, some of which may destroy harmful micro-organisms or prevent their growth.

However, some plant parasites increase and are spread on organic matter. They appear on diseased plant residue, manure, and composts. There is no scientific evidence that organic matter makes fruit or vegetables more nutritious than produce grown with commercial fertilizers. A combination of organic and inorganic commercial fertilizer is better for home vegetable production than either alone.

Besides insects and diseases, there is another common garden pest—the weed. A weed is a plant out of place. Thus, all wild plants are not weeds. Many serve as cover and food for wildlife, and also help prevent soil erosion. Continuity of growth and reproduction of wild plants is of great value because this is nature's bank from which we may draw valuable genetic material in the future.

In the garden environment, however, weeds are polluters. Some interfere with normal growth of grains, fibers, vegetables, and fruits. Some destroy the esthetic values of ornamental plantings. They clog ponds, lakes, and streams, and crowd out lawn grasses. Some make you sneeze in the spring and fall. Some have spines and thorns.

Some weeds have broad leaves and some are grasses. Some are annuals and some perennials; some are competitors and some are parasites.

Annual weed grasses you will commonly find in the garden include crabgrass, annual bluegrass, lovegrass, and goosegrass. Perennial weed grasses include Bermudagrass, dallisgrass, and nimblewill. There are many others.

Yellow and purple nutsedge are perennial weed plants that are making trouble for home gardeners.

Numerous annual broadleaf plants

are found in many home gardens. Some of the common species are chickweed, dodder, henbit, pigweed, lambsquarters, carpetweed, german knotweed, spotted spurge, knawel, spurry, smartweed, ragweed, and purslane.

Perennial broadleaf weeds include poison-ivy, trumpetcreeper, mugwort, greenbrier, morning-glory, ground-ivy, speedwell, and stinging-nettle.

The seed production of some kinds of weeds is fantastic. A single pigweed plant, for example, may produce more than 100,000 seeds, a purslane plant more than 50,000, and a nutsedge plant more than 90,000.

Perennial weed plants reproduce from seeds, or underground food storage organs such as rhizomes, stolons, tubers, corms, and bulbs. A single nutsedge tuber may produce 2,000 new plants and almost 7,000 new tubers in a year in a soil area 7 feet in diameter and 7 inches deep.

Weeds show remarkable ability to survive. Seeds of some species will remain dormant through many years of drought, finally germinating when conditions are just right for good growth. Some species will germinate when the soil is cultivated and the seeds are brought near the soil surface. Some, such as chickweed, germinate only in spring and fall or when the weather is cool. Others, such as goosegrass, germinate only in the heat of midsummer. Some, such as cocklebur, produce seeds of specialized dormancy requirements. Seed pods of cocklebur contain two seeds; one will germinate in 1 year and the other in 2 years. Many variations of seed dormancy are known in other weed plants.

Some weeds grow only in very moist soil or in marshes, lakes, and streams. Other weeds must have good drainage and aeration to survive. Some grow only in desert conditions. A number of weeds grow profusely only where crops are raised and fertility levels are high.

Some weeds grow best in the shade. Others grow best in full sun. Some, such as poison-ivy, grow equally well in sun or shade.

Weeds interfere with crop growth by

Morning-glory twines around young sweet corn stalk at right and stunts its growth.

competing for light, water, and nutrients. Some, such as morning-glory, kudzu-vine, and trumpetcreeper, restrict crop growth by twining around the plants. These also compete for water, light, and nutrients.

Some weeds are parasitic on green plants. The principal parasitic weed found in home gardens is dodder. It germinates from seeds, twines about the stems of green plants, and obtains its nutrients by sending rootlike feeders into the tissues of the host plant.

Weeds may be spread in many ways. Some weed seeds float easily and are carried in rainwater and streams. Seeds from dandelion and milkweed are carried by the wind. Birds eat poison ivy fruits and spread the seeds. Weed seeds are often present among crop seeds and are planted with them. Organic mulches and unsterilized animal manures contain many weed seeds.

Top soil and the soil around the roots of balled nursery plants often contain weed seeds, stolons, rhizomes, roots, and bulbs, and even entire weed plants. When you cultivate you will surely distribute some weed seeds and sections of roots, rhizomes, and stolons.

For effective control of annual weeds, you should attack them before they emerge. One way to do this is to spread a black polyethylene sheet on the soil surface. It acts as a mulch, conserving soil moisture by reducing evaporative loss, and it controls germinating weed seeds. It will also reduce fruit rots of watermelon, cucumbers, cantaloups, squash, and tomatoes.

Straw mulches are useful, too. You can use them for vegetable plantings and for such fruit plantings as strawberries, raspberries, and blackberries. If you use a straw mulch be sure it is sterilized to kill all small grain and weed seeds.

Wood chips or pine bark may be used around woody ornamental plantings. Pebble-size gravel of a range of colors is available and can be used effectively as a mulch in permanent ornamental plantings.

Mulches are discussed more thoroughly in the chapter on page 241.

Some herbicides, such as DCPA, sesone, chlorpropham, diphenamid, and others, are effective in the control of germinating weed seeds in vegetable and ornamental gardens.

Emerged annual weeds in home vegetables and annual ornamental plantings

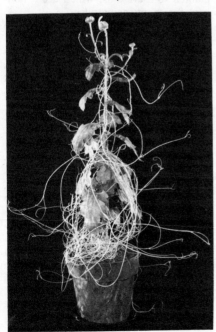

Dodder on a chrysanthemum.

are best controlled by hand pulling or hoe cultivation. Such weeds in plantings of woody ornamentals can be controlled by hand or by carefully applied wetting sprays of such herbicides as paraquat or stoddard solvent. These sprays must not touch the foliage of the ornamentals.

Perennial weeds such as poison-ivy, stinging-nettle, Bermudagrass, mugwort, and nutsedge can be controlled only with great difficulty by continual removal of all top growth by hoeing, mowing, or pulling. Such weeds are best controlled with herbicides. Amitrole carefully applied as a spray directly to the foliage of the broadleaf weeds or to the crown or whorl of weed grasses kills tops and roots.

Injury to your valuable plants can be avoided by carefully localizing the treatments.

Herbicides are necessary, effective, and safe when used with appropriate caution. Use an oil can to treat individual plants. Spray herbicides when there is no wind. Use low spraying pressure to produce large spray droplets that will minimize their movement in air. Purchase herbicides in small quantities and store in a locked cabinet outside of the house.

Follow the directions on the manufacturer's label. When in doubt, contact your county extension agent or weed research specialist at your State agricultural experiment station.

Nematodes are another common type of garden pest. Nematodes are microscopic worms, not to be confused with the large, beneficial earthworms. They occur in all soils and attack most commonly-grown vegetables. Plants weakened by nematodes are more susceptible to many plant diseases.

Because of their microscopic size and transparency, nematodes can be seen only after separation from the soil and plant roots.

Their exact identity is best made by a specialist using a microscope. You can take measures to prevent nematodes from increasing and there are ways to reduce hidden damage.

Over a hundred species of nematodes

attack crops grown in gardens. Characteristic symptoms on growing plants should alert the gardener to nematode attack. For convenience, they can be categorized into groups based on the type of plant damage.

Root-knot and related nematodes produce large knots or swellings on roots. A group of ectoparasitic nematodes feed externally on the roots, destroying the fine feeder roots. In extreme cases of infection this feeding results in a stubby root or coarse root condition. Many other nematodes invade the roots and cause extensive rotting. Foliar, bulb, and stem nematodes attack vegetative parts of plants, causing distorted and crinkled leaf or shoot formation, or discoloration and death of leaf tissues between the veins of leaves.

Regardless of the type of nematode, debilitated plants have certain common characteristics. They wilt easily during hot, dry weather because of impaired root systems. For the same reason, the top growth of plants is frequently stunted and yellow. Severe infestations may kill the plant. Infected plants will not grow normally, even after the addition of large amounts of water and fertilizer, since the plants are unable to use them effectively.

A number of species of destructive nematodes occur naturally in soils, where they live in ecological balance with other organisms. In this undisturbed condition, they are of no economic importance, but after a garden is established, their natural control agents are destroyed and the nematodes increase rapidly. The reason for this is that vegetable crops are highly susceptible to nematodes. Also, inadvertently, new pathogenic species can be introduced by the gardener. Once established, these nematodes thrive on their preferred succulent host plants.

There are a number of ways you can prevent nematode introduction and also suppress nematode populations. To prevent introduction, never transplant seedlings that are obviously infected with nematodes or have unhealthy looking roots. Purchase nematode-free transplants, or if you grow seedlings at home, raise them from seed in sterilized peat or soil.

Crop rotations can be used effectively to suppress nematode populations. Some plants are ideally suited for nematode attack, and if grown repeatedly in the same garden spot, nematode populations are sure to increase rapidly. Among these are tomatoes, beans of all types, squash, pepper, okra, melons, lettuce, carrots, and cucumbers. Radishes, mustard, turnip greens, onions, and corn are less subject to attack. Therefore, you should alternate the position of various crops in the garden each year.

Relocating the garden every 3 or 4 years will prevent nematode increase. In this regard, most sod and lawn areas, and especially wooded areas, are suitable sites for a new garden.

An alternate but equally satisfactory procedure is to use only part of your garden each year. You can plant part of the garden area to oats or rye (grain or grass) for 1 year; followed by vegetable crops for no more than 2 years. If you want flowers, a nematode infected section of the garden can be planted to marigolds, which are a non-host for many nematodes.

Plant breeders have developed a number of nematode-resistant vegetable varieties. These varieties are usually resistant to one or more species of root-knot nematodes. The resistant varieties are not necessarily adapted to all areas of the United States.

Here is a partial list of nematode-resistant vegetables; tomatoes—varieties, Nemared, Nematex, Pearl Harbor, Y91, and Urbana; pole beans—varieties, Alabama No. 1, 18, and 19, Winegard Wonder, Springwater Halfrunner, Isbell's Nematode Resistant, and Coffee Wonder; lima beans—varieties, Nemagreen; sweetpotatoes—varieties, Nemagold, Nemared, Heartagold, and Goldrush; crowder peas—variety, Mississippi Silver; peppers—varieties, California Wonder, Red Chili, and Mississippi Nemaheart.

Other varieties of vegetable crops are frequently listed in seed catalogs as having fair to moderate resistance to certain nematodes.

Because nematodes require a suitable host to maintain life and reproduce, the home gardener can interrupt their life cycles and prevent reproduction in several ways. As soon as the entire garden—or an individual crop within the garden—is harvested you should dig up the roots. Rake and burn them along with plant tops, or dispose of them as garbage. This stops reproduction of the nematodes, removes from the garden large numbers that are trapped inside the roots, and allows the soil to be partially sterilized by the drying action of wind and sun.

You can further accelerate this process by spading, plowing, or roto-tilling the soil several times during late summer when crops cannot be grown.

Organic matter not only creates better soil fertility and structure but provides nematode control. Decomposing organic matter supports parasites, predators, and diseases of nematodes; and certain chemicals from decomposing organic matter are toxic to some nema-todes. Therefore, if you add organic matter to your home garden it will help prevent nematode problems.

Good sources of organic matter are manures, lawn sweepings, leaves, chipped tree trimmings, peat or sphagnum-moss, and pine tree bark. Compost, made from a number of easily obtained products, such as leaves or grass clippings, also is highly beneficial when added to soil.

Organic matter is best worked into the garden soil in the fall or spring at least 4 weeks before planting time. If you apply too much organic matter, especially in the spring, you may have to add nitrogen to prevent nitrogen deficiency in the garden.

A number of nematocides and soil fumigants are available at home-garden centers for controlling nematodes. These chemicals give the highest degree of control possible, but should be used only to supplement the above control methods, and then only at the dosage and by the method recommended by the manufacturer for use on specific crops.

quarantines give thumbs down to hitchhiking plant pests

AN ESTIMATED $10 billion is lost every year by farmers, gardeners, homeowners, and others to the destructiveness of pests that attack plants.

The Japanese bettle that chews unsightly holes in the most beautiful rose, the gypsy moth that has no regard for the shade trees it defoliates in the backyard, the European chafer that picks the most lavishly landscaped lawn to destroy, all have one thing in common. They are pests that were accidentally introduced into this country and have become established. Even the lowly dandelion, now commonplace and almost tolerated, is an import.

Scientists estimate that between 2 million and 5 million different kinds of insects live on the earth. By the end of 1970, the number of insects that had already been named was estimated at over three-quarters of a million. About 85,000 kinds of insects are located in the United States. Of these, 10,000 are undesirable and several hundred destructive enough to agricultural crops and gardens to be of major importance. In addition, there are 1,500 plant diseases in the United States that must be dealt with.

Insect populations can multiply so enormously that numbers become almost meaningless. For instance, if all the descendants of one female garden aphid lived through a season and were placed end to end, they would stretch around the earth 86,000 times.

With the myriad of insects, caterpillars, mites, and disease he has to deal with, the gardener is painfully aware of the pest problem. But he may not know that at least half of the destructive pests and diseases in this country are of foreign origin—the gypsy moth, codling moth, San Jose scale, Argentine ant, and Asiatic garden beetle, for instance. Some of the imported diseases include chestnut blight, white pine blister rust, asparagus rust, cereal smuts, apple scab, and chrysanthemum rusts.

In their natural environment, few pests cause great damage. But when brought to a new environment that is favorable for their development—and beyond the range of natural predators that keep their numbers in balance—these pests can get out of hand and become an economic menace.

Plant quarantines play a major role in keeping the food and fiber industries—as well as the gardens—of the United States free from thousands of additional pests that might otherwise enter this country each year. Without organized effort, even the billions of dollars already lost every year to pests could be multiplied many times.

Until 1905, the United States had no law protecting itself against foreign plant pests. As a result, this country was said to be the dumping ground for poor quality, pest-carrying plants. The lack of protection resulted in great losses to agriculture and permitted the introduction of many pests that have gained such a strong foothold that their eradication appears hopeless even with modern methods.

———

Author H . V . AUTRY is Chief Staff Officer, Regulatory Services, Plant Protection Program, Animal and Plant Health Inspecting Service (APHIS).

Coauthor IVAN RAINWATER is Chief Staff Officer, Regulatory Services, Agricultural Quarantine Inspection Program, APHIS.

Coauthor E. E. CROOKS is Assistant Chief Staff Officer, Regulatory Services, Plant Protection Program, APHIS.

In 1905, an act prohibiting the importation of certain plant pests was enacted by Congress. However, this early legislation alone was not enough to stop the pest invasion.

Finally, in 1912, Congress passed the Plant Quarantine Act. This law gave the U.S. Department of Agriculture the authority to prevent importation of plants and other agricultural products which might contain insect pests and plant diseases that could not adequately be eliminated by treatment. This act also provided authority to control or if possible to eradicate a new pest should it become established within the country. In 1957, the Federal Plant Pest Act was passed to give more effective control over the entry and movement within the country of plant pests themselves. It superseded the act of 1905.

Since the quarantine law was enacted, $600 million in Federal and State funds have been spent to control or eradicate 40 economically destructive plant pests. Most of these pests were introduced before the 1912 law was passed. Parlatoria date scale, citrus canker, Hall scale, and Mediterranean fruit fly—all serious pests of the home orchard—have been eradicated from the United States. If these and a number of other seriously destructive pests had not been eliminated, they would still be eating and destroying the Nation's home gardens.

Many more acres of home gardens and lawns would be destroyed each year if there were no quarantines to regulate articles that might be carrying pests.

Home gardening would become more impracticable. And the apples on the apple tree known from childhood would almost be lost completely.

Pests are readily spread from place to place by the movement of diseased or infested plants, seeds, bulbs, fruits, crops, or soil. They may also travel as hitchhikers on vehicles, ships, and in aircraft.

It is man who usually upsets the natural balance by inadvertently carrying pests to new places.

In 1969, a young Florida boy vacationing in Hawaii with his family picked up an unusual looking snail and put it in his pocket. Unforunately, he got past agricultural quarantine inspectors when reentering the continental United States. The snail turned out to be the giant African snail, a pest that feeds on nearly all garden plants and leaves slimy trails all over yards and houses.

Because of this incident, the shrubs, trees, and lawns in some areas in Florida are now infested with these snails, requiring an extensive and expensive eradication program in an attempt to eliminate it.

In today's plant quarantine system, there are two lines of defense; the first is against foreign plant pests. More than 800 specially trained inspectors are located at all major airports, seaports, and border crossings into the United States to man this defensive line.

In the early days, it was relatively simple to maintain the necessary defenses at ports of entry. But today the situation is far different and the danger greater. More people travel more, farther, and faster. Plants and plant products can be brought from any part of the world in a few hours. This increases the chance that some traveler will unconsciously introduce a dangerous foreign insect or disease.

Alert USDA inspectors intercept an average of 129 plant pests each day at U.S. ports of entry—pests not now in this country. Most arrive in or on plants, fruits, and other plant material.

A potted shamrock from Ireland, or a rose plant from Italy, might be among the approximately 656,000 prohibited plants and plant products intercepted annually. More than 230 million returning Americans or visitors from abroad cross the borders into the United States each year. They bring with them 63 million pieces of baggage, all potential carriers of highly destructive pests.

Once an infestation is established, man and his products continue to spread the pests to uninfested areas. A truckload of sod, a camper trailer, or a delivery of nursery stock can spread destructive plant pests, to give some examples.

USDA's plant protection program is the second line of defense. It maintains an aggressive regulatory program to keep introduced insects and diseases from being spread into uninfested areas. Within an infested area, quarantines are imposed that control the movement of shrubs, sod, fruit trees—items that may be carrying a particular garden pest.

Thus, quarantines play a constructive role in protecting the Nation's ornamentals, gardens, orchards, and lawns, as well as its forests and farm crops.

Eradication of pests once established is very expensive. Living with introduced pests is even more costly. Many gardeners and farmers who continually battle gladiolus thrips, chrysanthemum rust, dandelions, European corn borers, and many other pests will readily verify this.

Continuing control of pests requires the use of agricultural chemicals which may add to the pollution of our physical environment. Quarantine protection, therefore, contributes to quality environment.

Travelers can help keep our gardens free of new pests by readily complying

Checking for citrus blackfly infestation in Brownsville, Tex.

with plant regulatory requirements. Inbound intercepted foreign pests, plus domestic plant pests which are moved into and between States contrary to quarantine regulations, are capable of rendering millions of dollars in damage and destruction to U.S. crops, gardens, forests, and ornamentals.

Gardeners who are planning to swap or move soil, plants, or articles that might harbor a destructive hitchhiker can provide valuable aid by first contacting their local agricultural officials. In many areas, State and Federal quarantines restrict the movement of plants and associated materials. Soil, sod, compost, plants, shrubbery, and decorative greenery may harbor microscopic cysts or insect eggs, subsurface grubs and worms, seeds from parasitic plants, or other pests.

Your county agent or agricultural inspector will tell you if your area is infested with a plant pest, how you control it, and how you can safely move plants, bulbs, tubers, and other gardening articles. Overseas travelers should check with the U.S. Department of Agriculture about items that can be safely brought into the United States. They may easily obtain this information by dropping a card to "Quarantines," U.S. Department of Agriculture, Washington, D.C. 20250.

plants for problem areas of the western states

ARID AND SEMIARID regions comprising the Great Plains west of the 100th meridian, the intermountain region between the Rockies and the west coastal ranges, and the Desert Southwest are problem areas when it comes to growing ornamental plants. Success in raising ornamentals is different than in areas of adequate rainfall but not necessarily difficult if you select adaptable species and use proper cultural methods.

The Great Plains and intermountain region is characteristically an area of low rainfall, low humidity, high wind movement, and medium to high altitude. The higher the altitude, the lower the atmospheric pressure in relation to sea level pressure. Low atmospheric pressure coupled with wind movement and low humidity allows moisture to evaporate quickly, thus contributing to drought conditions.

New residents are often surprised to learn that adequate water alone does not insure the survival, flowering, and fruiting of plants. Many factors of environment affect plant growth.

Some folks find that plants which were hardy and adaptable in the New England States will not survive in the cold, semiarid regions of the Great Plains. This shows the effect on plants of high wind movement and low humidity associated with cold. The effect is called desiccation or drying out. Unless plants have special mechanisms such as few or sunken breathing pores, an ability to store water, or small bark pores to prevent excessive desiccation, they often kill back or die in the central and northern portions of the Great Plains and the intermountain regions.

Another factor affecting plant growth in these problem areas is soil type. Problem soils make problem areas for plant growth. Such soils are common in areas between the Rockies and the coastal mountain ranges, and less common in the Great Plains east of the Rockies.

These soils are classified as saline

Author GENE S. HOWARD is a Horticulturist at the Cheyenne Horticultural Field Station, Plant Science Research Division, Agricultural Research Service, Cheyenne, Wyo.

alkali, saline nonalkali, and nonsaline alkali. All have a high pH and are commonly called alkaline soils as opposed to acid soils. Soil alkalinity or acidity is measured by a pH number; 7.0 is neutral, smaller numbers are acid and larger numbers alkaline.

The soils originated from weathered materials and from drainage waters of past geological ages. They may be modified by the use of specific compounds or amendments. However, the novice should get advice from competent soil scientists—either from commercial companies, or from State and Federal experiment stations.

Saline and/or alkaline materials are present in many western soils because there has not been enough rainfall or drainage since their deposition to remove them and render the soil neutral or acidic.

Some problem soils in farming districts occur where irrigation water accumulates or where good drainage is lacking. In some instances, the gardener or farmer may install drainage canals, or he may fracture and break up the subsoil to insure drainage and to leach out the salts and or alkali with water during the off season for production of plants.

A number of plants are more tolerant of highly saline or alkaline soils. Many of these are the native plants found growing in the area of the problem soil. They should be used in problem areas if soil amendment or leaching is not well understood or is not feasible.

In arid and semiarid regions, gardeners must take special care in order to successfully grow horticultural plants. They must eliminate competing vegetation by clean cultivation.

To limit the desiccating effects on ornamental plants in winter months, experimental researchers have developed ways of growing windbreaks. These windbreaks protect homesteads, orchards, gardens, barns and livestock areas, as well as highways and railroads. Experiments have also determined adaptable species and methods of growing them.

In regions of low annual rainfall, wind erosion of soils is more severe and widespread than water erosion. However, water erosion sometimes occurs during the spring runoff of melted snow and during flash floods after thunderstorms. These problems are more serious in cultivated fields than in areas around buildings where ornamentals are grown. Adequate plant cover is a solution.

A list of more than 250 plants for problem areas described in this chapter begins on page 156. Plant recommendations are classified by zones according to the average annual minimum temperature in degrees Fahrenheit. These zones are as follows: Zone 1, below $-50°$; Zone 2, $-50°$ to $-40°$; Zone 3, $-40°$ to $-30°$; Zone 4, $-30°$ to $-20°$; Zone 5, $-20°$ to $-10°$; Zone 6, $-10°$ to $0°$; Zone 7, $0°$ to $+10°$; Zone 8, $+10°$ to $+20°$; Zone 9, $+20°$ to $+30°$; and Zone 10, $+30°$ to $+40°$. See map inside the front cover of this book.

Recommendations by zones in the table apply specifically west of the 100th meridian and east of the Sierra Nevada and Cascade mountain ranges, although many of the species listed are adaptable ornamentals in other regions. The 100th meridian runs north and south on a line drawn through Bismarck, N. Dak., and Dodge City, Kans.

Zones IV and V east of the Rocky Mountains are areas of high wind movement, particularly during the cold winter months. Winds of 100 miles per hour are not uncommon and on several days each year 50 m.p.h. or more winds occur. High wind movement is also characteristic of the intermountain region west of the Rocky Mountains, although it usually is less extreme. For these reasons, you may consider adaptable plants in zones IV and V as windproof plants.

Similarly, you may regard plants that are adaptable in zones VI and VII as heatproof plants. They grow where summer temperatures often exceed the 100-degree mark.

In our region, only the lawn grasses listed in the table are acceptable traffic-proof plants. Two so-called noxious

Ornamental Plants for Problem Areas of the West

Adaptability to:

Common name	Annual rainfall: Less than 10"	Annual rainfall: 10"–20"	Zone III	Zone IV	Zone V	Zone VI	Zone VII	Salt or alkaline soils pH–8.0+	Altitude require-ment ft.+	Shade
Trees (Evergreen)										
Arborvitae, Eastern		x			x	x	x			x
Arborvitae, Oriental		x		x	x	x	x			x
Cypress, Arizona		x				x	x	x		x
Fir, White		x		x	x	x	x		3,000	x
Juniper, Alligator	x	x								
Juniper, Oneseed		x		x	x	x	x	x		
Juniper, Redberry		x	x	x	x	x	x			x
Juniper, Redcedar (many cultivars)		x	x	x	x	x	x			x
Juniper, Rocky Mountain (many cultivars)	x	x	x	x	x	x	x			
Larch, Siberian		x	x	x	x	x				
Pine, Aleppo		x			x	x	x			
Pine, Austrian		x		x	x	x	x	x		
Pine, Bristlecone		x		x	x	x		x	4,000	
Pine, Colorado Pinyon		x		x	x	x	x			
Pine, Limber		x		x	x	x	x			
Pine, Ponderosa		x	x	x	x	x	x	x		x
Pine, Scotch		x	x	x	x	x	x			
Pine, Swiss Mountain (mugo)		x		x	x	x				
Spruce, Black Hills		x	x	x	x	x				
Spruce, Colorado		x	x	x	x	x			3,000	x
Spruce, Engelmann		x	x	x	x	x			3,000	x
Shrubs (Evergreen)										
Juniper, Common		x		x	x	x	x			x
Juniper, Creeping		x		x	x	x	x			x
Juniper, Meyer Singleseed		x		x	x					
Juniper, Pfitzer Chinese		x	x	x	x	x				x

Juniper, Savin 'Tamarix'	x	x	x	x	x	x			
Pine, Mugho Swiss Mountain	x		x	x	x				x
Trees (Broadleaf)									
Albizzia, Silktree (Mimosa)	x				x	x			
Ash, Green	x	x	x	x					
Ash, European Mountain	x		x	x					
Birch, Cutleaf Weeping	x		x	x				4,000	
Buckeye	x		x	x	x	x			
Cottonwood	x+	x	x	x	x	x			
Crabapple, Flowering	x	x	x	x	x	x			
Elm, Lacebark Chinese	x				x	x			
Elm, Siberian	x	x	x	x	x	x	x		
Hackberry, Common	x	x	x	x	x	x			
Honeylocust (thornless)	x		x	x	x	x			
Jujube, Common	x			x	x	x			
Linden, American	x		x	x	x				
Linden, Littleleaf	x		x	x	x				
Locust, Black	x			x	x	x			
Maple, Amur	x	x	x	x	x	x			
Maple, Manchurian	x		x	x	x				
Maple, Norway	x		x	x	x	x			
Maple, Silver	x	x	x	x	x	x			
Maple, Sugar	x		x	x	x	x			
Maple, Tatarian	x		x	x	x				
Mulberry, Russian	x			x	x	x			
Oak, Bur	x	x	x	x	x	x			
Oak, Live (sometimes evergreen)	x				x	x			
Oak, Northern Red	x			x	x	x			
Oak, Pin	x			x	x	x			
Pecan	x				x	x			
Redbud, Eastern	x				x	x			
Russian-Olive	x	x	x	x	x	x	x		
Sweetgum, American	x				x	x			
Sycamore	x				x	x			
Walnut, Black	x			x	x	x			

Ornamental Plants for Problem Areas of the West—Continued

Common name	Annual rainfall		Zones					Salt or alkaline soils	Altitude require-ment	Shade
	Less than 10"	10"–20"	III	IV	V	VI	VII	pH–8.0+	ft.+	
Shrubs (Broadleaf)										
Adina (Adina rubella)		x				x	x			
Almond, Flowering		x				x	x			
Almond, Prairie (Prunus triloba x P. pedunculata)		x	x	x	x					
Almond, Russian		x	x	x	x	x				
Amorpha, Indigobush		x		x	x	x	x			
Apacheplume	x	x		x	x	x	x			
Beautybush		x			x	x	x	x		
Bitterbrush, Antelope	x	x			x	x	x	x	4,000	
Bluebeard (Caryopteris sp.)		x			x	x	x			
Buckthorn, Common		x	x	x	x	x				
Buckthorn, Dahurian		x	x	x	x	x				
Buckthorn, Rock		x	x	x	x	x				
Buffaloberry		x	x	x	x	x				
Butterflybush		x			x	x	x			
Ceanothus, Inland	x	x			x	x	x			
Chaste-tree		x			x	x	x			
Cherry, Manchu		x		x	x	x	x			
Chokecherry, Western 'Schubert'		x		x	x	x		x	4,000	
Cinquefoil, Bush		x	x	x	x	x			4,000	
Cliffrose, Stansbury		x		x	x	x		x	4,000	
Coralberry		x		x	x	x	x			
Cotoneaster, European		x		x	x	x	x			
Cotoneaster, Hedge		x	x	x	x	x	x			
Cotoneaster, Multiflora		x		x	x	x	x			
Cotoneaster, Peking		x	x	x	x	x	x			
Cotoneaster, Sungari Redbead		x		x	x	x	x	x		
Crapemyrtle		x			x	x	x			

158

Desertwillow	x	x				x	x	x		
Dogwood, Colorado Redosier		x		x	x					
Dogwood, Siberian		x		x	x					
Elderberry, Blueberry		x		x	x	x	x			
Elderberry, European Red 'Redman'		x		x	x	x	x			
Euonymus, European		x		x	x	x	x			x
Euonymus, Winterberry		x		x	x	x	x			x
Firethorn, Laland		x			x	x	x			
Fontanesia, Fortune	x	x				x	x	x		
Forestiera, New Mexican	x	x		x	x	x	x	x		
Forsythia, Border		x			x	x	x			
Forsythia, Fortune Weeping		x			x	x	x			
Goldraintree		x				x	x			
Greasewood	x	x		x	x	x	x	x		
Hawthorn, Cockspur		x	x	x						
Hawthorn, Downy		x		x	x	x				
Hawthorn, English		x			x	x				
Hawthorn, Russian		x		x	x	x				
Honeysuckle, Amur		x			x	x	x			
Honeysuckle, 'Arnold Red', 'Cardinal', 'Carlton', 'Valentia'		x	x	x	x	x				
Honeysuckle, Winter		x			x	x	x			
Honeysuckle, Zabel Blueleaf		x		x	x	x	x			
Leadplant	x	x		x	x	x	x	x		
Lilac, Early		x	x	x	x					
Lilac, French Hybrids		x		x	x	x	x			
Lilac, Hungarian		x		x	x	x				
Lilac, Japanese Tree		x	x	x	x	x	x			
Lilac, Late		x		x	x					
Lilac, Persian		x	x	x	x	x	x			
Mockorange, Lewis		x		x	x					
Mockorange, Sweet		x			x	x	x			
Mockorange, Virginalis		x			x	x	x			
Mountainmahogany, Douglas	x	x		x	x				4,000	
Nandina		x				x	x			x
Peach, Flowering		x			x	x	x			
Peashrub, Globe Russian		x	x	x	x					
Peashrub, Pygmy		x	x	x	x					

Ornamental Plants for Problem Areas of the West—Continued

Common name	Annual rainfall		Zones					Salt or alkaline soils	Altitude requirement	Shade
	Less than 10"	10"–20"	III	IV	V	VI	VII	pH–8.0+	ft.+	
Peashrub, Siberian			x	x	x					x
Perovskia, Russiansage		x		x	x	x				
Plum, Cistena		x	x	x	x					
Plum, Flowering		x	x	x	x					
Plum, Newport		x		x	x	x				
Privet, European		x		x	x	x	x			x
Quince, Flowering		x			x	x	x			
Quince, Japanese Flowering		x			x	x	x			
Rabbitbrush	x		x	x	x	x		x		
Rose, Austrian Copper		x	x	x	x					
Rose, 'Harison's Yellow'		x	x	x	x					
Rose, Hybrid Tea		x		x	x	x	x			
Rosewood, Arizona	x				x	x	x	x		x
Sagebrush	x			x	x	x	x	x		
Saltbush	x		x	x	x	x	x	x		
Serviceberry, Allegany		x		x	x	x	x			
Serviceberry, Saskatoon		x	x	x	x	x				
Serviceberry, Shadblow		x	x	x	x					
Shrubalthea		x				x	x			
Sibirea, Smooth		x		x	x	x				
Smoketree, Common		x			x	x	x			
Snowberry	x		x	x	x	x				
Spirea, Mongolian		x		x	x	x	x			
Spirea, Nippon		x		x	x	x	x			
Spirea, Sargent		x	x	x	x	x				
Spirea, Threelobe		x	x	x	x	x	x			
Spirea, Vanhoutte		x	x	x	x	x	x			
Sumac, Skunkbush		x	x	x	x	x	x			

Plant																								
																				x			x	x
Sumac, Staghorn	x	x															x	x					x	
Tamarix, Amur	x	x															x	x	x				x	
Tamarix, Kashgar	x	x															x	x	x				x	
Viburnum, Common Snowball	x	x													x		x	x					x	
Viburnum, European Cranberrybush	x	x															x	x	x				x	
Viburnum, Koreanspice	x	x															x	x	x	x			x	
Viburnum, Manchurian	x	x													x		x	x					x	
Viburnum, Nannyberry	x	x													x		x	x					x	
Viburnum, Wayfaring Tree	x	x															x						x	

Plants for the Desert Southwest

Plant																								
Agave			x	x	x	x	x	x	x	x	x	x	x	x			x	x	x	x			x	
Boojam Tree			x	x	x	x	x	x	x	x	x	x	x	x			x	x	x	x			x	
Brittlebush			x	x	x	x	x	x	x	x	x	x	x	x			x	x	x	x			x	
Broom Baccharis			x	x	x	x	x	x	x	x	x	x	x	x			x	x	x	x			x	
Cacti (many types)			x	x	x	x	x	x	x	x	x	x	x	x		x	x	x	x	x			x	
Catclaw			x	x	x	x	x	x	x	x	x	x	x	x			x	x	x	x			x	
Creosotebush			x	x	x	x	x	x	x	x	x	x	x	x			x	x	x	x			x	
Hackberry, Spiny			x	x	x	x	x	x	x	x	x	x	x	x		x	x	x	x	x			x	
Jojoba			x	x	x	x	x	x	x	x	x	x	x	x			x	x	x	x			x	
Mesquite			x	x	x	x	x	x	x	x	x	x	x	x		x	x	x	x	x			x	
Ocotillo			x	x	x	x	x	x	x	x	x	x	x	x			x	x	x	x			x	
Paloverde			x	x	x	x	x	x	x	x	x	x	x	x			x	x	x	x			x	
Sotol			x	x	x	x	x	x	x	x	x	x	x	x			x	x	x	x			x	
Tesota			x	x	x	x	x	x	x	x	x	x	x	x		x	x	x	x	x			x	
Yucca (many types)			x	x	x	x	x	x	x	x	x	x	x	x			x	x	x	x			x	

Vines

Plant																								
Clematis, Drummond			x	x	x	x	x	x	x	x	x	x	x	x	x	x	x							
Clematis, Jackman			x	x	x	x	x	x	x	x	x	x	x	x	x	x	x							
Grape (use the native species in each zone)			x	x	x	x	x	x	x	x	x	x	x	x	x	x	x			x				
Honeysuckle, Dropmore Scarlet Trumpet			x	x	x	x	x	x	x	x	x	x	x	x	x	x	x			x			x	
Honeysuckle, Everblooming			x	x	x	x	x	x	x	x	x	x	x	x	x	x	x	x		x			x	
Ivy, Engelmann			x	x	x	x	x	x	x	x	x	x	x	x			x			x				
Monkshoodvine			x	x	x	x	x	x	x	x	x	x	x	x			x			x			x	
Moonseed, Asiatic			x	x	x	x	x	x	x	x	x	x	x	x	x	x	x	x		x			x	
Rose, Climbing			x	x	x	x	x	x	x	x	x	x	x	x	x	x	x	x						
Silkvine (Grecian and Chinese)			x	x	x	x	x	x	x	x	x	x	x	x			x			x				

Ornamental Plants for Problem Areas of the West—Continued

Common name	Annual rainfall — Less than 10"	Annual rainfall — 10"–20"	Zones III	Zones IV	Zones V	Zones VI	Zones VII	Salt or alkaline soils pH–8.0+	Altitude requirement ft.+	Shade
Silverlacevine		x				x	x			
Trumpetcreeper, Common 'Mme. Galen'		x			x	x	x			
Virginia Creeper		x	x	x	x	x	x			x
Perennial Flowers										
Althea, Perennial		x	x	x	x	x				
Aster, Perennial		x		x	x					
Babysbreath 'Pink Star'		x	x	x	x	x				
Bellflower, Top		x		x	x	x				
Bugloss, Italian		x	x	x	x	x				x
Campion, Maltesecross		x		x	x	x				x
Centaurea, Globe		x		x	x	x				
Centaurea, Persian		x		x	x	x				
Chrysanthemum (hardy garden forms)		x	x	x	x	x	x			
Cinquefoil, Northwest		x		x	x	x				x
Cinquefoil, Small Nepal		x		x	x	x				x
Cinquefoil, Sulfur		x		x	x	x				x
Clematis, Caripensis		x		x	x	x				
Clematis, Douglas		x		x	x					
Clematis, Solitary		x		x	x					
Columbine, Colorado		x		x	x	x	x			
Coneflower, Cutleaf		x		x	x					
Coreopsis, Bigflower		x		x	x					
Daylily (many cultivars). Some daylilies are subject to chlorosis		x			x	x	x			
Delphinium		x	x	x	x	x				
Dianthus (Carnation, Pinks, Sweet-william)		x	x	x	x	x				
Dittany, Gasplant		x		x	x	x				

Plant	
Euphorbia, Cushion	
Euphorbia, Cypress	
Euphorbia, Myrtle	
Flax, Perennial	
Four-o'clock, Colorado	
Gaillardia, Perennial	4,000
Geranium, Meadow	
Globethistle, Small	
Goutweed, Bishops	
Hen-and-chickens	
Iris (many cultivars)	
Larkspur, Slender Siberian	
Lily, Henry	
Lily, Madonna	
Lily, Tiger	
Lily, Turkscap	
Lily, Western Orangecup	
Nepeta, Persian	
Peavine, Perennial	2,000
Penstemon, Beardlip	3,000
Penstemon, Oneside	3,000
Penstemon, Sawsepal	3,000
Peony (many cultivars)	
Periwinkle	
Phlox, Summer	
Prairieconeflower, Upright	
Sage, Perennial (*Salvia* sp.)	
Speedwell, Bastard	
Speedwell, Wooly	
Stonecrop (Liveforever, Showy, Tworow)	
Tansy	
Thermopsis, Carolina	
Wormwood, Common	
Yarrow, Sneezewort	

Ornamental Plants for Problem Areas of the West—Continued

Common name	Annual rainfall		Adaptability to: Zones					Salt or alkaline soils	Altitude require-ment	Shade
	Less than 10"	10"–20"	III	IV	V	VI	VII	pH–8.0+	ft.+	
Annual Flowers										
Most of the common kinds are satisfactory. Set as bedding plants in all zones. The large seeded kinds may be planted directly in the garden in all zones.										
Hardy Bulbs										
Daffodil		x	x	x	x					
Grape Hyacinth		x		x	x	x				
Tulip		x	x	x	x	x				
Tender Bulbs (harvest and store over winter)										
Canna		x	x	x	x	x	x			
Dahlia		x	x	x	x	x	x			
Gladioli		x	x	x	x	x	x		3,000 (in zones VI & VII)	
Lawn Grasses (irrigated)										
Bermudagrass (and its cultivars)		x				x	x			
Centipedegrass		x				x	x			x
Fescue (the fine bladed species and cultivars)		x	x	x	x					x
Kentucky Bluegrass (and its cultivars)		x	x	x	x	x				
Lawn Grasses (dryland)										
Buffalograss		x	x	x	x	x	x			
Crested Wheat, Fairway		x	x	x	x	x				
Grama, Blue		x	x	x	x	x	x			

weeds, creeping bellflower (*Campanula rapunculoides*) and bindweed (*Convolvulus arvensis*), are excellent traffic-proof plants if they could be accepted.

All ornamental plants which are adapted to arid regions profit by irrigation water. Some species should not be watered late in the growing season, as they need to mature their growth before cold weather arrives.

Plants that require acid soils are not adaptable to the problem areas discussed in this chapter.

In the region covered by the chapter, you must give intensive care to all newly-set woody plants until they become well established, usually a period of 2 to 5 years. Put up wind barriers in dry, windy winters, and thoroughly water ornamentals at monthly intervals. Cultivate so that competing vegetation (other than lawn grass) is eliminated around ornamental plants.

Prepare soil for ornamental planting by deep spading or plowing. Organic materials such as well-rotted barnyard fertilizer, leafmold, compost, peat moss, or vermiculite are beneficial when incorporated during soil preparation. They improve soil texture and water-holding capacity.

If you are having a new home built, make sure if you can that the contractor stockpiles the good topsoil. After the building construction is completed, remove the surplus subsoil and spread the good topsoil on the yard.

Any area of the yard or garden with poor or thin soil will profit by the addition or substitution of fertile topsoil. Topsoil usually is available from commercial sources at a reasonable price.

Fertilizer elements apt to be deficient in our soils are nitrogen, phosphorus, and iron, and in some areas, potassium. There are plenty of iron compounds present in western soils, but these become tied up and unavailable to plants. The use of chelated iron compounds and various iron salts will help eliminate the problem of iron deficiency chlorosis on a year-to-year basis. Plants with yellow leaves having green veins demonstrate this deficiency.

Bags of prepared fertilizer show three numbers separated by dashes—for example 20–10–5. These refer to the percent nitrogen, phosphorus, and potassium respectively. Calculate the percent of actual fertilizer in any package and purchase the most economical kind.

Transplant all dormant woody and herbaceous ornamentals during the first month or 6 weeks after the soil thaws in the late winter or early spring. Iris, peonies, and oriental poppies are the few perennials planted in early fall. You may plant container-grown and balled-and-burlapped ornamentals throughout the summer months, but the earlier the better as they must become established before frost and cold weather return in the fall.

Mulching of ornamental plants is not a common practice except for winter protection of perennial plants that are not completely hardy. Mulching with organic materials helps control weeds and maintain moisture.

A few ornamentals require the support of stakes or trellises. These include dahlias, climbing or trailing plants, and tall perennials such as peonies which tend to break or fall over in wind or rain.

Perhaps no cultural treatment, other than providing enough water, is more necessary and less understood by home gardeners than proper pruning methods.

Prune ornamentals regularly, except the small slow-growing types. You may maintain woody plants at a predetermined size by adequate pruning. You can shape any species of woody plants into a hedge by shearing the size pattern desired from the time the plants are small seedlings. Hedges should be slightly wider at the base than at the top.

I recommend pruning in early spring, but it also may be done in the fall or summer in our area.

The purpose of pruning is to remove branches that cross each other, branches that are parallel, and all other branches that spoil the balance and symmetry of the tree. Anyone can become a satisfactory pruner if he has good sharp tools, and learns how to make proper cuts and how various ornamentals should be pruned.

To make a proper cut, you must cut close to the branch or branchlet from which the part is to be removed—never leave a stub. Favor the strong branches on the windward side and cut back those on the sheltered side. Many shade trees will grow away from the wind in arid and semiarid regions.

Shrubs branch at the soil level and have few to many canes or shoots. Depending on the number of canes on each plant and the time between each pruning, you should remove 15 to 25 percent of the oldest, largest canes. Select a similar number of the strongest new shoots to replace them. In this manner shrubs may be completely renewed every few years.

Shape the shrub with the remaining branches maintained all the way to the ground, and prune these so the lower branches are slightly longer than the upper branches. This allows sunlight to reach all the parts of the plant and promotes normal leaf and branch growth.

The home gardener often sets new plants too close together. As they grow and become crowded, alternatives arise. You either must remove some plants,

or annually prune and shape them so they fit the available space.

Some gardeners become attached to their ornamental plants and will not remove or discard any of them. Others desire variety in the landscape and either move plants to a different location (at the proper season) or discard and replace them with new cultivars and species. A plant cultivar is a cultivated variety available from commercial sources.

Most plants are subject to injury or loss from insects, nematodes, and diseases. You must be aware of such possibilities, and use methods of control when injury or damage is first noted. Effective chemicals which are not known to be harmful to the environment are available.

Many of our ornamental plants in semiarid and arid parts of the West are low plants—grass, annual and perennial flowers, and short shrubs. Perhaps in our cities with their visual air pollution problems we need to grow more large plants in each unit area. Several ornamentals make excellent tall hedges—Colorado spruce, chokecherry, Siberian peashrub. Perhaps we need to grow more large trees also.

In the arid and semiarid region of

Hedge of Colorado spruce on the High Plains.

the West we have learned to modify our environment by irrigation, through developing tree windbreaks, by using both native and exotic adaptable plants, and by improved cultural practices. We have learned to remove excess salts from our soils by leaching and by using soil amendments.

In spite of the problems which confront us, many people in the region have beautifully landscaped homes, whether they live in city or suburb, on farm or ranch.

For further reading:
Burnham, D. R., and Johnson, E. W., *Shrubs for Northeastern New Mexico.*

New Mexico A & M College Bulletin 358, 1950.

George, Ernest J., *Shelterbelts for the Northern Great Plains.* U.S. Department of Agriculture Farm Bulletin 2109, Washington, D.C. 20250, 1966.

Howard, Gene S., *Herbaceous Perennials for the Central Great Plains.* U.S. Department of Agriculture, ARS Publication 34–71, Washington, D.C. 20250, 1965.

Johnson, E. W., *Ornamental Shrubs for the Southern Great Plains.* USDA Farm Bulletin 2025, 1958. For sale by Superintendent of Documents, Government Printing Office, Washington, D.C. 20402, 20¢.

Guide to the Boyce Thompson Southwestern Arboretum. A visitor's bulletin, University of Arizona, Tucson.

song of the lazy gardener, or minimum care plantings

MANY PEOPLE avoid having plants in their daily lives because of the regular care that must be given to help them thrive. But while the planning and planting of any garden can consume a lot of time and energy, you can develop plantings which may be maintained with only 1 or 2 hours of care a week.

The decision to have a minimum-care garden starts with planning the garden area, deciding the kind of vista that you wish to create, and—most important—selecting the plants to be grown.

A minimum-care garden immediately eliminates many favorites which are grown by avid gardeners. To survive, some plants require frequent watering, pruning, staking, and spraying for disease and pest control. They may also be very sensitive to drought, freezing, or inadequate drainage. The gardener must apply protective mulches, set up screens, and hope for mild weather. Some plants grow so vigorously that they cannot be retained within the desired space.

A minimum-care garden starts with deciding on the functions of the plants —a foundation planting, screening, traffic control, controlling water movement, color and fragrance, or shade. Other chapters in this book give specific information on how to plan and select plants to perform all of these functions. This chapter will offer specific approaches just for a low-maintenance garden.

Mature plantings around old homes are examples of low-maintenance gardens. The yard is filled with large plants, all meshed together. Plants susceptible to disease and insects died many years ago. All of the plants which needed staking have been broken and developed into quaint forms. Because of their age and the neglect through the year, the plants which are left in the garden are the resistant types and thus low-maintenance plants.

You can seek clues from the plants

Author HENRY M. CATHEY is Leader of Ornamental Investigations in the Plant Science Research Division, Agricultural Research Service.

growing in a mature garden as to what you should be doing. Become aware of the size of mature trees and shrubs. Realize that the number of plants needed for a landscape effect are minimal. A garden effect throughout the growing season can be created with a few hardy herbaceous perennials, bulbs, and shrubs. And finally, keep in mind that some plants will not survive under minimum care.

Certain kinds of plants are adapted to minimum care because of their growth characteristics. Within almost every type of plant are species or cultivated forms which are slow growers.

It is often difficult to pick out a slow growing form of a plant, unless the plant is labelled as such. A simple way is to move your hand along the main stem of the plant. The stem should be smooth for the entire length of the current season of growth. Your fingers will feel and then your eyes will see a ridge circling around the stem. This is the scar from the previous growth season. Observe the length of growth made during the previous season and the distances between the leaves on the stems.

The shorter the length of the previous season's growth and the closer the spacing of leaves on the stem, the more likely the plant is slow growing. Select the slow-growing over the rapid-growing plant, for a minimum care garden.

There are also true dwarf forms of many kinds of plants. They are called dwarfs because of the restricted growth which is produced each year. True dwarf plants are often difficult to propagate. They develop into useful sizes for landscape purposes only after many years of culture in the nursery. True dwarf plants are thus much more expensive to buy than their normal counterparts in the garden.

The dwarf characteristic of growth may be an indication of poorly formed or functioning root systems or restricted movement of water and nutrients within the plant. Dwarf plants must be given more protection to survive than normal plants.

Another approach open to the gardener on a limited budget is to plant more vigorous types of plants and plan to prune them at frequent intervals. Many gardeners prune their plants at the wrong time of year. Consult Home and Garden Bulletin No. 165, *Pruning Ornamental Shrubs and Vines,* on how to prune many kinds of garden plants.

As a rule, spring flowering shrubs should be pruned immediately following flowering. They can be severely cut back at this time and still permit the development of new shoots prior to winter. Most spring flowering shrubs will flower every year with an annual pruning.

Summer flowering shrubs blossom on current season growth. They should be pruned either before growth resumes in the spring or after the flowers fade in late summer. Pruning of these plants after growth starts will delay or inhibit their flowering for the current season of growth.

Conifers and broad- and narrow-leaf evergreens should be sheared while they are dormant. This means trimming during the winter. Pruning at the correct time for the individual plant will help retain any plant within desired bounds and need be done only once a year.

Deciduous flowering shrubs are often the forgotten plants in the new garden. Unfortunately, they do not retain their foliage over the winter. However, they do give maximum areas of color in the garden for a limited period of time. By careful selection of species of plants, the gardener can have a procession of flowers throughout the growing season.

A list of 25 easy-to-care-for shrubs and trees is given on the next page. These flowering plants have only one problem: if left alone in the garden, they eventually become very large. All, however, can be retained within any space requirement when pruned yearly or every other year. Pruning should require only a few minutes during the gardening year but will permit the gardener to control the space occupied by each plant.

The plants were selected to give a

Spiraea, a spring flowering shrub, can be retained in any garden space if the plants are given a yearly pruning following flowering. This is Spiraea x vanhouttei.

progression of blooms from early spring to late fall. Many are currently out of common use because of rapid advances in the development of other showy flowering shrubs. The listed trees and shrubs, however, do not need the intense care that some of our new hybrids require and will provide the gardener with a succession of color throughout the gardening season.

Underneath the flowering trees and shrubs are spaces for ground covers and herbaceous perennials and bulbs.

As with the woody plants, many of the favorite garden plants must be excluded from a minimum-care garden. They require frequent lifting and division, survive only a few years, or demand intensive pest and disease control. Other herbaceous plants can flourish in a garden with but little care and actually will maintain themselves for many years.

The plants listed on page 170 suggest a sequence of bloom of 25 herbaceous perennials and bulbs. For their

---

Sequence of Flowering of 25 Minimum-Care Shrubs, Vines, and Trees
ORDER OF BLOOM: *From late winter to fall*

Hamamelis sp.—Witch-hazel
Cornus mas—Cornelian-cherry
Forsythia sp.—Forsythia
Pieris japonica—Japanese andromeda
Amelanchier canadensis—Serviceberry
Chaenomeles japonica—Japanese quince
Magnolia x soulangeana—Saucer magnolia
Spiraea x vanhouttei—Vanhoutte spirea
Spiraea thunbergii—Japanese spirea
Cercis canadensis—Redbud
Cornus florida—Flowering dogwood
Deutzia grandiflora—Deutzia
Kerria japonica—Kerria

Syringa vulgaris—Common lilac
Kolkwitzia amabilis—Beauty-bush
Weigela florida—Weigela
Kalmia latifolia—Mountain-laurel
Hydrangea arborescens—Hills-of-snow
Calluna vulgaris—Heather
Abelia x grandiflora—Glossy abelia
Buddleia davidii—Butterfly bush
Caryopteris incana—Bluemist-spirea
Hibiscus syriacus—Althea, Rose of Sharon
Lagerstroemia indica—Crapemyrtle
Sophora japonica—Japanese pagoda tree
Vitex agnus-castus—Chaste-tree

Sequence of Flowering of 25 Minimum-Care Herbaceous Perennials and Bulbs

ORDER OF BLOOM: *From late winter to fall*

Helleborus niger—Christmas rose
Galanthus—Snowdrop
Crocus vernus—Crocus
Muscari—Grape-hyacinth
Narcissus—Daffodil
Leucojum aestivale—Snowflake
Scilla hispanica—Bluebell
Convallaria majalis—Lily-of-the-valley
Dicentra spectabilis—Bleedingheart
  and *D. cucullaria*—Dutchmans-breeches
Aquilegia hybrids—Columbine
Paeonia—Peony
Lilium candidum—Madonna lily

Astilbe—False goatsbeard
Heuchera hybrids—Coralbells
Iris—Bearded and beardless iris
Primula hybrids—Primrose
Oenothera—Evening-primrose
Lilium regale—Regal lily
Hemerocallis—Daylilies
Canna—Canna
Sedum sp.—Stonecrop
Eupatorium—Bluemist-flower
Lycoris squamigera—Lycoris
Colchicum autumnale—Autumn-crocus

maximum survival they should be planted at greater distances apart than recommended in the previous chapters of this book. Extra space between the plants will allow more room for each plant to develop prior to the crowding of the individual clumps of the plants.

These plants should be fertilized and watered throughout the growing season, and only the minimum amount of foliage should be removed. Functioning of the leaves throughout the growing season will insure more than adequate growth of the plants for flowering the following season. Maximum development of the storage organs must be realized with each season of growth to insure flowering the following season. Premature removal of leaves may make for a more tidy garden but at the sacrifice of the bloom the next year.

Following the selection of plants and placing them in the garden, plans should be made to insure their maintenance. Most local newspapers and monthly garden magazines carry columns on what the gardener should be doing to help maintain plants.

Make it a routine practice to refresh your memory on what should be done at a specific time in the year. There is an ideal time to do everything in the garden. Doing it at the right time always greatly reduces the labor involved and insures that the plants will flower the following season.

The gardener should install a simple automatic watering system to help get the plants established in the garden. Details for installation are described in pages 66 to 67. Automatic watering, even though it is just an oscillating sprinkler, will permit thorough watering of the entire garden area without hours of hand labor of holding a garden hose. The initial investment in a sprinkler system is quickly offset by the reduced labor for maintenance.

The period of enjoyment and the time for working in the garden can be extended with the use of nighttime lighting. Several kinds of lamps may be used. Ordinary incandescent flood lamps are the most common.

Light the plants only in the early evening. If you keep the light on later than 9:30 to 10 p.m., the extra daylength will alter the growth and flowering of many plants. Some plants will flower early while others will be delayed in flowering. Serious cold damage may well result when plants continue to grow in the fall.

A final aspect of the minimum-care garden is to limit the space in which you wish to garden and the number of plants you wish to grow. Over-ambitious activities in the spring planting season can cause problems later with the time pressures which will develop through the growing season.

For further reading:
  U.S. Department of Agriculture, *Pruning Ornamental Shrubs and Vines.* Home and Garden Bulletin No. 165, Washington, D.C. 20250.

searching the world to obtain
new and better plants

MOST OF OUR garden plants, like our crop plants, have been derived from wild species native to distant lands.

We have been favored also with a number of ornamental plants that are native to our own country. Some of our natives such as the dogwood, holly, magnolia, assorted pines, hemlocks, and rhododendrons are, indeed, among the finest of their kinds and they will remain important for as long as we have gardens and parks.

To these, however, must be added the thousands of species and varieties of plants which were brought to our shores first by the colonists and since then by a variety of means which have increasingly made more and varied garden plants familiar to the public.

Origins of our garden plants are as diverse as the migrations of man. For wherever he settled man brought with him plants that reminded him of his homeland. In return, he sent newly-found trees, shrubs, and herbs back to his origins.

Japanese emissaries to the courts of China sent home to Japan the chrysanthemum, flowering apricot, and peony. Scholars and physicians employed in the Dutch and English East India Companies and their Portuguese counterparts first introduced azaleas, camellias, and many other choice garden plants into Europe during the 16th and 17th centuries. At the same time, many missionaries provided vast amounts of information on the botanical resources of the Orient. Although they actually introduced few plants, their letters and writings markedly stimulated others to do plant collecting.

In our own country, the colonists brought many of their Old World garden favorites to the New World.

These contributions to the culture of our country can be seen today in the restored gardens of Colonial Williamsburg, in Virginia. At that historic center only the garden and herb plants of colonial times are used in landscaping the restored area.

Efforts to introduce ornamental plants in the early 1800's were largely those of wealthy landowners who received plants on every ship arriving from Europe to grace their estates. H. H. Hunnewell, of Massachusetts, was such a person. He reportedly imported over 2,000 forest trees, fruit, and ornamental plants in 1847 alone. Undoubtedly, many of these early importations failed, for this was strictly a trial and error approach. Similarly, plantation owners in the South introduced camellias and other broadleaved evergreens from Europe.

Many of our garden plants are native to the Orient. Most of the European collectors had sent these plants from Japan and China to Europe in earlier centuries. Indirectly at first from Europe, these broadleaved evergreens, flowering trees and shrubs, and perennials have become our major landscaping resources.

An American, Dr. George R. Hall (a physician turned foreign trader), was responsible for the first direct shipments of ornamentals from Japan to the United States shortly after the reopening of that country by Admiral

Author JOHN L. CREECH is Chief of the New Crops Research Branch, Plant Science Research Division, Agricultural Research Service. During 1971 he traveled to Soviet Siberia in search of trees, shrubs, and other plants for use in environmental improvement.

Perry. In 1861–62, Dr. Hall, on returning to his home in Rhode Island, sent many of the plants he had assembled in his Yokohama garden to Francis Parkman, noted historian and horticulturist, and to the famous Parsons Nursery, at Flushing, N.Y.

Some of Hall's first introductions were Japanese maples, cryptomerias, hydrangea, procumbent juniper, star magnolia, Japanese red pine, dwarf Japanese yew, wisteria, and zelkova.

Establishment of the Arnold Arboretum in Boston, Mass., in 1872 provided for the first extensively organized effort to collect and introduce ornamentals from foreign countries.

Of the several collectors sent out by the Arnold Arboretum, Ernest H. Wilson was the most famous. During his travels throughout the Orient, Wilson introduced more than a thousand species not previously cultivated, not to mention his many collections of the best azalea varieties of Japan.

Along with its many sister arboretums in the United States, the Arnold Arboretum has continued to introduce plants from foreign arboretums, nurseries, and similar institutions.

Today there is less emphasis on the collecting of wild plants by our arboretums because of greater quarantine restrictions and cost of conducting field work. The exploration programs of the U.S. Department of Agriculture attempt to serve the needs of arboretums and nurserymen for new plants through the efforts of the Agricultural Research Service. This is done by the New Crops Research Branch and our own National Arboretum.

In USDA the first organized efforts to conduct plant exploration began in 1898 under the leadership of David Fairchild. While the Department's interests were chiefly economic plants, ornamentals could scarcely be overlooked. During this grand period of plant collecting by Americans, 1890

World Contributions to American Horticulture—Some Familiar Ornamentals

OLD WORLD PLANTS		
Southern Europe/Mediterranean	Crabapple	Dendrobium orchid
Anemone	Daylily	Magnolia
Boxwood	Deutzia	Primula
English holly	Flowering cherry	Rhododendron
Hyacinth	Forsythia	
Iris	Holly	*Australia*
Ivy	Hydrangea	Acacia
Narcissus	Iris	Eucalyptus
Pansy	Juniper	Melaleuca
Privet	Lily	
Snapdragon	Magnolia	NEW WORLD PLANTS
Sweet pea	Peony	
Yew	Philadelphus	*Mexico/Central America*
	Privet	Agave
Central/Southern Africa	Tea rose	Cacti
African-violet	Yew	Cosmos
Begonia		Dahlia
Calendula	*Near East*	Epidendrum orchid
Calla	Daylily	Marigold
Geranium	Iris	Poinsettia
Gladiolus	Lilac	Zinnia
Succulents	Poppy	
	Pyracantha	*South America*
Eastern Asia	Spring bulbs	Amaryllis
Aster	Tulip	Begonia
Azalea		Canna
Camellia	*Indo-Burma-Assam*	Cattleya orchid
Chrysanthemum	Begonia	Fuchsia
Cotoneaster	Camellia	Nasturtium
	Crapemyrtle	Petunia
		Zinnia

to 1930, we find flowering cherries, bamboos, Chinese elms, lawn grasses (zoysia), roses, and lilacs among the plants that were made especially popular through USDA collections.

One USDA collector, Frank N. Meyer, crossed the Asian continent several times by cumbersome horsecart between 1905 and 1918 and gathered both economic and ornamental plants. His collections of wild Callery pear for resistance to pear blight became famous not for that reason but rather because of the fine ornamental shade tree selected from his seed shipments. In the 1950's the 'Bradford' ornamental pear was developed by USDA and is now widely planted in the Eastern United States as a street and lawn tree.

Following World War I, J. F. Rock was the leading American collector of ornamental plants. He roamed the great Snow Range on the China-Burma border in a search for rhododendrons, lilies, conifers, and primulas. Between 1920 and 1924, as a USDA explorer, he sent back some of the finest collections of new rhododendrons.

In 1925, Rock collected important tree and shrub species in Kansu Province, China, for use in the Midwestern Prairie States and Canada. His collecting travels in China extended to 1934, taking him into areas such as the land of the Tebbu tribes, never before entered by a white man.

From 1920 to the early 1930's several USDA scientists on other missions in the Orient sent back ornamental plants. Two USDA collectors, P. H. Dorsett and W. J. Morse, traveled in the Far East between 1924 and 1932 to collect soybeans and other Chinese plants, including ornamentals. They introduced a number of plants from Korea and Manchuria.

A USDA pathologist, R. Beattie, studying chestnut blight in Japan from 1927 through 1930, visited Japanese nurseries and assembled a large collection of azaleas. These have become known as the "Beattie Azaleas" and figured greatly in USDA's development of the Glenn Dale hybrid azaleas. He also sent home numerous lilies as well as many Oriental chestnuts for hybridizing with our dying American species (*Castanea dentata*).

From this period until mid-1950, collecting of ornamental plants was largely restricted. Some collecting in Tropical America was undertaken by special plant groups, chiefly for orchids, bromeliads, and foliage plants. These have contributed greatly to the displays that may be seen in conservatories and public gardens in our major cities.

You can now understand the many ways by which ornamental plants have found their way into American gardens over past years. The explorations by more than 60 plantsmen over the last four centuries have indeed contributed to the wealth of beauty that we have acquired.

Swift transportation and ingenious use of plastic films for packing have now reduced the losses of plants. But plant quarantines necessary to protect our economic crops, and nationalistic attitudes in many countries, have virtually stopped collecting by individuals and private institutions. This has placed a heavy responsibility on public institutions at a time when the environment and its improvement is receiving its greatest attention. As a result of these facts, USDA has become the focal point of plant exploration activities for economic and ornamental plants.

In 1956, Longwood Gardens, a private horticultural institution at Kennett Square, Pa., joined forces with USDA to conduct explorations specifically to collect ornamentals. The basic concepts behind the USDA-Longwood agreement are to explore those regions of the world where ornamental plants are native and yet inaccessible except through official cooperation between governments; and to survey and collect improved varieties developed by botanic gardens and other horticultural centers in foreign countries.

Since 1956, a total of 13 ornamental expeditions have been completed, one of the most recent to New Guinea for rhododendrons. Other collection trips include seven to temperate Asia, reflect-

Taking a cutting of kolomikta vine, an ornamental native to Siberia, during 1971 plant collection trip there. Because of vine's extreme hardiness, it is useful in coldest regions of the United States. The fruit is edible.

ing the importance of this region to horticulture; one each to Australia and Brazil; and two to Europe to assess progress in plant breeding with ornamentals in Europe. A trip was undertaken to Siberia in the Soviet Union in the summer of 1971, primarily for hardy tree species.

Plants collected on USDA expeditions are carefully inspected for insects and diseases at plant quarantine stations and are sent to plant introduction gardens for propagation and testing in cooperation with State experiment stations, arboretums and botanic gardens, and nurseries. Ultimately, the best of the introductions appear in your garden.

Plant explorers cross stream in New Guinea in search for rhododendrons.

175

It is difficult to estimate how long is required to develop a plant introduction into a new ornamental. Some are used directly, others must be incorporated into breeding programs.

For most plants where hardiness is already known from earlier experience, a new woody shrub or tree can become popular in the nursery trade within 5 to 7 years after release. Herbaceous plants, such as coleus and chrysanthemum varieties, are accepted almost immediately. Only if a variety or seedling is superior to those now in use will a new introduction find its place in horticulture.

A single illustration demonstrates one process of developing an introduction to full use. In 1961, while collecting on the beaches of the north coast of Honshu, Japan, near Ibaraki, I encountered long stretches of a prostrate juniper, *Juniperus conferta*. This juniper grows in solid stands like a gray-green carpet. Seed gathered on this collecting trip failed to grow.

In 1967, during a trip to Taiwan, I arranged for a local Japanese collector to visit this same beach site to gather cuttings for use by USDA's Soil Conservation Service. The cuttings were duly gathered and shipped back to the United States, rooted, and planted out for test by SCS plant specialists in New Jersey and at Beltsville, Md. This introduction grows vigorously and remains uniformly prostrate so that it is a handsome ornamental. USDA now plans to name this selection and release it to nurserymen in the autumn of 1972.

Just as for economic plants, we are able to identify the regions of the world where our favorite ornamental plants originate. It is important to know these regions in order to plan collecting trips as well as to encourage efforts to prevent the aimless destruction of these plants. Because many ornamental species have little other economic value, they are the first to be destroyed when remote areas are opened for industrial development.

For further reading:
U.S. Department of Agriculture, *Sixty Trees from Foreign Lands*. Agriculture Handbook 212, Washington, D.C. 20250, 1961.

adventures with native plants that passed their 'tests'

THERE ARE MANY thousands of plants native to the United States. Many of them have great beauty and many can be found growing in American gardens today. But there are hundreds of others yet to be tried and yet to be appreciated.

The plants growing wild in the United States have grown here for thousands of years. The fact of their presence is ample proof of their ability to survive in our climate. Plants from foreign countries must usually be tested for a period of years in various places to find out whether they are adapted to our climate. But the native American plants have long since passed their most important "tests".

Many of our native American plants have been used in breeding better garden varieties. For example, some of our wild azaleas have been used along with other species to produce what are perhaps the finest flowering shrubs in existence. These are the Exbury or Knaphill azaleas. Much of their beauty and fragrance comes from our flame azalea of the Appalachians, the Pacific azalea from the California mountains, and two other pink-flowered wildings from the Eastern United States.

The Exburys may ultimately be

Wild plum, Prunus americana, *blooms in springtime in the Nation's Capital.*

found to survive in most regions of our country. Some can withstand temperatures down to 40 degrees below zero, as well as summer temperatures up to 100 degrees. All require acid soil.

When you attempt to grow native plants in your garden, keep the following suggestions in mind:

1. Grow the plants under conditions that resemble as closely as possible the plant's wild habitat. Plant water-loving plants in wet places. Plant shade-tolerant species in shade, and sun-loving plants in the sun.

2. Be liberal with peat moss. Gardeners have found that sedge peat moss (not sphagnum) does something to the soil that helps. Sometimes the peat moss makes the difference between success and failure.

3. Get your plants from nurseries or seedsmen who specialize in native materials. There are a number that do, and they usually advertise in gardening magazines. Collecting wild plants is often a chancy business unless you know plants better than most people do.

4. Use the plant zone map that appears on the next page. In the lists of trees and shrubs, note the numbers attached to each plant. Find your own number on the map, based on where you live. If the shrub or tree has your number, it will probably grow in your garden—providing you treat it right. If it does not have your number, trying it in your garden can be a disappointment or an interesting test, depending on how you look at it.

5. If you have an area—of small or large size—where you want conditions to be as natural as possible, use native plants. The American plants can stand the competition of other plants better than foreign species can.

Author WILLIAM R. VAN DERSAL is an ecologist and author of *Native Woody Plants of the United States* and of *Ornamental American Shrubs.* He is a deputy administrator in the Soil Conservation Service.

6. Wild plants often become more luxuriant in a garden than they appear in the wild. For example, sage brush out West is scarcely beautiful because the plant is almost always chewed on by livestock. Grown in a garden, the plant is a lovely, shapely, silvery-white bush of great character and beauty.

There are certain relationships between the growth regions shown on the map. For example (for native plants)—

• Plants from regions 12 and 13 are usually successful in regions 24, 25, 27, and 28. The reverse is rarely true.

• Plants from regions 27 and 28 are usually successful in regions 1, 2, 24, 25, and 29.

• Plants from regions 1, 2, and 4 will usually grow in regions 2, 29, and 30.

• Plants from region 5 usually will

177

PLANT GROWTH REGIONS OF THE UNITED STATES

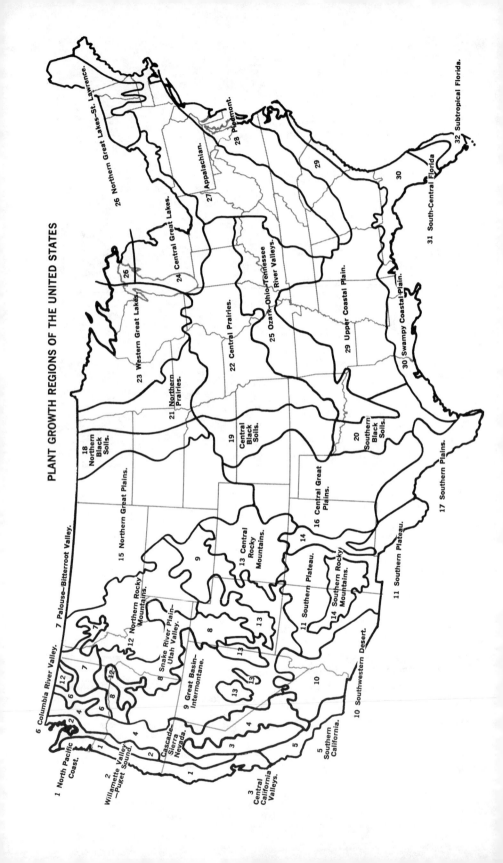

6 Columbia River Valley.

7 Palouse—Bitterroot Valley.

1 North Pacific Coast.

2 Willamette Valley—Puget Sound.

Cascade-Sierra Nevada.

3 Central California Valleys.

5 Southern California.

10 Southwestern Desert.

9 Great Basin-Intermontane.

8 Snake River Plain—Utah Valley.

12 Northern Rocky Mountains.

15 Northern Great Plains.

18 Northern Black Soils.

13 Central Rocky Mountains.

14 Southern Rocky Mountains.

11 Southern Plateau.

16 Central Great Plains.

17 Southern Plains.

19 Central Black Soils.

20 Southern Black Soils.

21 Northern Prairies.

22 Central Prairies.

23 Western Great Lakes.

24 Central Great Lakes.

25 Ozark-Ohio-Tennessee River Valleys.

26 Northern Great Lakes-St. Lawrence.

27 Appalachian.

28 Piedmont.

29 Upper Coastal Plain.

30 Swampy Coastal Plain.

31 South-Central Florida.

32 Subtropical Florida.

succeed in regions 31 and 32, and the reverse also seems true.

• Plants from region 20 usually do well in region 29.

Nine times out of ten, such moves as these will be successful, always provided the plant is grown in a situation similar to its wild habitat.

A comprehensive listing of all the native plants that have been grown in gardens, or that have possibilities for use, would more than fill this book. For trees, the list on pages 181-3 indicates some of the very best ones for various parts of the United States. The shrubs list on this and the next page includes those considered by many horticulturists and gardeners as being the very best of American shrubs.

There is no chart for mosses because their names are familiar to very few people. Mosses are little used in gardens, but they are invaluable between stepping stones, in nooks of a rock garden or around pools, and some will succeed on hot dry areas where nothing else will grow. Your best bet is to place some sample clumps in your garden under conditions reasonably similar to the wild situation.

Noteworthy Native Shrubs for Gardens

Common name	Latin name	Growth region (see the map on page 178)	Special comment
Flame azalea	Rhododendron calendulaceum	1, 2, 3, 20, 22, 24, 25, 27–29	Flowers yellow, orange, or red, brilliant. Rated by many as the finest native ornamental.
Flannel bush	Fremontia mexicana	5	Waxy yellow flowers. Closely-related California fremontia has golden flowers, not quite as showy, but excellent. The latter can be grown in regions 3, 4, 5, 10; if seed comes from high elevations, probably can be grown in regions 1, 2, 29, 30, 31, and possibly 28. Evergreen.
Mescalbean	Sophora secundiflora	11, 16, 17, 20, 29, 30	Wisteria-like clusters of violet-blue flowers, deliciously fragrant. Forms a little tree in favorable situations. Pods hard, seeds red or carmine.
Mountain-laurel	Kalmia latifolia	1, 2, 24–30	Pink-white flowers in clusters; highly floriferous. Evergreen.
Santa Barbara ceanothus	Ceanothus impressus	5 (possibly 29 and 30)	Foliage deep green; flowers dark blue. Prolific bloomer. "Clean, tailored" shrub, often wider than tall.
Fringe-tree	Chionanthus virginica	1, 2, 3, 20, 22, 24, 25, 27–30	Lacy, white flowers; very fragrant. A large shrub or small tree.
Mountain stewartia	Stewartia ovata var. grandiflora	1, 2, 20, 22, 24, 25, 27–30	Waxy-white flowers up to 4 inches across. Orange and scarlet fall color.

Common name	Latin name	Growth Region (see the map on page 178)	Special comment
Yaupon	Ilex vomitoria	20, 28, 29, 30 (probably 1, 2, 3 and 5)	An evergreen valuable for its profusion of red berries.
Cranberrybush ...	Viburnum trilobum	1, 2, 4, 12, 13, 15, 18, 21, 27	White, flat-topped flower clusters. Fruits bright red, highly attractive.
Oakleaf hydrangea	Hydrangea quercifolia	1, 2, 24, 25, 28–30 (Freezes in 27)	Large panicles of white flowers later turning copper to brown. Leaves large, oakleaf shaped. Very tolerant of shade.
Oregon-grape	Mahonia aquifolium	1, 2, 4, 6, 7, 11–16, 22, 24, 25, 27–29	Hollylike, shining green foliage. Flowers bright yellow; fruits grapelike, blue. There is a form with a dull leaf, not as good.
Creosotebush	Larrea tridentata	9, 10, 11, 16, 17	Excellent, yellow-flowered shrub for desert gardens. Foliage evergreen.
Anacahuita	Cordia boissieri	11, 17, 30; possibly 29–32	Very rare evergreen. Flowers white, with yellow centers, clustered. Fruits ivory white.
Sage brush	Artemisia tridentata	2, 4–13, 15, 27, 28	A very fine silver-white bush. Requires alkaline soil (use a little lime or crushed shells around it).

Gardeners are more familiar with ferns, but even these are not too well known by name. Maidenhair, woodsia, licoricefern, oakleaffern, swordfern, and dozens of others are highly attractive in appropriate garden locations. Catalogs of growers will help you choose ones you might like to try. Your local library will have a fern book, usually with pictures, for your area.

There is a host of wild flowers that have made—or that you can use to make—excellent color and variety in a garden. Some that are especially choice are—

Lilies, all of which are choice, especially the Turk's Cap that grows up to 8 feet tall. The spider-lilies of the Southeast are not true lilies, but they, too, are noteworthy, as are the lovely mariposa lilies of the West.

Orchids, especially pink ladyslipper and the showy ladyslipper. A number of orchids in southern Florida are choice subjects. Noteworthy also are the habenarias, orchis, and pogonia.

Trilliums, including all of the eastern and western species.

Xerophyllums, both eastern and western species, are spectacular plants with large clusters of cream-white flowers.

Iris, of many colors and sizes. Most of them are superb in the garden.

Buttercups, which deserve greater attention, produce sheets of yellow that are highly attractive.

Cactus varieties are prolific bloomers with spectacular flowers. There is at least one that will grow outdoors year around in every State.

Columbines, not as spectacular as

Common name	Latin name	Growth region (see the map on page 178)	Special comment
White fir	Abies concolor	4, 5, 9–14, 27, 28	Evergreen, shapely, fine foliage
Huisache	Acacia farnesiana	5, 10, 11, 17, 20, 29, 30	Grows larger with moisture. Deciduous.
Red maple	Acer rubrum	19–30	Red fall color; rapid growing
Sugar maple	Acer saccharum	2, 15, 18, 21–29	One of our most brilliantly-colored trees in autumn.
Ohio buckeye . . .	Aesculus glabra	22, 24, 25, 27, 28, 29	Successfully planted in recent years in region 13 at lower elevations.
Madrona	Arbutus menziesii	1–3, 5, 10	Difficult to transplant, a beauty.
Hickory	Carya spp.	20–30	Usually hard to transplant.
Catalpa	Catalpa spp.	21–23, 25–30	Leaves very large, flower clusters showy.
Hackberry	Celtis occidentalis	15–30	Drought resistant. Much planted in the Great Plains.
Paloverde	Cercidium torreyanum	10–11	Excellent in desert gardens.
Port Orford cedar	Chamaecyparis lawsoniana	1, 2, 28, 29	70 or more varieties, some exceptionally pleasing.
Flowering dogwood	Cornus florida	1, 2, 20, 22–25, 27–30	Pink, white, and double flowered forms known, also a weeping form
Pacific dogwood	Cornus nuttallii	1–5, 12	Somewhat difficult to grow; forms from region 12 will probably grow in 27 and 28.
Monterey cypress	Cupressus macrocarpa	1, 5	Growth form highly picturesque, especially along the seacoast.
American beech	Fagus grandifolia	20, 22–30	Magnificent specimen tree.
White ash	Fraxinus americana	20, 22–25, 27–30	
Red ash	Fraxinus pennsylvanica	15, 18, 20; and 12 and 17 for green ash, a variety	
Honeylocust	Gleditsia triacanthos	16, 20, 22–30	There is a thornless variety. Highly resistant to drought.
American holly	Ilex opaca	20, 25, 27–30	Many varieties available, some better than the wild form.
Walnut	Juglans spp.	18–30	

Common name	Latin name	Growth region (see the map on page 178)	Special comment
Juniper (Red cedar)	Juniperus spp.	Different species occur in western mountains and in the East	Eastern red cedar is rapid growing. Western species are slower.
Larch	Larix spp.	Eastern larch 22–24, 26, 27. Western larch 4, 12	The eastern species occurs in swamps, but grows quite well on dry land. Deciduous.
Incense cedar	Calocedrus decurrens	1, 4, 5, 29, 30.	Elegant evergreen foliage.
Sweetgum	Liquidambar styraciflua	2, 20, 22, 25, 27–30	Exceptionally brilliant fall color.
Tuliptree	Liriodendron tulipifera	2, 21–29	Very rapid growing. Excellent specimen tree.
Catalina ironwood	Lyonothamnus floribundus	5	Much planted in southern California.
Magnolia	Magnolia spp.	Generally 28–30, 27 for some	The evergreen magnolia is especially beautiful; planted also in 1, 2, 3, 5. Bigleaf magnolia has the largest leaves of any American tree (25, 27–30).
Red mulberry	Morus rubra	16–25, 27–30	Highly attractive to birds.
Blackgum	Nyssa sylvatica	20, 22, 24, 25–30	Brilliant fall color.
Sourwood	Oxydendron arboreum	25, 27–30	Very attractive in flower.
Blue spruce	Picea pungens	9, 12–14, 27–29	Many cultivated varieties. Exceptional form and color.
	(White, black and sitka spruces are also in cultivation.)		
Pines	Pinus spp.		
	(About 40 species, nearly all cultivated. Use any "good" pine native to your region. Big trees, except for the pinyon or nut pines of the Southwest.)		
Sycamore	Platanus spp.	Eastern S. 16, 20–22, 24–30. California S. 3, 4, 5. Arizona S. 10, 11	Majestic trees with "blotched" bark. Fine specimens. Best adapted to wet places, rich soil.
Douglas-fir	Pseudotsuga menziesii	The Rocky Mountain variety 9, 11, 13, 14, 16, 25, 27, 28, probably 29. The Pacific variety 1–6	The Rocky Mountain species is the only one successfully grown in the East.

Common name	Latin name	Growth region (see the map on page 178)	Special comment
Oaks	Quercus spp.	About 70 species, one or more in every growth region	Very slow growing, but superb trees, generally long-lived.
Black-locust	Robinia pseudoacacia	1–8, 12, 15, 16, 20–23, 25–29	
Cabbage palmetto	Sabal palmetto	30 (a related species, the Texas palm occurs in 11, 17)	
Sassafras	Sassafras albidum	2, 20, 22–30	
Redwood	Sequoia sempervirens	1	Has failed in the Eastern U.S. after many years of trial. Our tallest tree.
Sequoia	Sequoiadendron giganteum	4	Our most massive tree. Failed in the East over many years of trial.
Cypress	Taxodium spp.	17, 20, 25, 28–32	
Western red cedar	Thuja plicata	1, 2, 4, 6, 7, 12	
Basswood	Tilia spp.	Some 14 species, generally found in Eastern and Southeastern United States	Excellent shade trees.
Canadian hemlock	Tsuga canadensis	22, 25, 27–29	Excellent hedge, as well as specimen tree.
Western hemlock	Tsuga heterophylla	1, 2, 4, 6, 12	
Mountain hemlock	Tsuga mertensiana	4, 12	Slow growing. Fine specimen tree.
American elm . . .	Ulmus americana	1, 2, 15, 16, 18–23, 25–30	Handsome, vase-shaped shade tree.
Yucca	Yucca spp.	Generally southwestern	Desert gardens.
Palms	Washingtonia spp.	Generally southwestern	The California species is much grown in 5.

the long-spurred hybrids, but neverthe-less of great delicacy and beauty.

Erythroniums, the avalanche-lily or lamb's-tongue, with nodding and bell-shaped flowers.

Gentians, especially for rock gardens, but many varieties are useful in the general garden. All are blue flowered and lovely.

Goldenrods, some of exquisite color for fall blooming. They require plenty of room.

Lupines, especially the western ones.

Phlox, forming tight or loose mats of white, pink, blue, or red, depending on the species.

Saxifrages, perhaps of greatest value in rock gardens.

Spiderworts or tradescantias, with blue or purple flowers, or (in one species) rose-colored ones.

Violets, with yellow, white, blue, or bicolor flowers.

Yuccas, with dagger leaves and great bursts of creamy flowers each year.

Especially fine are the Georgia mal-low (*Hibiscus coccineus*) that makes 8-foot stems with red flowers 6 inches across; the cardinalflower with spires of startling red; the Virginia bluebells with soft pink to blue flowers; blood-root which is remarkably showy in established clumps; jack-in-the-pulpit, with its odd flowers and stalks of red fruit in the fall and exceptionally good growth in wet places; wild ginger, an overlooked but handsome ground cover, easily grown; the skunkcabbage of the Pacific Coast, smelly if handled, but with great showy yellow flowers highly prized in English gardens.

Passionflower vines, with curious and beautiful flowers in white, purple, and pink, are a conversation piece in any garden. And the lovely blue flowers of western camas should certainly not be overlooked.

There are many, many others. A good idea is to send away for catalogs of nurserymen who specialize in "wild flowers." Comparing names with those in books on wild flowers for your area (in *your* library) will help you decide what you want to try. There are tre-mendous adventures here to be had for little expense and relatively little effort.

Above, yaupon in North Carolina with loads of red berries. Right, Arizona palms grow-ing in a mountain canyon in the South-west.

breeding plants for beauty, form, and survival

MAN HAS BEEN INTRIGUED by decorative plants ever since esthetic feelings were first aroused. It has been said that attention to ornamental plants is an indication of a nation's increasing sophistication. This is certainly reflected in the intricate horticulture of such countries as Japan and China, the great importance of gardens in the estate life of early Europe, and the development of botanic gardens and of arboretums in cities in every country of the world, no matter how impoverished.

With this interest comes the urge to improve garden plants, first by simple selection and later by advanced breeding methods. Most of the plants we grow in our gardens have been the subject of attempts to improve them by breeding. This has ranged from individuals, special plant societies consisting largely of amateurs, public research organizations, to industry. All have had a hand in this effort.

As might be expected, not all plants have received the same degree of attention from plant breeders. Herbaceous plants have been improved tremendously through plant breeding and many of the highly sophisticated techniques that have been applied to crop plants have been used to good advantage. Considerably less advancement through breeding has been made with woody plants because of the long period of time between generations.

Azaleas and rhododendrons—because of their great diversity, adaptation, and heavy flowering—rank second only to roses in popularity and in hybridization research. Well known and widely grown are the Gable hybrids bred by Joseph B. Gable and the Glenn Dale hybrids and Back Acre hybrids developed by the late B. Y. Morrison.

Other notable accomplishments include the Beltsville dwarfs and the Belgian Glenn Dale hybrids developed by the Agricultural Research Service respectively at Beltsville and Glenn Dale, Md.; and the Rutherford hybrids by Bobbink and Atkins, East Rutherford, N.J.

Hybridizing efforts designed to develop new races of azaleas and rhododendrons for the nursery trade and for improved adaptation are numerous. To extend the range of azaleas northward, scientists at the University of Minnesota and at Michigan State University are evaluating seedlings for the production of more hardy varieties. Similarly, breeders at West Virginia University are concentrating upon improving the cold and drought hardiness of the rhododendrons native to Appalachia.

R. L. Schwind, a private breeder in Atlanta, Ga., is hybridizing native and oriental azalea species to achieve greater heat resistance for the lower Piedmont and coastal plain areas of the Southeastern States. At Oregon State University and at the North Willamette Agricultural Station, scientists are busy breeding and selecting superior rhododendrons adaptable for the West Coast.

The Ohio Agriculture Research and Development Center has a project to evaluate rhododendrons for greater resistance to *Phytophthora* wilt and root rots. Similarly, a project at the Georgia Coastal Plain Station is designed to evaluate azalea collections for resistance to several wilt diseases.

———

Author WILLIAM L. ACKERMAN is research horticulturist in charge, U.S. Plant Introduction Station, Agricultural Research Service, Glenn Dale, Md.

Research efforts are being directed toward the transfer of superior yellow flower color from deciduous to evergreen azaleas. Also, recent introductions of the oriental azalea *R. japonicum,* showing a wide range of color variants in the yellow, orange, and red range, are being crossed between themselves and hybridized with other species at the U.S. Plant Introduction Station, Glenn Dale, Md.

The range of adaptation of varieties of the "true" rhododendrons is more restrictive than the azaleas. A number of plant breeders have utilized the early "Ironclads" of *R. catawbiense* ancestry, Dexter hybrids, and Asiatic species in crosses with many of our native rhododendrons to develop new heavy flowering hybrids with greater color range, desirable growth habit, and greater hardiness.

Camellias are another broadleaved evergreen group of plants that have attracted the interest of breeders.

Camellia varieties today are largely chance seedlings selected by camellia fanciers, which frequently have resulted from open pollinated seed gathered from garden plants of two species, *Camellia japonica* and *C. sasanqua.* Varieties of these two species make up the majority of all camellias grown in the United States and Europe. Less frequently cultivated species are *C. hiemalis, C. reticulata, C. saluenensis,* and *C. vernalis.*

There are approximately 30 camellia species presently in the United States, besides more than 60 others never successfully imported from the Orient. This offers great possibilities for further improvement. Although flower size and form of most of these lesser-known species are inferior to that of the cultivated varieties, they do possess many valuable plant characteristics not present in our varieties of today.

During the past decade advances have been made to improve flower and plant qualities of the garden camellia through interspecific (crosses between different species) and intergeneric (crosses between species of different genera) hybridization.

Since few of these first generation hybrids are of commercial value, the recent results will not have a significant impact among new varieties for some years to come.

A review of camellia varieties registered by the American Camellia Society during a 9-year period (1962 to 1970) shows that among 582 camellias registered, 493 were chance seedlings, 50 were sports (spontaneous mutations), 19 were varietal crosses of known parentage, and 20 were interspecific hybrids. Thus, although less than 4 percent of the new varieties during this period were interspecific hybrids, it is in this field that the greatest future advances will be made.

Several objectives which have received considerable attention from camellia breeders are greater cold hardiness of plants and flower buds, flower fragrance, and yellow flower color.

Breeding for cold hardiness has been undertaken at the University of North Carolina and at the Glenn Dale Plant Introduction Station. The North Carolina crosses are primarily among selected cold tolerant varieties of *C. japonica.* Large numbers of seedlings have been distributed to cooperators for field testing in New Jersey, Pennsylvania, and Maryland.

The work at Glenn Dale has concentrated on breeding and selection among camellia introductions collected by U.S. Department of Agriculture plant exploration in the northernmost areas of Japan where camellias grow wild. One selection of *C. japonica* resulting from field tests was named 'Frost Queen' by USDA's Agricultural Research Service in 1970. Hybrids utilizing less-known species, such as *C. oleifera,* also appear promising as sources of greater cold hardiness.

Pleasing floral scent, long sought in camellias, has been achieved in hybrids developed by several plant breeders. Interspecific hybrids utilizing a small flowered species, *C. lutchuensis,* from Okinawa, have proved to be the most promising.

One of the major difficulties has been the high sterility of these hybrids. They are poor breeding parents for carrying the breeding beyond the first generation. We have, however, developed fragrant hybrids of merit. One such hybrid, Fragrant Pink, named by the Agricultural Research Service in 1966, is highly sterile. Treatments of this variety with the drug colchicine have changed it to a fertile form, allowing plant breeders to use it in further hybridization.

Cotoneasters are valued chiefly for their bright-colored berries and range of plant types from prostrate forms to shrubs 18 feet in height. They include deciduous, semi-evergreen, and evergreen types. Unfortunately, they have many troubles including defoliation by red spiders and susceptibility to fire blight.

Disease-resistant cotoneaster strains with good ornamental characteristics are being developed. A semi-pendulous selection from seed introduced from Japan, showing resistance to fire blight, will soon be released to the nursery trade.

Development of varieties adapted to the rigorous climate and short growing seasons of the Great Plains with tolerance to alkaline soils is in progress at the U.S. Horticulture Field Station, Cheyenne, Wyo., and at the University of Nebraska.

Crapemyrtle (*Lagerstroemia*) has been a traditional ornamental of the Southeastern States. Greater hardiness, mildew resistance, and increase in flower color range have been three objectives of recent breeding. Otto Spring, a private breeder of Okmulgee, Okla., has produced a series of dwarf types in a wide color range. The U.S. National Arboretum, Washington, D.C., has released four hardy, mildew-resistant varieties.

At the University of Arkansas a scientist is breeding for mildew-resistant types which in addition have desirable growth habits, good flower color, and are adaptable to Arkansas.

Crosses between Lagerstroemia species offer possibilities of more disease-resistant plants with graceful growth habit. The National Arboretum is pres-

ently evaluating first and second generation interspecific hybrids for inheritance of mildew resistance.

Firethorn (*Pyracantha*) has experienced an increase in popularity as a hedging and screening plant for suburban landscaping. Research has largely stressed improvement of horticultural characteristics with emphasis on hardiness and disease resistance, especially against fire blight disease.

There is no reliable red-fruited variety that will withstand temperatures lower than about 20° F. Scientists at Rutgers University, N. J., and at the National Arboretum are actively engaged in breeding to extend the northern limit of cultivation of firethorn species now grown only in the more southern areas.

Many of the seedlings grown at the National Arboretum are hardy and have heavy foliage that persists during the winter in Washington, D.C. Recently crosses between firethorn and the related hawthorns, crabapple, and mountain-ash have been made to acquire greater hardiness and resistance to disease.

The new varieties of the future may be trees or shrubs, bear apple- or firethorn-sized fruits with red, orange, or even new fruit colors, have evergreen or deciduous foliage, and be adaptable to either hot or cold climates.

Flowering-quince (*Chaenomeles*) hybridization work today depends heavily upon the many varieties resulting from the early work in America of W. B. Clarke, who originated the Clarkiana and the California groups. More recent breeding at the University of Illinois has resulted in seven varieties. This breeding emphasizes desirable plant form, a good range of flower colors, disease resistance, and cold hardiness.

Holly (*Ilex*) has acquired a variety of ornamental uses. These include foundation plantings, hedges, ground covers, accents, screens, windbreaks, and orchard specimens for holiday greens. The broad usage of this plant is reflected in a diversity of breeding objectives, although most varieties registered to date are chance seedlings.

Pollinating hibiscus in breeding project at U.S. National Arboretum.

From 1952 to 1958 the American Association of Nurserymen registered 22 holly varieties, only one of which had resulted from a controlled cross. Among 113 varieties registered by the Holly Society of America from 1959 to 1970, only 16 were the result of controlled crosses.

Hybridization work attempting a variety of combinations both among and between species is presently underway at State and Federal institutions and by private plant breeders. These efforts may greatly increase the number of holly varieties that are derived from controlled crosses.

Research varietal releases include an American holly, Reynolds, and a Chinese holly, Cairo, by the University of Illinois; an American holly, Jersey Knight, by Rutgers University; and a Japanese holly, High Light, by the National Arboretum.

Many complex hybrids have gained prominence in recent years as a means of incorporating new genetic combinations in superior varieties. Monongahela (*I. myrtifolia* x *I. opaca*) has been registered by West Virginia University. Six new hybrids by the National Arboretum are Lydia Morris female, and John T. Morris male, both *I. cornuta* x *I. pernyi* crosses; Elegance female and Accent male, both *I. integra* x *I. pernyi* crosses; *and* Tanger and Oriole, both females, *I. myrtifolia* x *I. opaca* crosses.

Five varieties of *I. cornuta* x *I. ciliospinosa* include three females, Albert Close, William Cowgill, and Edward Goucher, and two males, Howard Dorsett and Harry Gunning, by the Glenn Dale Plant Introduction Station. Another recent variety of *I. cornuta* x *I. ciliospinosa* parentage is Byram K. Stevens, selected by T. Delatush, a nurseryman of Robbinsville, N. J.

Hybrid varieties of *I. rugosa* x *I. aquifolium* include Blue Boy and Blue Girl developed by Mrs. F. L. Meserve, a holly specialist of St. James, Long Island, N. Y.

Lilacs (*Syringa*) exhibit a diversity of flower forms, growth habits, hardiness, and prolonged season of bloom which have made them popular as landscape objects for suburban plantings. Varieties developed in America by A. M. Brand, W. B. Clarke, J. Dunbar, and T. A. Havemeyer have complemented the French hybrids of the early 20th century.

Objectives of modern research, as typified by the work at the University of New Hampshire, are toward mildew resistance, a greater hardiness, free flowering, true flower colors, and good foliaged, compact varieties.

Roses have been the subject of the greatest efforts in hybridization among woody ornamentals. Of 647 plant patents issued between 1963 and 1968, a total of 232 were for new rose varieties. The next largest numbers were 53 patents assigned to gladiolus and 40 to azaleas.

Modern rose hybridization is handled mostly by plant breeders associated with the large commercial rose companies. Among the prominent breeders are J. S. Armstrong, E. S. Boerner, W. E. Lammerts, R. V. Lindquist, R. S. Moore, H. C. Swim, and O. L. Weeks.

Emasculating viburnum flowers in research at the National Arboretum.

Perfection from shrub rose and hybrid perpetuals to hybrid tea, floribunda, and grandiflora is a progression in research that cannot be equaled in other woody ornamentals. In addition to superior flowering varieties, breeding emphasis has been to increase hardiness, disease resistance, flower production, and vigor, and to improve growth habit.

Despite the great advances that have been made, roses continue to be plagued with diseases—particularly canker, black spot, and mildew. In these areas there are still opportunities for considerable improvement.

Viburnum, represented by over 250 species, is extremely diverse in flower, fruit, foliage, and growth habit types. This allows breeders a magnitude of potentialities. Plant breeders are attempting to combine the best of the ornamental characteristics of several species in superior hybrid forms. Ten varieties recently released by the National Arboretum exhibit characteristics such as floral fragrance, attractive fruit, evergreen or semi-evergreen, disease-resistant foliage, and a compact growth.

Trees have received less attention from plant breeders than other woody ornamentals. Perhaps this has been due to their long life cycles with the resultant protracted periods needed for evaluation of the seedling populations. Many of the newly named varieties are chance seedlings and more the result of observation and selection than of hybridization.

Crabapple (*Malus*) varieties are a good example of this, since most are either chance seedlings, selections from open-pollinated progeny, or byproducts of fruit tree breeding. The early efforts of N. E. Hansen, Isabella Preston, A. den Boer, and others have contributed many of the earlier crabapples that are the parents of recent varietal releases.

Hansen's 1905 introductions of *M. baccata* and *M. pumila* from Russia have in particular served as an important source of hardiness in many of today's varieties. More recently, research at the University of Minnesota has been directed toward developing hardy varieties with double flowers, longer blooming periods, small highly-colored fruits which persist on the trees, and resistance to cedar apple rust and fire blight.

A number of our native crabapple species such as *M. coronaria, M. ioensis, M. angustifolia*, and *M. lancifolia* could perhaps be exploited more fully than they have been. New forms of crabapples recently introduced extend the variation hitherto seen; thus, there is the medium dwarf, weeping 'Dainty', and the non-fruiting sterile 'Spring Snow'. Other outstanding new crabapples include the 'American Beauty',

Pollinating viburnum flowers.

'Crimson Sunset', 'Royalty', and 'Pink Spires'.

The ornamental pear, *Pyrus calleryana* 'Bradford', developed at the Glenn Dale Plant Introduction Station, has gained general acceptance as a medium-sized tree for street and landscape plantings throughout much of the country east of the Mississippi River and in parts of the West Coast.

Called the "tree of all seasons" because of its attractive spring flowers, summer foliage, and autumnal coloration, the Bradford pear is presently offered by more than 50 nurseries located in 25 States. Presently, several narrow columnar forms of *P. calleryana* are under evaluation for their possibilities as hedging, screen, or specimen plants where space is severely restricted.

Rhododendron in a container.

Recent magnolia breeding has been directed toward hardiness, flower fragrance, color and time of bloom, dwarf and semi-dwarf growth habits, and ease of propagation. Major breeding efforts have been undertaken by the National Arboretum, the University of Illinois, Michigan State University, and the Brooklyn Botanic Garden.

Seedling selections from the native *M. virginiana* have resulted in the variety Henry Hicks; from *M. grandiflora* in such varieties as Alabama Everblooming, Cairo, Gallissoniensis, Fastigiate clone, Miss Bogue, Majestic Beauty, Madison, Praecox, and St. Mary. Crosses between these two species at the National Arboretum resulted in varieties Freeman and Maryland.

D. Todd Gresham, a breeder from Santa Cruz, Calif., used *M. liliflora* as one parent in separate crosses with *M.* x *veitchii* and *M.* x *soulangiona,* producing five named varieties from each of the two combinations. Besides, five new patented magnolia varieties developed by other private individuals have been recently introduced.

A number of maple (*Acer*) varieties have been introduced into the nursery trade in recent years. Emphasis has been on superior autumnal foliage coloration as well as crown form and attractive summer foliage in greens, reds, and purples. Six maple varieties received plant patents during the period 1963 to 1968.

Similarly, new forms of thornless locust (*Gleditsia*) with attractive foliage in summer greens and yellows and/or autumnal brilliant yellows have gained popularity.

Interest also has developed in species and strains of *Zelkova* as a possible shade tree replacement for the disease-plagued majestic elm (*Ulmus*). *Zelkova* Village Green is an example of a recently patented variety.

Woody ornamental breeding has advanced in recent times from largely the selection of chance seedlings to systematic breeding involving controlled crosses both within and between plant species. Among many ornamentals the full impact of these scientific efforts has not as yet been appreciably observable at the nursery. However, the foundations have been established and the range of obtainable goals has been defined for more extensive research in the future.

Man's rapidly changing environment provides an added challenge to future generations of plant breeders to originate new and adaptive trees and shrubs for the beautification of America.

For further reference:

THE NATIONAL ARBORETUM, 13½-min. USDA color film, available to organizations on loan from State film libraries (usually at State universities), 1968.

good seeds for plant propagation and how they get that way

TO MOST PEOPLE, propagating plants from seeds seems a rather simple matter. You buy seeds at the hardware store or garden center, take them home, and put them in the soil. If conditions are right, in a few days you'll have some seedlings.

Many people do this year after year, blissfully unaware of the vast amount of work that has gone into making sure that the seeds they buy will yield disease-free plants, good wholesome vegetables, or beautiful flowers.

Seeds are the product of the labor of many men. Research scientists, geneticists, plant breeders, and seedsmen all had a hand in improving the seed that you buy.

They maintain the seed's heredity, and see that the seeds are free of diseases, are not contaminated with the unwanted seeds of weed pests, have good vitality and germination ability, and are protected against fungi and insects in the soil.

Heredity of a seed is as important to a plant breeder as it is to a breeder of thoroughbred racehorses. And, with seeds, heredity is more difficulty to protect. Many of the seeds we use today are from varieties developed for certain valuable characteristics. Once a particularly valuable strain is developed, care must be taken to maintain it. Cross-pollination from other strains must be prevented.

Another important characteristic of good seed is freedom from seedborne diseases. Some diseases such as halo blight and anthracnose of beans may be carried from one season to the next or from one field to another on the seed. One of the best methods of preventing this perpetuation and spread of certain diseases is to produce the seed in dry regions of the Western United States where those diseases rarely occur. Also, seed crops must be inspected for presence of those diseases.

Certain field and turf seeds are often contaminated with seeds of serious weed pests. One method of avoiding such contamination in crops grown for seed is to plant clean seed in fields that are free of the more objectionable weeds. Ingenious seed cleaning machines are used to remove contaminants. They work on the basis of weight, size, shape, or even the roughness of the seed coat.

Another significant seed quality characteristic is the ability to germinate. Because seeds cannot always be planted under ideal conditions, the ability to germinate over a wide range of conditions is especially desirable. That ability is often related to the seed's vitality.

The development and maintenance of good germinating ability and vitality in seeds require not only good production procedures but also careful harvesting, processing, and storage. Too much moisture on mature seed prior to harvest, mechanical injury during harvesting or processing, or storage at too high a seed moisture content or too high a relative humidity may be injurious to both germinability and vitality.

Seeds planted in soil often find themselves in a hostile environment. Nonsterilized soil contains fungi that can attack unprotected seeds. Some insects

Author B. E. CLARK is Professor of Seed Investigations, New York State Agricultural Experiment Station, Cornell University, Geneva, N.Y.

Coauthor A. A. KHAN is Associate Professor of Seed Physiology at the experiment station.

191

may also attack seeds before they can germinate. The seed corn maggot is an example. For these reasons, the proper treatment of seeds with seed protectants makes them more valuable.

Fortunately, we have laboratories for testing seed quality. Some of these are maintained by seed companies for their own use. Some are private laboratories that provide services for various clients. Others are governmental (State or Federal) laboratories which are usually maintained at least partially to enforce laws requiring the labeling of seed quality. Most State laboratories will conduct tests for State residents for an established fee.

Seed testing laboratories can't measure all aspects of seed quality. Varietal purity is difficult to measure in a laboratory except for a few kinds of seeds. Freedom from seedborne diseases is also difficult to ascertain in laboratory tests. But the presence of objectionable weed seeds, seeds of other kinds of crops, and chaff or other nonseed contaminants can readily be detected by examination of the seed.

Ability to germinate can be determined by placing the seeds on moist material in controlled temperature chambers and also by chemical means. There are some tests of seed vitality that are now being used to a limited extent, but the science of testing seeds for vitality is still in the early stages of development.

All States have laws covering field seeds (corn, for example), turf seeds (such as lawn-seeding mixtures), and vegetable seeds. The laws of some States cover flower seeds, and in certain States tree and shrub seeds are also covered. The State laws regulate seeds distributed within each State and there is a Federal Seed Act which regulates interstate distribution of seeds. At present, the Federal Seed Act covers field, turf,

and vegetable seeds but does not cover flower or tree and shrub seeds.

When you buy seeds, you can select them on the basis of required labeling information. If you are purchasing a lawn-seeding mixture, for instance, you can determine from the label the kinds of seeds that are in it, the percentage germination of each kind, and the date that the seeds are tested. After you have determined from a reliable source the kinds of lawn seeds that are best suited to your situation, you can use the required label information to select a mixture containing those kinds.

Anyone buying seeds from a commercial source is taking advantage of many services provided for him, varying all the way from the knowledge and skill of professional plant breeders to the protection of seed laws. In spite of this, there is sometimes a temptation to save one's own seed. If you are tempted to do so you should recognize that many of the safeguards of purchasing seed at a commercial outlet are lacking. Thus, your risk of failure in propagating plants from the seed you save is increased.

There are times when a gardener finds he has seeds left over from a

Checking germination of seeds on moist paper in a temperature-controlled chamber, during a germination test.

```
         LAWN SEED MIXTURE

Fine-Textured Grasses:              Germination    Tested
  Kentucky bluegrass      30.00%       75%         1-72
  Red fescue              20.00%       80%         2-72
Coarse Kinds:
  Annual Ryegrass         20.00%       90%        11-71
  Ky 31 Tall fescue       24.00%       90%        12-71
Other Ingredients:
  Inert matter             5.55%
  Other crop seeds         0.20%
  Weed seeds               0.25%
Noxious-weed seeds-None
Lot No. B-256
ABC Seed Company
Philadelphia, Pa.
```

A sample seed label.

previous season and he may wonder whether to use them or buy new ones. Some seeds are now being packaged commercially in hermetically sealed containers. Such seeds are specially dried before they are packaged and, if the package is kept sealed without being opened, the seeds can be expected to stay germinable as long as 3 years.

The storage life of seeds that are not put in hermetically sealed containers will vary with their environment. They may die completely after a few weeks of storage under moist conditions, or they may live for several years under dry conditions. If you store any seeds from one year to the next you should have them retested for germination before you use them. You can test small quantities of seeds which would not justify the cost of a laboratory germination test by planting a few of them in a flower pot or other container filled with soil, sand, or peat moss.

Germination of a seed is one of the dramatic phenomena of nature. How efficiently a seed can be transformed to a seedling not only preoccupies seed growers and gardeners, but also offers a challenge to the seed technologist who is constantly experimenting to learn more about germination.

The biochemical revolution of the past decade has left an indelible mark on seed technology. We now understand more clearly some of the mechanisms governing germination. Recent studies have enabled us to predict and control germination to a greater extent.

Seed germination is a result of an interplay of environmental factors such as light, temperature, and moisture with a vast array of chemicals inside the seed. That these factors would have different effects on different seeds is only to be expected as no two seeds (even seeds of the same lot belonging to a species) are chemically identical.

Scientists have known for a long time that during germination of a seed there is a mobilization of storage chemicals followed with their breakdown into smaller molecules. Recent discoveries have shown that the plant hormones—promoters as well as inhibitors—play a decisive role in initiating or stopping these changes.

The hormones primarily responsible for controlling germinations are the gibberellins, cytokinins, and inhibitors. Each of these hormones has a different function in seeds.

Gibberellins play a central role in germination. The actions of cytokinins and inhibitors are secondary, and are essentially permissive and preventive respectively. The cytokinins will permit the completion of a gibberellin-induced germination when it is blocked by the inhibitors.

Based on the presence or absence of these three hormones, there are several hormonal situations or combinations likely to occur in nature in various seeds. Thus, depending on a particular hormonal combination, a seed could remain dormant or germinate. Dormancy in a seed can result not only from the presence of an inhibitor, but also from the absence of a gibberellin (primary stimulus) or a cytokinin (permits gibberellin action by opposing the effect of an inhibitor).

If all this seems too complicated, think of dormancy as a jailbreak that didn't happen, for one of several reasons. Either there was a guard on the wall to prevent it (the presence of an inhibitor); or the convict didn't want to break out because there was snow on the ground and he had holes in his shoes (absence of a primary stimulus or gibberellin); or he couldn't persuade a friend (a cytokinin) to restrain the guard while he escaped. So he stays in prison.

Gibberellins appear to be a must for germination of all seeds. In the absence of these hormones, germinative processes such as production of certain key enzymes are not initiated. Post-harvest dormancy of many grasses and grains of cereals is released by a treatment with gibberellins alone. A short moist prechilling treatment (5 days at 50° F.) or prolonged dry storage will also break the dormancy of these seeds. Both treatments increase the level of gibberellin in the seed, an example of changes in hormone level resulting from environmental changes.

The bur of the cocklebur contains two seeds, one of which is smaller than the other. The larger seed will germinate at maturity but the smaller seed is usually dormant. Gibberellin is ineffective in releasing the dormancy of the smaller seed. This seed contains an inhibitor which appears to block the action of gibberellin, thereby causing the dormancy. Dormancy in this or other seeds when clearly resulting from such a block can be released by treatment with a cytokinin. Cytokinins, thus, permit the action of gibberellin by opposing the action of inhibitors.

Some seeds, among them apple and pear, are dormant and have to be moist prechilled at 35° to 40° F. for extended periods of time to break their dormancy. Such prechilling occurs naturally in moist soil during fall, winter, and spring or it can be provided artificially by storing seeds in moist sphagnum moss in a refrigerator. The content of inhibitors is decreased by such treatment. Dormancy of the seeds can also be released to some extent by gibberellins as well as by cytokinins. A combination of these hormones is more effective than either one alone.

Another instance of a direct relationship between an environmental factor and a hormone is provided by Grand Rapids lettuce seeds. These seeds will germinate in light, but are dormant in darkness. If treated with gibberellin, however, they will germinate in the dark as well.

Some seeds with impermeable or semipermeable seedcoats fail to germinate even with the right complement of hormones. Seeds of geranium, okra, morning-glory, and various other kinds contain anywhere from a few to a large percentage of seeds in this "hard-seeded" category. To speed up germination, these seeds require abrasion of the seedcoat by mechanical or chemical means. Rubbing them against sandpaper or soaking them in sulphuric acid for a short time will bring about their immediate germination.

In nature, the impermeable seedcoats are eventually made permeable through the action of bacteria or by physical or chemical means as they lie in the soil.

Certain seeds have still more elaborate systems of dormancy and of germination. Instances are the so-called "two-year seeds," "double dormancy," "root dormancy," and "epicotyl dormancy," and combinations of two or more of these. In the case of the tree peony, the root develops normally when the seed germinates, but the epicotyl, from which the above-ground portion of the seedling develops, requires a low temperature treatment for 2 to 3 months before a complete plant can be produced.

In the case of freshly harvested Indian rice grass, seed scarification alone is not enough to promote germination. A moist cold treatment or gibberellin treatment after scarification is also essential for maximum germination. For *Trillium,* a common wild flower, roots as well as shoots must undergo low-temperature treatment interspersed with warm temperatures for development of normal seedlings.

In nature, self-preservation sometimes requires that a seed remain dormant when conditions are not suitable for survival of a young seedling. The seed finally becomes germinable with the advent of a new growing season. This environment-sensing capability of a seed is a highly evolved trait and appears to work principally through changes in hormonal balance.

For example, depending upon its

physiological state, a seed can be induced to germinate with no hormonal treatment (if essential hormones are present in the proper balance and concentrations), or by treatments with gibberellin (if gibberellin is lacking and there is no inhibitor), cytokinin (if gibberellin and an inhibitor are both present), or a combination of gibberellin and cytokinin (if gibberellin is lacking and an inhibitor is present).

Although propagators of certain trees and shrubs and a few kinds of grasses and flowers will encounter seed dormancy that has to be overcome before they can obtain germination, most gardeners will be using kinds of seeds that are not ordinarily dormant at planting time.

Even nondormant seeds, however, have relatively precise requirements for germination.

All seeds, of course, need the proper amount of moisture for germination, and that moisture is supplied from the medium in which they are planted. Satisfactory transfer of moisture from the medium to the seed requires good contact between the two. It is usually necessary to compact the germination medium over the seed to provide a good contact.

Germinating seeds also require oxygen. The amount of water applied to the germination medium affects the amount of oxygen available. If you use too much water the air is driven out of the medium and not enough oxygen is available to the seed. Therefore, the medium should be kept moist but not too wet.

Each kind of seed has its own temperature requirements for germination. Some germinate best at a temperature as low as 40° F. while others germinate best at temperatures above 70°. Still others germinate better when the temperature is alternated daily between a low and high temperature than at any constant temperature.

Most seed packets and various garden books and Extension publications provide instructions for planting individual kinds of seeds to meet their water, oxygen, and temperature requirements. For the successful propagation of plants from the different kinds of seeds, those instructions should be followed very carefully.

For further reading:
U.S. Department of Agriculture, *How to Buy Lawn Seed.* Home and Garden Bulletin 169, Washington, D.C. 20250, 1969.

propagating from cuttings; other vegetative methods

PLANTS HAVE THE ABILITY to regenerate a new root system or shoot system or both or to unite to another plant by grafting. Therefore, it is possible to produce an entire population of plants from a single individual. All the plants produced will have the same characteristics as the parent.

The genetic background of plants propagated from cuttings is so diverse that plants propagated from seeds taken from these plants tend to be highly variable. If you plant the seeds from that red delicious apple, for example, the chances are very remote that any of the new plants will produce apples even remotely resembling the original. However, by grafting buds or twigs from the same tree onto seedlings, an entire orchard of red delicious apple trees just like the one you planted can be established.

Plants may be propagated vegetatively by cuttings, division (also called separation), layering, grafting, and budding. We will describe each of these techniques but will place special emphasis on propagation by cuttings.

Cuttings may be made from a variety of plant parts. Cuttings made from stems have to generate new roots, cuttings made from roots have to develop new shoots, and cuttings from leaves have to form both shoots and roots. Roots regenerate more readily than do shoots and therefore the range of plants propagated by stem cuttings is much greater than that propagated by root cuttings. Only a few plants, such as the African-violet, can be propagated by leaf cuttings.

Stem cuttings vary by the condition of the tissue used.

Herbaceous cuttings are made from stems of annuals or herbaceous perennials, such as chrysanthemums. The tissue is very soft and succulent.

Softwood cuttings are made from woody plants and the tissue is also relatively soft and succulent, but slightly more woody than for herbaceous cuttings. Softwood cuttings are usually made during the first 6 weeks of the growing season.

Semiripe cuttings are made from tissue which is harder and less succulent. The stem may still be growing in length. Semiripe cuttings are usually made during mid to late summer.

Hardwood cuttings, also called mature or dormant cuttings, are made from stems taken after growth has stopped in the fall. Hardwood cuttings of narrow- and broad-leaved evergreens have leaves, but no leaves are present on deciduous hardwood cuttings.

There is no "best" medium to use for rooting cuttings. A good medium must hold the cutting in place, supply adequate water and oxygen, and be free from disease and insects. A wide variety of materials can be used for rooting. Coarse sand, perlite, vermiculite, cin-

Author WILLIAM E. SNYDER is Professor of Ornamental Horticulture at Rutgers, the State University of New Jersey, New Brunswick.

Coauthor CHARLES E. HESS is Director of the New Jersey Agricultural Experiment Station and Associate Dean of the College of Agriculture and Environmental Science at Rutgers.

ders, and even soil are used successfully. Peat moss is frequently added to sand or perlite and should be used with acid-requiring plants, such as rhododendrons, azaleas, blueberries, and Japanese andromeda.

Plants can even be rooted in water. However, a deficiency of oxygen in the water will cause rotting instead of rooting for many plants. The roots formed in water are frequently brittle and make transplanting and establishment in a growing medium a problem.

Here is a good general-purpose medium. Use 2 parts perlite and 1 part peat moss by volume. The medium should be 4 to 6 inches deep and the base of the cutting should be inserted to a depth of 1 to 2 inches.

Careful selection of the plant from which the cuttings are to be made is a must. The stock plant should be healthy and vigorous, and show no evidence of water deficiency (wilting) or disease. Plants which have been recently fertilized, especially with a high nitrogen fertilizer, should not be used as the source of cuttings.

If the soil is dry, a thorough watering a day or so before you take your cuttings can be beneficial.

Leafy stem cuttings are cuttings with leaves or needles and should be made early in the day when the tissue is crisp. Use a sharp knife or pruning shears and cut the stem pieces several inches longer than the final length of the cutting.

Herbaceous cuttings should be about 3 or 4 inches long. Other kinds of leafy stem cuttings are usually cut 6 to 8 inches long.

To keep the cuttings from drying out, place them in polyethylene bags or put the bases of the stems in water and keep them in the shade. Take only as many cuttings as can be processed in a short time. If a delay of several hours is necessary, the stems can be stored in a refrigerator in the polyethylene bags.

In making the cutting, trim off the lower third of the leaves and make a smooth, diagonal cut at about a 45° angle. If the plant has hollow stems, the basal cut should be made just below a node (the point at which a leaf arises).

During the late 1930's the use of chemicals to aid in the formation of roots became a standard practice. One of the growth-regulating chemicals produced by plants is indole acetic acid (IAA). This substance works in conjunction with other chemicals produced by the plant itself to initiate the growth of roots.

A number of synthetic chemicals, related to IAA, will also stimulate rooting. Two of these, indole butyric acid and naphthalene acetic acid, are commonly included in the proprietary products available to the plant propagator.

One of the easiest ways to treat cuttings with root-inducing chemicals is the method known as the "powder dip." The chemical is dispersed in talc powder. It is available in several different strengths at your nursery or hardware store. The lower inch of the stem should be dusted lightly with the powder. Detailed directions are included with the materials available on the market. These root-inducing chemicals should be used only on stem cuttings since they inhibit the development and the growth of shoots on leaf and root cuttings.

As soon as the cuttings have been made and treated with the root-inducing chemical, they should be inserted in the medium to a depth of 1 to 2 inches depending upon the length of the cutting. Make a hole in the medium to the depth the cutting is to be inserted and large enough in diameter to accommodate the stem. A pencil or large nail can be used. With thumb and fingers, press the medium firmly around the cuttings and then water the medium thoroughly. Firming and watering will insure that the medium and the water are in contact with the base of the cuttings.

Care of the cuttings while in the rooting medium is very important. The cuttings need water, a certain temperature range, and sunlight. A plant takes in water through the roots and loses water from the leaves. A leafy cutting, thus, has been deprived of its main source of water and only a small amount enters through the basal cut surface. The leaves will continue to lose water. If the cuttings are allowed to dry out, rooting will be prevented. The medium should be kept moist but not saturated with water. This will assure maximum water uptake by the unrooted cutting.

The major methods we can use to reduce water loss are to keep the atmosphere surrounding the cuttings at the highest relative humidity possible and to keep the leaf surfaces covered

Herbaceous stem cutting of poinsettia.

with a thin film of water. Techniques and structures to accomplish this will be discussed later in the chapter.

Temperatures of the medium and atmosphere should be maintained between 65° and 85° F. Rooting is inhibited at temperatures above and below these levels. If possible, the night air temperature should be 5° to 10° cooler than the day temperature.

Sunlight is necessary for successful rooting of most species of plants. In general, the more light, the faster the rooting response. However, sunlight supplies heat—and heat increases water

potting. In general, cuttings should be potted when there are 10 to 15 roots 1 to 2 inches long. Ideally, roots should be formed all around the stem—not on one side only.

Rooting should occur first at or near the base of the cutting and then gradually up the stem to the top of the medium. If the bottom of the cutting rots, rooting may occur above the rot. Basal rot may develop if the medium is too moist (causing a deficiency of oxygen), if the cutting or medium is contaminated with a disease organism, or if too strong a concentration of root-

Rhododendron
stem cutting (left)
and leaf-bud cutting (right)

loss. Thus, indirect sunlight is preferable. At least you should avoid direct and strong sunlight on the cuttings from mid-morning to mid-afternoon and for the first 10 days after the cuttings are planted.

Cuttings of some plants, mostly herbaceous and softwood, will root in 7 to 21 days. Cuttings of semiripe wood will take 3 to 6 weeks or longer. Hardwood cuttings of narrow- and broad-leaved evergreens will require 2 to 6 months to root. Cuttings of some kinds of plants are considered impossible to root no matter how long they are left in the medium.

Cuttings should be potted for further growing when well rooted. It is difficult to establish a definite stage for

inducing chemical has been used.

The ability of stem cuttings to develop roots varies with the kind of plant. Some are easily rooted, while others are very difficult to root. Plants which are difficult to root show the greatest variability in rooting.

Closely related plants may show a wide range of rootability. Upright growing junipers are difficult to root, but the spreading types are relatively easy. Some selections of the American holly root easily ('Arden' and 'Old Hale and Harty') and others are difficult to root ('Cumberland'). Rhododendrons with red flowers are more difficult to root than those with white or pink flowers.

Certain selections of the tropical hibiscus (*Hibiscus rosa-sinensis*) are relatively easy to root and others are difficult. Studies have shown that the more difficult to root selections of hibiscus do not produce all of the chemical materials which, together with IAA, are necessary for rooting.

The time of year to make cuttings is learned primarily by experience. This time actually refers to the condition of the plant rather than to a calendar date.

With easily rooted cuttings, "timing" is relatively unimportant. Chrysanthemum and geranium cuttings, for example, can be rooted any time of the year there is new growth. However, during the winter months a longer period of time is usually necessary for rooting.

California privet, forsythia, and many other ornamental shrubs can be propagated in the early summer as softwood cuttings, in mid to late summer as semiripe cuttings, and during the winter as deciduous hardwood cuttings.

Cuttings of some plants, however, root well at certain times and poorly at others. French hybrid lilacs, which are generally considered to be a difficult-to-root plant, will give the best results if the cuttings are made about the time the plant is in flower.

Rhododendrons and azaleas can be propagated by softwood cuttings taken after bloom or as semiripe cuttings made in September. A variation of a week or 10 days, however, may spell the difference between success and failure.

American holly will give the best results with cuttings made in the late summer or early fall. Narrow-leaved evergreen cuttings root best if taken in late fall after the plants have been subjected to one or two heavy frosts.

Another factor which sometimes can be related to rooting ability is the chronological (developmental) age of the plant.

The horticulturist has recognized that plants undergo a developmental aging—from juvenility to maturity. In some plants there are visible differences between juvenile and mature forms, but in others there are no visible differences.

The plant propagator has learned that cuttings made from juvenile plants are easily rooted but that cuttings from mature plants may be difficult to root. English ivy (*Hedera helix*) is a good example. The juvenile form commonly used as a ground cover has lobed leaves, forms aerial rootlets, has red pigmentation in the stems, and does not produce flowers and fruit. Cuttings from juvenile plants are easy to root.

In contrast, mature English ivy plants have entire leaves, do not form aerial rootlets, grow upright, have green stems, and can flower and fruit. Mature cuttings are difficult to root. Research has revealed that, like the difficult-to-root hibiscus, mature English ivy does not produce all of the chemicals necessary to interact with IAA to cause rooting.

Cuttings from seedling trees which are not over 5 or 6 years old can be rooted without too much difficulty. However, as the trees become older, success in rooting rapidly decreases. Cuttings made from many trees which have reached the flowering stage are frequently difficult to root. Sucker stems which may arise at or near the soil line or from roots are more easily rooted. Some trees may be cut back, as described later for mound layering, to induce the development of such sucker shoots.

Several special techniques may be helpful for difficult-to-root cuttings. The deliberate wounding of the base of the cutting is one of these techniques.

A light wound is made by drawing the tip of a knife down the base of the cutting for about 1½ inches. The cut should be made through the bark and slightly into the wood. Several such wounds can be made around the base of the stem. Care must be taken not to cut entirely through the stem.

A more severe treatment, called heavy wounding, can be made by removing a thin slice of the bark and wood from one or two sides of the stem. Care must be taken to cut only slightly into the wood.

Wounds should be made before treatment with a root-inducing powder.

Another technique which may be helpful is known as etiolation. The piece of stem which will be used as the base of the cutting is covered with black paper or tape so as to exclude all light. This should be done several weeks before the cuttings are to be made. The black paper or tape is removed just prior to making the cuttings.

A third technique is to girdle the stem just below the point where rooting is desired. The stem may be girdled by wrapping a piece of wire or string tightly around the stem or by removing a thin circle of bark. The girdle should be made a month or more before the cuttings are to be made. This girdling interrupts the downward movement of carbohydrates, growth-regulating chemicals, and other substances involved in the rooting process. There is a buildup of these materials above the girdle.

Deciduous hardwood cuttings are made from the current season's growth. The cuttings should be gathered soon after the dormant season has started or until mid-winter. The cuttings can be made with a knife or a pruning shears.

An ideal size for these cuttings is equal to a new lead pencil in both diameter and length. Finished cuttings should be tied together in convenient size bundles (25 to 50) and covered with a moist medium (peat moss, sawdust, shavings, etc.).

The cuttings are first subjected to a temperature of 50° to 55° F. for 3 to 4 weeks, then stored at a temperature below 40° but above freezing. They can be buried outdoors or placed in your refrigerator.

In the spring the cuttings should be planted to a depth that will expose only the uppermost bud above the soil.

Easily rooted species, such as pussy willow and forsythia, will root in water. However, this method is unsatisfactory for most hardwood cuttings. Treatment of deciduous hardwood cuttings with a root-inducing chemical is of questionable value.

Plants which readily produce suckers can frequently be propagated by *root cuttings*. Root cuttings are usually made in fall or winter. For woody plants, select roots which are about the thickness of a lead pencil. These should be cut into lengths of 3 to 4 inches. Plant horizontally or with the thicker end of the root upward (the end closest to the stem).

Cuttings may be planted in flats for greenhouse propagation or in prepared beds for outdoor propagation. Root pieces should be covered to a depth of 2 to 3 inches. Outdoor plantings in temperate zone areas should be mulched over winter.

Greenhouse propagated plants can be transplanted outdoors in the spring. Outdoor propagated plants should be transplanted following the first growing season.

Leaf cuttings are used to propagate many herbaceous tropical plants which have thick leaves. For the various fibrous-rooted begonias, the main veins of the leaf's blade are cut in several places and the leaf is then anchored firmly upon the rooting medium. New plants will develop at these cut places.

For *Sansevieria,* the elongated sword-like leaf is cut into sections about 3 inches in length. The basal end of each section is inserted in the medium to a depth of about ½ to 1 inch. If the upper end is placed downward, neither roots nor a new shoot will develop.

Plants developing from leaf cuttings of *Sansevieria* will have entirely green leaves regardless of whether the parent plant has variegated (part green, part nongreen) or entirely green leaves. A *Sansevieria* with variegated foliage should be divided (division is discussed later in this chapter).

Peperomia, African-violet, and gloxinia are also propagated by leaf cuttings. For these plants, the leaf is cut from the stock plant so that the leaf-stalk is ½- to 1-inch long. The leaf-stalk is inserted in the medium deep enough so that the leaf blade is just above the medium.

Leaf cuttings will develop roots in about 3 weeks; another 3 to 4 weeks may be required for new shoots to grow. Leaf cuttings of many plants, in-

An effective method for rooting a few cuttings. Plastic bag covers the container and is supported by framework made of two wire coat hangers. Bag is tied tightly to prevent evaporation of water. Unit should be placed in a moderately light place, but never in direct sunlight.

cluding the woody species, will readily form roots, but new shoots may not develop.

Successful propagation can occur in the field, where there is little control over the environment, and in controlled-growth chambers, where light, temperature, humidity, carbon dioxide, and other environmental factors can be precisely controlled.

Seeds and deciduous woody cuttings are examples of propagation under field conditions. Meristem tissue culture (use of just the very tip of the stem) of orchids, carnations, and geraniums are examples of propagation in controlled-growth chambers.

The structures most feasible for use by the commercial propagator or by the homeowner lie between these two extremes and may be as diverse as is human ingenuity.

Of paramount consideration in selecting a propagation structure is how to restrict the volume of air surrounding the cuttings. This is essential to conserve water in the cutting and thus to prevent wilting.

The simplest way is to use a wide-mouthed jar. Invert it over one or two cuttings. Many of us will remember our mother or grandmother sticking a "slip" (cutting) of her favorite rose in the flower bed and placing a fruit jar over the cutting.

With the larger jars, a moist-rooting medium can be placed inside the jar, the cuttings inserted, and the opening covered with a piece of polyethylene tightly tied. The polyethylene permits exchange of oxygen and carbon dioxide but markedly restricts loss of water. Aquariums and large metal or plastic food trays can also be used. Care must be taken not to overwater because there is no place for excess water to drain away.

Even tied plastic bags can be used if only a few cuttings are to be rooted.

Wooden flats and clay pots make excellent propagation structures. A plastic bag can be inverted over a pot and sheets of polyethylene can be spread over wire hoops (clothes hangers are excellent) affixed to the flats. Since the bottom of the flat and pot are not enclosed, some water loss may occur and occasional watering may be necessary.

Coldframes are easy to construct and are an effective structure for propagating almost any kind of plant during the warmer part of the year. Sides and ends of coldframes should be tight to reduce air movement and water loss.

Coldframes may be any size; however, they commonly are 3 by 6 feet so that window sash can be used for the cover. If the top is a wooden frame covered with polyethylene, then the size can be varied as desired.

The back side of the coldframe is 18 inches high and the front is 12 inches. This height will permit use of long cuttings and the slope will help prevent water from dripping onto the cuttings. There should be good drainage underneath the coldframe.

A 2- to 3-inch layer of the rooting-medium is spread over the soil and the cuttings are inserted no deeper than about three-fourths the depth of the medium. Rooting will occur in the medium and the roots will grow into the soil beneath.

Shading the coldframe, the plastic covered flats, and pots or other structures from direct, strong sunlight is essential. The shade will prevent a buildup of heat in the closed structure and will help to keep the cuttings from wilting. The shade should be removed on cloudy days and gradually as the cuttings become rooted.

Needless to say, greenhouses and similar plastic structures are good propagation units. If heated, they can be used during colder months of the year as well as during summer. Greenhouse benches can be covered, as described for coldframes, or left uncovered. If left uncovered, the foliage should be syringed (sprayed with water) several times each day to keep the cuttings from wilting.

Since the early 1950's commercial propagators have used controlled intermittent mist and full sunlight for the rooting of cuttings. Water is sprayed through nozzles placed above the cuttings so that a fine mist settles on the foliage. The intervals of mist may be controlled by timeclocks or electronic devices.

Frequent intervals of mist keep the foliage moist at all time. Even when the cuttings are exposed to full sunlight, the film of water lowers the temperature of the leaf tissue and thus reduces water loss. Fertilizers, insecticides, and fungicides can be supplied through the mist system.

You can construct a simplified version of a mist system for use with outdoor beds during summer propagation. Affix oil burner-type nozzles at 3-foot intervals to a piece of water pipe. One end of the pipe must be sealed. Suspend the pipe over the propagation bed at a height of about 30 to 36 inches. Fasten a garden hose to the open end of the pipe and turn on the water. Cuttings should be placed in the area covered by the mist.

The mist should be turned on early in the morning and off about sunset. No mist is necessary on cloudy, humid, or rainy days. Good drainage is an absolute must for all mist systems.

Propagating plants by cuttings can be fun and rewarding. If you've had little or no experience, then start with a simple propagation structure and easily rooted cuttings. As you gain experience, the use of more complex structures and harder-to-root plant material will be challenging.

Besides rooting a cutting in a medium there are other ways to propagate vegetatively. One of them is layering. Layering consists of rooting a stem before it is detached from the parent plant. One of the major advantages of layering is that the parent plant continues to supply nutrients and water to the shoot while roots are developing. The four most common methods of layering are simple, tip, mound, and air.

For *simple layering,* a branch is bent to the ground before growth commences in the spring. A 5- to 10-inch portion of the center of the stem is covered with soil. Several inches of the tip are left exposed to form new leaves. It is advisable to anchor the stem firmly in the ground and to stake the exposed tip in an upright position.

A notch cut from the lower side of the stem, the removal of a ring of bark around the stem, or making a diagonal cut about one-third the way through the stem will frequently improve rooting. A light dusting of the stem with a root-inducing powder will also be beneficial. Divide and plant when well rooted.

Tip layering is another common type of layer. Tip layering is done by placing the tip of a branch into 1 to 2 inches of soil. The tip should be firmly anchored. Black raspberries, blackberries, and a type of golden bells with drooping stems (*Forsythia suspensa*) are easily propagated by tip layers. Divide and plant when well rooted.

Mound layering is also known as stooling. This method consists of covering the bases of stems with moist soil.

During the dormant season the plant should be cut back severely—almost to soil level. As soon as new shoots start to grow in the spring, the bases are covered with soil. As growth continues, more soil is mounded over the base of the stem until about 6 to 8 inches of the stem is covered. Never cover the stem tip.

By fall these layered stems will be rooted and can be cut off and stored or planted.

Gooseberry, currant, quince, hydrangea, and spirea 'Anthony Waterer' are examples of plants which can be mound layered and which will root the first year.

Magnolias and rhododendrons can also be mound layered; however, two growing seasons will be required for rooting.

Air layering is also known as pot and Chinese layering. Many of the woody tropical plants (dracaena, rubber plant, croton, pandanus) are commonly propagated by air layering. Propagators at the Arnold Arboretum at Jamaica Plain, Mass., have demonstrated that a wide variety of woody trees and shrubs can be successfully air layered outdoors.

Remove the leaves about 2 to 4 inches above and below the point where you want the stem to make root. Make a diagonal, upward cut of about 1 to 2 inches. The cut should be nearly to the center of the stem. The cut surfaces may be dusted with a root-inducing powder and should be held apart with a small pebble or stick.

Place about a handful of moist sphagnum moss around and between the cut surfaces and tie tightly with string. Wrap polyethylene film, such as a freezer bag, carefully and tightly about the sphagnum moss. The cut edges of the polyethylene should be folded several times to afford a watertight seal. Fasten the upper and lower ends of the polyethylene firmly to the stem with a waterproof tape. When properly made the sphagnum moss will remain moist for over a year.

The air layer should be shaded to prevent a buildup of excessive heat from the sun. Cut off and plant the rooted layers.

Another method of propagation is by division. Division is the simple act of producing two or more complete plants by splitting apart the parent plant. A sharp knife, pruning shears, or spade may be used.

Early flowering woody plants are usually divided in late summer or early fall after the plant has become dormant. Woody plants which bloom in mid to late summer are divided in the early spring before the buds begin to swell. Easiest to divide are the woody plants which have multiple crowns (branches) arising below the soil surface or which produce sucker shoots.

Herbaceous perennials which form multiple crowns should be divided as described above. Plants that are rampant growers should be divided every 1 to 2 years.

Perennials which require several years after planting before starting to flower should be divided only occasionally. Iris rhizomes, for example, should be divided in mid-July and about every 3 to 4 years. The rhizomes are cut into sections and immediately replanted. Each rhizome section should have a visible growing point.

Dahlia and peony roots should be divided so that each root piece has a bud (eye) on the stem piece at the top of the root. Peonies should be divided every 6 to 7 years. Dahlia, which is not hardy, is dug each fall, stored, and may be divided in the early spring just prior to planting.

Hardy bulbs, such as daffodils, narcissus, tulips, and lilies, are divided, but only when the planting becomes crowded. During the summer, after the tops have died down, dig, clean, and allow the bulbs to air-dry. Separate the bulbs and replant in the late summer or early fall. Bulbs, corms, and similar plant parts which are not hardy and must be dug each fall should be handled as described for the dahlia.

The most precise forms of plant propagation are grafting and budding. Considerable skill is required in preparing the graft union so the parts fit together properly. The botanical relationship of the graft partners must be known. In general the closer plants are related to each other, the better will be the chances for having a successful graft union.

Although grafting is normally left to the professional horticulturalist with the facilities to control temperature, humidity, and light during the grafting process, there are some techniques which can be handled outside with a minimum of equipment.

The ones we will discuss are the bridge graft that can be used to repair tree trunks which have had extensive areas of bark damaged by rodents, lawnmowers, or children; the cleft graft that can be used to change or add a new variety to the top of a fruit tree; and budding, that can be used to propagate a wide range of ornamentals which are very difficult to propagate by cutting.

The *bridge graft* is used to provide a span of living tissue over an injured area on a tree trunk. If over 50 percent of the bark on a tree trunk is damaged it is essential to provide a bridge of living tissue to carry food manufactured in the leaves to the root system. The best time to make a bridge graft is in early spring just as the buds are beginning to break.

If possible, shoots one-fourth to one-half inch in diameter should be taken from the injured tree several weeks before grafting. You can cut them and put them in a refrigerator to keep them dormant.

Damaged tissue around the wound should be removed. Cut the shoots (scions) on the diagonal and insert them in the live tissue above and below the wound. The scions may be held in place with small, flat-headed wire nails. A shoot is inserted every 2 or 3 inches, starting on one side of the wound.

Be sure to insert the shoots right side up. If they are placed upside down, the transport of nutrients to the upper part of the tree will be hindered.

After inserting the shoots, cover the area with grafting wax to prevent drying out and the entrance of disease organisms. Any buds which grow out of the shoots used to make the bridge should be removed.

The shoots will enlarge and completely cover the wounded area within a few years.

The *cleft graft* is used to topwork (grafting individual branches) to change or add a variety on an established tree. It can also be used to insert a male branch in a female holly tree to insure pollination.

Cleft grafting can be done any time the plants are dormant, but it is best to do it just before buds begin to swell in the spring.

Cut off a branch not over 4 inches in diameter, and split the stub vertically

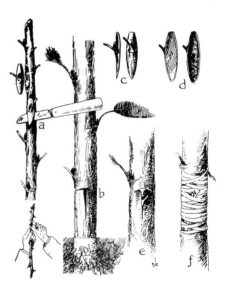

Budding or bud grafting, using the T-bud or shield bud technique.

a. Bud-stick. Proper method of holding knife and cutting bud is shown in lower left-hand corner.

b. T-cut on stock.

c. Side and front view of a "bud."

d. Inside view of bud with and without wood.

e. Stock with bud inserted.

f. Bud in place and tied with rubber band.

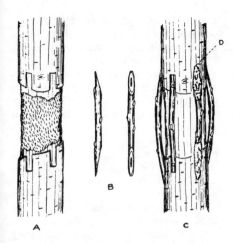

into opposite sides of the split. The outer edge of the shoot should match the outer edge of the branch stub so that a union can be formed.

After you have inserted the shoots, remove the screwdriver or wedge so the shoots will be firmly held in place. Cover the top of the stub and the union between stub and shoots with grafting wax.

Budding or *bud grafting* consists of inserting a single bud of the desired variety into the bark of a seedling or rootstock (the plant which is used as the root for a budded or grafted plant). This technique is used extensively for propagating roses and fruit trees.

Budding should be done when the bark is easily separated from the wood. The bud is inserted between the bark and the wood. Most budding is done in the fall since there is more time for the union to form before new shoot growth starts the following spring.

Bridge Grafting. a. Injured trunk showing ragged edges of bark trimmed and the rectangular sections of bark removed. b. Two views of a scion cut properly. c. Scions in place and nailed. Note the bow of the scions and the exposed wood under the scions is painted. d. The scions waxed properly.

for a distance of 2 to 3 inches. You can do this by using a mallet to pound a heavy knife or wedge into the stub. If a knife is used, a screwdriver or wedge should be inserted to hold the split open.

Two shoots (scions) 3 to 4 inches long with a gently sloping cut on the basal 2 inches of the shoot are inserted

For further reading:

Hartmann, Hudson T., and Kester, Dale E., *Plant Propagation—Principles and Practices.* Prentice-Hall Inc., 1968.

Mahlstede, John P., and Haber, Ernest S., *Plant Propagation.* John Wiley & Sons, Inc., 1957.

U.S. Department of Agriculture, *Home Propagation of Ornamental Trees and Shrubs.* Home and Garden Bulletin 80, Washington, D.C. 20250, 1967.

how to use controlled lighting to propagate and grow plants

WITH THE DEVELOPMENT of efficient sources of artificial light, you can now completely control one of the most important factors which affects plant growth. For centuries, individuals have been starting and growing plants in their homes, gardens, and greenhouses. But before the development of artificial light, all these gardeners were at the mercy of the sun to supply enough light.

By using artificial light in laboratory experiments, we have consistently grown larger, healthier, and more desirable plants than similar ones grown under sunlight. This is also possible for the average homeowner.

For success in growing plants under artificial light, you need to consider several things. These include the use of high-quality seed and stock plants;

a suitable growing medium; and simultaneous control of all environmental factors. For good growth you must have a medium with the following properties: good moisture conditions, high nutrient level, and proper aeration. In addition to controlling light, you need to regulate temperature, relative humidity, carbon dioxide (CO_2), and air movement.

The term *light* by definition is related to the sensitivity of the human eye. Sunlight or "white light" is the combination of photons of energy from all colors in relatively equal amounts. The color of light is determined by the relative level of the energy emitted at various wavelengths. For instance, the incandescent lamp appears somewhat yellow because it emits more energy in the yellow and red regions of the spectrum. The mercury lamp appears blue because that is the predominant wavelength emitted.

As far as the plant is concerned, at least two light-sensitive systems operate within it. These systems are photocontrol and photosynthesis.

The photocontrol mechanism controls many processes and responses within the plant. Among these are seed germination, stem elongation, branching, and flowering. Photocontrol requires only a low level of energy in the red and far-red region of the spectrum.

The photosynthesis mechanism is the food-producing system. It requires high energy and, in general, light of all wavelengths is utilized, although blue and red light are used more efficiently.

Lamps are rated by manufacturers in lumens, a measure of the total light emitted by a lamp. If you divide this by the input wattage of the lamp, you have a measure of the lamp's efficiency in terms of lumens per watt.

The light that strikes a leaf is meas-

ured in lumens per square foot or foot-candles (ft-c). Frequently, these values are given in metric units. In metric units, light intensity is measured in lux (1x) or kilolux (klx). One lux is equivalent to a lumen per square meter. To convert ft-c to lux, multiply by 10.764. Thus, 1,000 ft-c equals 10,764 lx or 10.764 klx.

The foot-candle light meter is the most widely used instrument for measuring light. Relatively inexpensive foot-candle light meters are commercially available.

A photographic light meter may be used if a foot-candle meter is not available. A photographic meter indicating an ASA exposure index of 75, a lens opening of f/8, and an exposure time of 1/60th of a second would be measuring a light level of about 1,000 ft-c. A light level of 500 ft-c would show the lens opening one f-stop larger or a doubling of either the ASA index or the exposure time. A level of 2,000 ft-c would cause a change of any one in the opposite direction.

Light sources for controlled lighting are classified in three groups. These are fluorescent, incandescent, and high-intensity discharge (HID) lamps.

Fluorescent lamps are the most widely employed for providing artificial light for growing plants. Researchers, commercial growers, and home gardeners make wide use of these lamps. They are relatively inexpensive, easily obtained, and simple to install. They are fairly efficient and have an average life of 7,500 to 12,000 hours.

These lamps are available in a wide range of colors, although we have found that the standard cool white fluorescent lamp is one of the best fluorescent light sources for growing plants.

Perhaps one of the most important and least understood aspects of fluorescent lamps is that they are manufactured in different energy levels. This level is based on the electrical current used and is called "loading". For instance, the standard 48-inch fluorescent tube comes with three levels of loading: light loading, also known as the

Author HERSCHEL H. KLUETER is an Agricultural Engineer in the Agricultural Engineering Research Division, Agricultural Research Service (ARS).

Coauthor DONALD T. KRIZEK is a Plant Physiologist with the Plant Science Research Division, ARS.

40-watt lamp; medium loading, known as the high-output lamp; and heavy loading, known as the 1,500 milliampere (ma) lamp. These lamps are not interchangeable and each requires a different type of lamp holder and ballast (electric current controller).

Fluorescent lamps also come in various lengths. For growing plants, 4-, 6-, or 8-foot lamps are used.

Many different kinds of fixtures are available for fluorescent lamps. You can get single-lamp, two-lamp, three-lamp, and four-lamp fixtures with and without reflectors. The uniformity of light distribution is affected both by the type of fixture and the spacing between the fixtures.

In general, you will have reasonably uniform lighting when you place the lamps at a distance from the plants equal to or greater than the spacing between fixtures. To raise the level of light near the edges and to increase uniformity, you might install white window shades or some other highly reflective material around the lamps. The shades will be extended during normal operation. When you work with your plants, the shades can be raised.

The major disadvantage of fluorescent light is that as the lamps age, the light from them decreases. A lamp lighted for 8,000 hours may give less than half the light of a new one. To maintain a fairly uniform light level over a period of time, you may have to move the plants closer to the lamps. Another way would be to replace part of the lamps on a fixed schedule every so often. A good rule might be to sequentially replace one-fourth of them after every 2,000 hours of use. If the lamps burned 12 hours per day, you would do this about every 6 months.

Incandescent lamps are the ones most commonly used around the home. They are the least expensive and easy to install. However, they have a low efficiency and a short operating life (1,000 hours). Because of this, they are not used extensively as a primary source of light for photosynthesis.

Growers and researchers use incandescents for photoperiod control because they emit considerable energy in the red and far-red region of the spectrum. They are also used with fluorescent light as a supplement to increase the rate of photosynthesis.

A number of lamps are classified as high-intensity discharge lamps (HID). They include various mercury, sodium, xenon, and metal halide lamps. In general, these lamps are expensive and require special equipment and knowledge before they can be safely operated. Once the lamps are installed, however, they are efficient, and have a long life and good spectral quality if used in the proper combination.

All HID lamps have essentially a point source of light emission and a high-bulb temperature. So when these lamps are used, a greater distance between lamp and plant is required to maintain light uniformity and the proper temperature for plants.

There is great interest in these new HID lamps and some growers are using them on a trial basis. However, more testing is required before we can make specific recommendations.

When any lamp fixture is installed, make sure a grounded three-wire cord, plug, and outlet are properly used. Also you should be sure to comply with your local, State, or national electric code.

For starting seedlings of most vegetables and ornamentals, a minimum of 1,000 ft-c of cool white fluorescent light is required. This should be applied from the time of seeding. For growing plants beyond the seedling stage, 1,500 to 2,000 ft-c should be maintained. That level can be obtained about 12 inches from new 1,500 milliampere lamps and about 1 inch from new 40 watt lamps spaced 6 inches apart.

An additional benefit can be obtained by adding about 20 percent additional energy from incandescent lamps. The incandescent lamp supplies the red and far-red light that is low in most fluorescent lamps. For the optimum seedling growth, 2,000 to 2,500 ft-c is required. For some plants you need even higher levels.

Continuous light may be used on most seedlings for the first 2 or 3 weeks. But as they get older, many seedlings—tomatoes, for example—will do better if given a dark period of at least 4 to 8 hours. This adjustable night break can be easily provided by including a 24-hour timeclock in the lighting system.

So, by using at least 50 watts per square foot of cool white fluorescent light (heavily loaded lamps on 6-inch centers), 10 watts per square foot incandescent light with reflectors around the sides, and a timeclock in the system, you can provide the requirements for intensity, quality, and duration of lighting.

million (ppm). This is considerably below the optimum for plant growth under high levels of light. Fortunately in most homes the CO_2 level is higher than normal (often up to 600 ppm) because of the CO_2 exhaled by humans. There is also a localized depletion of CO_2 around the leaves, especially at their surfaces, when there is little air movement. This effect can be minimized by moving the air through the plant area with a small household fan.

Too low an air or soil temperature often limits germination and seedling growth. Most seeds germinate rapidly,

Seedlings of 21-day-old lettuce grown on a 16-hour photoperiod. Plant at left was grown in greenhouse with 200 foot-candles of cool white fluorescent light added. Middle plant was grown under 2,000 ft-c of artificial light (cool white fluorescent plus incandescent). Both had a minimum of 400 parts per million of carbon dioxide (CO_2). Plant at right had artificial light and a minimum of 1,000 ppm CO_2.

The importance of beginning light treatment early in the life of the plant is frequently overlooked by both the amateur and the professional grower. Studies conducted in the Phyto-Engineering Laboratory at Beltsville, Md., have demonstrated that petunias and many other ornamental and vegetable plants may be given a "head start" by beginning light treatment from the time of planting the seed rather than waiting until after the seedlings emerge.

Light is not the only ingredient for successful culture indoors. Other factors need to be considered as well. One that has been frequently ignored is carbon dioxide (CO_2).

The normal level of CO_2 found in the atmosphere is 300 to 350 parts per

emerge quickly, and begin rapid growth when kept at an air temperature of about 80° to 85° F. during the light period. This is the most desirable temperature when the light level is high and the CO_2 content sufficient.

During the dark period a cooler temperature of 70° to 75° F. is generally desirable. As the seedlings get older, this temperature should be gradually reduced, if possible, before transplanting to the outside.

The simplest way to provide the proper temperature is to maintain the dark temperature at 70° to 75° F. With the addition of heat from the lighted lamps, a day temperature of 80° to 85° can easily be maintained by the use of a circulating fan. If a large lamp canopy is used, you may need to exhaust the air to the outside to prevent overheating.

To obtain the most rapid growth, keep the humidity as high as possible. Also, the soil should be kept moist. You can do these things by watering frequently or by misting. If misting is used, the growing areas will have to be enclosed to avoid wetting the lamps.

Fairly simple and inexpensive watering systems are available from most garden supply houses. Water soluble fertilizers should be added to the water to satisfy the plant's nutritional needs.

Frequent watering or misting calls for a light porous growing medium if the roots are to get enough oxygen. A mixture of sphagnum peat moss and fine vermiculite (peat-lite mix) provides an excellent growing medium for propagating plants. Mixtures are supplied under various trade names and are ideally suited for this purpose. They are lightweight and provide good aeration for the roots. They are also relatively sterile and therefore reduce dangers of fungal diseases.

By direct seeding under high intensity light, elevated day/night temperatures, and CO_2 enriched atmospheres, it has been possible to obtain 3-week-old seedlings that weigh 10 to 50 times more than those grown under conventional greenhouse conditions. You probably won't do this well, but you can grow a leaf lettuce crop or have flowering petunias from your own home with controlled lighting in 5 weeks from seed.

The use of controlled lighting in growth rooms, plant growth chambers, or your basement or apartment garden is no longer a dream of the future. Several large vegetable and bedding plant growers in this country and abroad are already using these techniques successfully on a commercial basis to start seedlings.

In the years ahead, there is little doubt that the market pack you buy from your garden center will be started under controlled environments because of the knowledge and the cooperation of growers and researchers throughout the world.

 ## small greenhouses provide year-round pleasure

Who loves a garden loves a greenhouse too.
Unconscious of a less propitious clime,
There blooms exotic beauty, warm and snug,
While the winds whistle, and the snows descend.

THESE LINES by William Cowper describe some of the pleasures of growing plants in a weather-proof garden.

A greenhouse can be part of the house, blending with the outdoor patio and enabling the gardener to live with plants the year around. It can be used as a pleasing entrance to the house or garden. Or it can be entirely separate.

You can bring any growing season with its flowers or colors into your garden greenhouse at any time of year you wish. You can hasten springtime through forcing of hyacinths, tulips, and azaleas, and lengthen summertime with roses that bloom far into the autumn. You may brighten winter with carnations, camellias, and rare tropical flowers. And you may also harvest tomatoes in January, and vegetables or greens any time of the year.

A greenhouse consists of a heated structure that traps the sunlight and keeps the plants in it alive, thriving, and multiplying while the same plants outside would go dormant or perish.

In a greenhouse, there is excitement and satisfaction for everyone in the family. Men are likely to be attracted to hybridizing, air-layering, and grafting, or they may want to specialize in some hobby plants like Easter lilies, poinsettias, begonias, camellias, or even orchids. Women usually are more interested in roses, African-violets, and cut flowers and flower arrangements for the house. Children are absorbed in what happens to the seeds they sow.

When the first green tip breaks the soil, or bulb spear turns green, it is unbelievably fascinating. As you watch true leaves form on seedlings, and each small seedling develop into a choice specimen, you sense an affinity for this child of nature that is your own to care for right up to the rewarding fullness of colorful and fruitful maturity.

Most people start their gardening activities without a greenhouse. Very soon, though, they learn the handicaps they work under and the opportunities that are closed to them. The greenhouse vastly enlarges the scope of your gardening. It saves the cost of buying many kinds of plants, enables you to propagate your chosen varieties, and provides a supply of vegetables for the dinner table.

When you place glass over a plant, you give the plant a new world of its own. This glass-enclosed microcosm—lighted and heated by the sun—is a warmer and safer place for plants on cold days and frosty nights than the natural environment. Within this shelter, spring comes earlier and summer carries on.

The use of glass or any other transparent cover to provide shelter for plants does not necessarily imply a greenhouse, however. This shelter can be anything from a simple wax paper cone, to cover early-started melon

plants or tomatoes, to a coldframe for your winter salads and cuttings. It may be a glassed-in porch off the living room, dining room, or bedroom, a window sill "conservatory," a reach-in window greenhouse, or the very latest greenhouse that cares for its plants automatically.

Selection of a plant shelter depends on whether you want a purely functional device or a structure designed as part of the garden or house; whether you want to use it the year around or only at special times; whether you plan to use it exclusively for growing plants or expect to furnish part of it as a living or family room; whether you want to grow many different kinds of plants requiring different conditions or only one or two kinds requiring similar conditions; how much money you have to spend; the location and space you have available; and how much time you can spare to take care of your plants.

Before you make your selection, take a broad look at all the types of plant shelters available. Learn what each one can do for you and approximately how much it will cost.

Individual and multiple plant protectors are available from garden suppliers or you can easily make them. Protectors are particularly useful for covering transplants or seedlings of warm-weather vegetables or flowers set out ahead of the normal planting season. The farther north you live, the greater their usefulness, since they make it possible to set plants out earlier and thus lengthen the normal growing season. The heavy wax paper cone costs only a few cents, and it will last more than one season if you handle it with care.

You can make a plastic-covered wire cone from 8- by 14-inch material by attaching it to a 1- by 1-inch anchor stick. Also a plastic and wire 7-inch open top cylinder can be made from 10- by 22-inch material, and attached between two pointed anchor sticks.

The European cloche (tent, barn, or rectangular shape) is usually built in 2-foot sections that vary in height

Author ROBERT C. LIU is an Agricultural Engineer in the Agricultural Engineering Research Division, Agricultural Research Service.

Coauthor WILLIAM A. BAILEY is Agricultural Engineer and Leader, Crop Structures Investigations, in the same division.

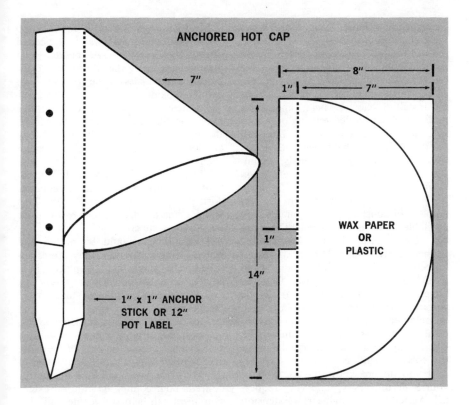

ANCHORED HOT CAP

7"

8"

1" | 7"

WAX PAPER
OR
PLASTIC

1"

14"

1" x 1" ANCHOR
STICK OR 12"
POT LABEL

from 9 to 24 inches and 15 to 26 inches in width. It is made of four panes of glass held together with heavy galvanized wire fittings. It has a handle for ease in carrying and for operating the ventilation system. It can be taken apart easily and moved from one spot to another.

Several cloches placed end to end will make a long miniature greenhouse.

A tunnel-like plant protector can be made with a 5-foot strip of plastic laid over 6-foot wire hoops placed 3 feet apart. Elastic tiedowns over the top near each hoop will hold the plastic.

A coldframe is a covered garden that is too small and low to accommodate the gardener along with the plants. It is simple and inexpensive but it begins to approach the greenhouse in scope.

With a coldframe, you can do many of the same things you do in a greenhouse. You can sow summer flowers and vegetables weeks before outdoor planting. Often, you will gain sufficient

time to grow an extra crop. You can start vegetables, annual flowers for fall and winter, and perennials for next year's bloom.

In a coldframe, plants are protected from the harsh weather and will grow to transplant size quickly. You can root cuttings of deciduous and evergreen shrubs and trees. Softwood cuttings of chrysanthemums, geraniums, and fuchsia, and leaf cuttings of rex begonias, African-violets, and succulent and foliage plants take root faster in a coldframe, particularly during the warmer months.

You can also grow your own lettuce, chives, endives, parsley, and green onions right through the winter in a heated coldframe (sometimes called a hotbed).

Portable coldframes can be built in the gardener's workshop. These coldframes make good use of surplus materials you may have on hand. Several readily built plant protectors are described in a Sunset Book, *Garden and Patio Building Book*.

Coldframes are constructed from sections of 3- by 4-foot or 3- by 6-foot millwork sash or plastic covered panels. They can be made for use in all seasons by installing electric heat, and automatic clock controlled misting or watering. Inexpensive and easy to build all season coldframes have been developed over the years by individuals, manufacturers, and research and extension agencies.

The following plans which are examples of current developments are available at a small cost: USDA Plan No. 5971, Hotbed and Propagating Frame; USDA Plan No. 6080, Mini-hotbed and Propagating Frame; and USDA Plan No. 5941, Plastic Covered Greenhouse Coldframe. Large-scale working drawings of these plans may be obtained from the extension agricultural engineer at your State university. There may be a small charge to cover the cost of printing.

If you do not know the location of your State university, send your request to Agricultural Engineer, Extension Service, U.S. Department of Agriculture, Washington, D.C. 20250. He will forward your request.

To assist home gardeners in propagating their favorite plants, one horticulturist from the National Arboretum suggested an inexpensive and effective technique for root cuttings, the windowsill greenhouse. This consists of a two-quart nonperforated plastic bag.

An artificial soil mixture of 2-part peat and 1-part sand by volume is suitable for rooting a wide range of plants in the windowsill greenhouse. Water is gradually added until a few drops of water will emerge when a handful of the mixture is tightly squeezed. Too much water may rot the cuttings.

The moist mixture is placed in the bag to a depth of about 4 inches. Compress the mixture gently and the greenhouse is ready to receive the cuttings. The closed "greenhouse" is now ready for placing on a north windowsill or any location which will receive abundant light but no direct sunlight.

Most cuttings will root in 6 to 10 weeks. No additional water is needed during this interval. The polyethylene plastic bags have the ability to retain moisture but pass some oxygen and carbon dioxide.

To determine whether the cuttings have rooted, tug the cuttings gently. If they resist, roots have formed. If they are loose, wait 2 weeks before testing again.

When the cuttings are rooted, gradually open the windowsill greenhouse during a period of several days. This will acclimatize the cuttings to the drier outside atmosphere.

The cuttings should be potted and watered frequently until they are established. The plants can be placed in a coldframe until they are large enough to be put in a permanent location in the garden.

Almost every serious gardener eventually reaches a point where he wants a greenhouse. Before buying or building one, however, give careful thought to the size, style, type, and kind of control desired. Your county agricultural extension agent can help you locate and visit a few of your neighbors who have garden greenhouses. Learn about their problems so that you can choose the best house for you. Local building codes and zoning laws may require a license before you start construction.

Too many greenhouses stand empty, are poorly managed, or are used for storage. The safe rule of thumb is this: don't get one that's too large. It is easier to find room for just one more plant in a small greenhouse than it is to find time to attend a greenhouse that is too large.

Let your skill and interest dictate the size of your greenhouse. It is easy to add a section later on, particularly if you get one of the knockdown sectional types.

You will be surprised by the number of types, styles, and sizes of greenhouses that are commercially available. For the handyman, a prefabricated glass or plastic greenhouse can provide do-it-yourself satisfaction and can also reduce cost. USDA Plans No. 5946,

A Plastic Covered Greenhouse and No. 6097, Tri-Penta Greenhouse are readily available from your State university to serve your needs.

No matter how you choose your greenhouse, you must take into account the problems of heating, ventilating, and cooling as well as general maintenance and working space.

There are two basic types of greenhouses: free standing and attached. A free-standing greenhouse is generally even-span (symmetrical roof) while an attached greenhouse may be even span, lean to, or window mounted.

A free-standing greenhouse is generally a balanced independent structure that has two sides and two ends with a door on one end or side. It has the advantage of providing maximum exposure to sunlight.

An attached greenhouse is ideal when space and budget are limited. It is usually half of the even span and can be attached over a door for convenient access. An attached greenhouse usually has the advantage of an available supply of heat, water, and electricity from the house, but you should be warned that a 12- by 14-foot greenhouse takes approximately the same amount of heating and cooling as a 3-bedroom house.

For year-round use, greenhouse heating is essential in all sections of the continental United States.

Greenhouses can be classified according to the average temperature maintained in them as:

The cold house . . 35°—45°F.
The cool house . . 45°—55°F.
The warm house . . 55°—65°F.
The hot house . . 65°—75° or higher

A window greenhouse will allow space to grow a few more plants than in a regular window, at relatively low

Plastic-covered greenhouse, Tri-Penta type.

cost for heating and cooling. This reach-in greenhouse is available in many standard sizes, either in single units or in tandem arrangements for large windows. Only simple tools are needed to remove the regular window from the frame and fasten the prefabricated window greenhouse in its place.

For each of the above types of greenhouses there is a range of plants which are naturally suited to the conditions that can be maintained inside the house. For greatest success: fill the house only with plants from the range appropriate to it; do not attempt to maintain a "mixed" greenhouse; remember that the higher the temperature maintained, the more work is involved because the plants are growing faster and need more watering and attending; and avoid overcrowding.

*A variety
of
greenhouses.*

214

Working in a greenhouse.

The size of the heater your greenhouse requires is determined by the lowest expected outside temperature, the maximum inside temperature desired, and the greenhouse surface area. In general, a heater should be large enough to overcome a heat loss from a glass greenhouse of 1.2 BTU per hour or 0.35 watt of electric heat multiplied by square foot of exposed surface multiplied by degree Fahrenheit of temperature difference (highest inside degree F. minus lowest outside temperature).

There are many types of heaters and heating systems that are satisfactory for small greenhouses if your home heating system can't handle the job. The best heating system will depend on size of the greenhouse, the availability of fuel, economy of operation, and possibly the initial cost.

Electric heat is generally more expensive, but very convenient to control automatically. A warm air overhead heating system equipped with plastic distribution tubes and automatic control, using natural gas fuel, will generally be more economical and have the best air distribution.

Adequate ventilation is essential for healthy plant growth. It is generally accomplished by means of ridge vents, side vents and/or exhaust fans, or perhaps a combination of these.

The combined use of an intake or exhaust fan and a perforated transparent plastic tube makes an ideal method of introducing fresh air into a greenhouse in the winter without a cold draft. Development of this principle has produced automatic climate control systems which can heat, dehumidify, ventilate, or recirculate the air in a greenhouse for proper climate control in the fall, winter, and spring seasons.

Excessively high summer temperatures are a serious problem to greenhouse owners across most of the United States. This problem can be reasonably solved either by conventional shading or by whitewashing the greenhouse, but the purpose of growing plants in natural daylight then becomes partially defeated.

There's a better way. You can cool the outside air before it passes through the greenhouse. A well-engineered evaporative cooling system can effectively and economically bring the temperature down 10° to 15° F. below the outdoor dry bulb temperature in humid areas and 20° to 30° F. in dry areas.

For example, if air at 95° F. and 50 percent relative humidity passes through a wet pad, it would pick up water from the pad to increase its water content (latent heat) and to reduce its dry bulb temperature (sensible heat) until it approaches its wet bulb temperature which theoretically should be 75° F. Thus, the wet bulb temperature of outside air tells how much the greenhouse air can be theoretically cooled by evaporative cooling. In actual practice only 85 percent efficiency can generally be obtained. The greenhouse temperature in this case should be cooled down to 78° F.

Since solar heat is measured on the basis of square feet of ground-surface area, the air flow rate for cooling is

Small plastic-covered greenhouse or coldframe that could be a starter for a home gardener. It may be either heated or unheated.

also determined on a cubic feet per minute (CFM) for each square foot of ground area. For small home greenhouses, a compact evaporative cooler often called an "Arctic" or "Swamp" cooler can be used. It consists of a blower fan, three cooling pads, a motor, a recirculating water pump, and an air control louver, all in a package, to fit outside and against the greenhouse.

Selection of the right size cooler is a simple and straightforward matter. Multiply the floor area by a factor of 12 to obtain the appropriate CFM rating of the cooler required. For improved ventilation, turn off the water system and use the cooler fan for air circulation.

For further reference:

Acme Engineering and Manufacturing Corp., *The Greenhouse Climate Control Handbook: Principles and Design Procedures.* Acme Engineering and Manufacturing Corp., Muskogee, Okla., 1970. $2.00.

Biles, Roy E., *The Complete Book of Garden Magic.* J. G. Ferguson Publisher, Chicago, 1953.

Blake, Claire L., *Greenhouse Gardening for Fun.* M. Barrow and Company, Inc., New York, 1967.

Courtier, J. W., and Curtis, J. O., *A Simple Rigid Frame Greenhouse for Home Gardeners.* Cooperative Extension Service, Circular 880, University of Illinois, College of Agriculture, Urbana, 1964. Out of State, 10¢.

————, *Home Greenhouses for Year-round Gardening Pleasure.* Cooperative Extension Service, Circular 879, University of Illinois, College of Agriculture, Urbana, 1964. Out of State, 10¢.

Edison Electric Institute, *Electric Gardening.* Edison Electric Institute, 750 Third Avenue, New York, 1970. (Available from your electric power supplier.)

Liu, R. C., Bailey, W. A., Klueter, H. H., and Krizek, D. T., *New Shapes of Hobby Greenhouses.* U.S. Department of Agriculture, ASAE Paper 68–925, Phyto-Engineering Laboratory, Beltsville, Md. 20705, 1968.

Lord and Burnham, *Your Gateway to Year-round Gardening Pleasure.* Burnham Corporation, Irvington, N.J., 1971. (Free)

————, *Greenhouse Gardens that Take Care of Themselves.* Burnham Corporation, Irvington, N.J., 1971. (Free)

Sunset Book, *Garden and Patio Building Book.* Lane Magazine and Book Co., Menlo Park, Calif., 1971. $1.95.

Sunset Book, *Garden Work Centers.* Lane Magazine and Book Co., Menlo Park, Calif., 1970. $1.95.

U.S. Department of Agriculture, *Electric Heating of Hotbeds.* Leaflet 445, Washington, D.C. 20250, 1959.

————, *Plastic Covered Greenhouse Coldframe.* Miscellaneous Publication 1111, Washington, D.C. 20250, 1969.

————, *Windowsill Greenhouse,* Slide set No. C 135; address inquiries to the Photography Division, Office of Information, Washington, D.C. 20250.

————, *List of Sources of Information on Greenhouses,* Correspondence Aid 34–134, Washington, D.C. 20250, 1970.

UNDERSTANDING
PLANT
GROWTH

day and night in the plant world,
or the rhythm must be right

FROM ITS BEGINNING, spacecraft earth has been in rotation. As a consequence, all living things on our planet have had to evolve under an alternating pattern of day and night.

Like all living things, plants have a biological clock. This clock works without ticking and it doesn't need to be started by man. But, like the clock on your mantle, it can be reset to run faster or slower depending on how it is handled.

Nearly every living organism, from the most simple to the most complex, shows some biological response to the rhythms of nature.

Some of the better known rhythmic patterns within the plant are the daily fluctuations that occur in root growth, shoot growth, photosynthesis, water uptake, and transpiration. These rhythmic patterns are imposed on the plant by the alternation of day and night. Scientists call these diurnal patterns since they occur in a 24-hour period.

In many kinds of plants, though, the pattern is not exactly 24 hours. Instead, it is somewhere between 21 and 28 hours. Rhythms of this type are called circadian rhythms ("circa" meaning about, "diem" meaning day).

Examples of circadian rhythms are leaf movement in bean plants and petal movement in *Kalanchoë* plants.

The need for different day and night conditions was recognized early in controlled-environment studies as investigators tried various combinations of photoperiods and temperatures. These studies show that, paradoxically, many plants need a dark period or a change in temperature for normal development. If you deprive them of it, you will damage the plant.

If, for example, you were to grow a tomato plant under continuous illumination, or under constant temperature, instead of under alternating conditions, the difference in growth would amaze you. The plant under constant conditions would weigh less, the leaves would be small, stiff, and yellow, and there would be a lot of dark areas of dead tissue. But if you were to simply interrupt the illumination with a dark period once every 24 hours, all of these abnormalities would be prevented.

If the dark interruptions do not come at 24-hour intervals, the plants will be damaged just as if they were growing in continuous light. This shows that the tomato requires a specific rhythmic environment.

After much experimenting, scientists have found that a 6-hour light, 6-hour dark regime is as damaging to a tomato plant as a 24-hour light, 24-hour dark regime, and that best growth is obtained in a 12-hour light, 12-hour dark regime. Evidently, it's not the amount of light the plant receives that's most important, it's whether the light and dark periods are in keeping with the plant's internal rhythms.

Researchers have found for this plant and many others, that to achieve a normal growth and development, the rhythmic needs of the plant must be synchronized with the internal rhythms of the plant. If they aren't, the plant will probably be severely damaged.

Another question that has long intrigued scientists is what time of the

Author DONALD T. KRIZEK is a Plant Physiologist with the Plant Science Research Division, Agricultural Research Service. Since 1966, he has worked in the Phyto-Engineering Laboratory at Beltsville, Md., on the effects of controlled environments on plant growth and development.

day or night do cell division, leaf expansion, stem growth, and other growth processes take place in the plant.

Prof. E. Bünning, working at the University of Tubingen, in Germany, attempted to answer this question by growing various short-day and long-day plants on a schedule of 12 hours light and 12 hours dark. By measuring leaf growth every 3 to 4 hours throughout a 24-hour light-dark cycle, he found that leaves of the short-day plant, *Chenopodium amaranticolor,* had the highest growth rate during the first hours of the light period. The lowest growth rate occurred at the beginning or in the middle of the dark period.

In contrast, leaves of another short-day plant, Biloxi soybean, had the highest growth rate in the middle of the night and the lowest growth rate in the middle of the day. In the long-day plant, henbane, the maximum growth rate was reached at the end of the dark period.

Surprisingly, fluctuations in leaf growth in these plants continued for 3 to 5 days after the plants were placed in complete darkness.

This indicates that a rhythm within the plant itself was involved, just as in the case of leaf movements, which also often persist for several days under constant environment of light or darkness.

Researchers have shown that rhythmic phenomena are not confined to intact whole plants but also may occur in detached leaves, strips of leaf tissue, and even single cells.

Scientists have found that plants are able to measure day and night with considerable precision despite changes in temperature. In nature, the two most obvious forces showing definite rhythms are light and temperature.

The response of the plant to changes in daylength is known as photoperiodism. This phenomenon was first described fully more than 50 years ago by two investigators at the U.S. Department of Agriculture—W. W. Garner and H. A. Allard. Their work led to further studies at Beltsville, Md., by H. A. Borthwick and S. H. Hendricks and their colleagues which re-

sulted in the eventual extraction and identification of an important pigment system in the plant called phytochrome.

This pigment occurs in two interconvertible forms: phytochrome 660 (P_{660}), with an absorption maximum in the red portion of the spectrum; and phytochrome 730 (P_{730}), with an absorption maximum in the far-red region of the spectrum. P_{730} is believed to be the physiologically active form of phytochrome. Its function is to trigger the basic changes in the metabolism of the plant that lead ultimately to such photoresponses as stem elongation, leaf growth, anthocyanin formation, floral induction, seed germination, and a wide range of other responses in the plant.

In contrast to photosynthesis, photoperiodism and photomorphogenesis (light influence on form of growth) require relatively small amounts of energy. By increasing the amount of irradiation, it is sometimes possible to override the responses in the plant attributed to the lower energy responses. Such light responses in the plant have been called high-energy reactions. A typical example of a high-energy reaction is seen in certain seeds which do not respond to wavelengths of light in the red or far-red portion of the spectrum when given high intensity light.

Garner and Allard classified plants as to whether they flowered on long days or short days, or were indifferent to the length of day.

At the time, they thought that only length of day was important. It wasn't until some time later that plant physiologists began to realize that night length and not daylength was the important factor in the regulation of flowering and other photoperiodic responses.

More recently, scientists have found that light itself is not the critical factor in seed germination, flowering, and many other photoperiodic responses, but rather a rhythmic response which is decisive in these processes.

The quality, intensity, and duration of light are not only critical for photoperiodism, they are also important in determining the form of growth the plant takes. Seedlings grown in the dark are typically elongated, with much smaller leaves. In contrast, those grown in the light are normal in appearance, and have normal looking leaves.

The forces of nature that are responsible for the change in day and night length are also responsible to some extent for the accompanying changes in temperature and relative humidity.

As these changes occur, they occur together. Relative humidity, temperature, photoperiod, light intensity, light quality, air flow, the amount of carbon dioxide and oxygen in the air are all important in the development of a plant. Nevertheless, they are often very difficult to separate and identify and measure.

For the past 50 years or so, scientists have been trying to separate and identify these factors and find out which ones exercise control over the growth of a plant and how much control they exercise.

The need to identify the role of these factors in plant growth and development led to the development of plant growth chambers and special controlled-environment facilities known as phytotrons ("phyto" meaning plant and "tron" which means a machine or an instrument).

A phytotron consists of a number of greenhouses and artificially lighted rooms in which plants can be grown to maturity under precisely controlled environmental conditions.

The first phytotron was built by Dr. Fritz W. Went in 1948-49 at the California Institute of Technology in Pasadena. It served as the forerunner of modern-day phytotrons.

Since then, phytotrons of various sizes have been constructed at nearly a dozen research facilities throughout the world. In these facilities, investigators can subject plants to a variety of day and night temperatures and photoperiods approximating the growing conditions of any climate in the world.

The advantage to having a number of different but precisely controlled environments available is that scientists can study the interactions among temperature, light intensity, photoperiod, carbon dioxide, and other plant needs. In this way, they can find out how each factor acts, singly and in concert, to cause a plant to grow the way it does.

Controlled-environment studies have shown that each successive stage of plant growth and development or part of the plant may have a different optimum day and night temperature. Similarly, the optimum temperature for plant growth may vary from one species to another and even among individuals and populations within a single species.

Studies conducted in the Phyto-Engineering Laboratory at Beltsville, Md., have indicated that the optimum temperature for early seedling growth of many vegetables and ornamental plants is relatively high, about 86° F. during the day and 75° during the night. Raising or lowering this temperature results in reduced growth, as shown in the photos on page 221.

Large fluctuations of temperature between day and night are of great importance in the growth of certain plants such as the coast redwood, while night temperature is the crucial factor in controlling the growth of other plants, such as spruce and digger pine.

Tomatoes do best when grown under moderate daytime temperatures followed by cool nights. Potatoes produce tubers only when grown in climates where the night temperature falls to 50° to 60° F. Peppers also do best when grown under cool night conditions. Similarly, low night temperatures greatly improve the flowering, quality, and flavor of fruits such as strawberry, apple, and plum.

Certain species, such as African-violet and zinnia, behave in just the opposite way; these plants grow best in the growth chamber under conditions in which the nights are warmer than the days. Other species are not affected appreciably by diurnal variations in temperature.

Various processes in the plant are vitally affected by day and night temperature. Among these are photosynthesis; respiration; water and nutrient uptake; and shoot and root growth.

Cucumber plants, top, and tomato plants, bottom, were grown for 20 days under controlled environment conditions at five different day/night temperatures, starting from 75°/65° F. and increasing at 5° intervals to 95°/85°.

Before the development of plant growth chambers and other controlled-environment facilities, reproducibility of experiments and experimental plant material was virtually impossible. Now a scientist can duplicate experiments at any time of the year.

At present, there are hundreds of growth rooms in use throughout the world, with varying ability to control the plant's environment. Most growth chambers are presently not equipped with automatic watering systems or facilities for enriching the atmosphere's carbon dioxide content.

USDA studies conducted in specially designed growth chambers at Beltsville have demonstrated that many plants need to be fertilized several times a day. Carbon dioxide also has been shown to be one of the most important yet least controlled factors in plant growth chambers.

Whether one grows plants in an elaborate growth chamber in the laboratory or an inexpensive propagation unit in the home, the needs are the same. For best results all environmental factors must be optimum during both day and night. If light, temperature, carbon dioxide, or other environmental factors are limiting, photosynthetic rates and overall growth will be greatly reduced.

Whether indoors or outdoors, virtually every aspect of plant behavior from seed germination to the ultimate death of the plant is under the rhythmic control of day and night conditions.

For further reading:

Evans, L. T. (ed.), *Environmental Control of Plant Growth.* Academic Press Inc., New York, 1963.

Leopold, A. C., *Plant Growth and Development.* McGraw-Hill Book Co., New York, 1964.

Salisbury, F. B., and Ross, C., *Plant Physiology.* Wadsworth Publishing Co., Inc., Belmont, Calif., 1969.

Went, F. W., *The Experimental Control of Plant Growth.* Chronica Botanica Co., Waltham, Mass., 1957.

——————— and Sheps, Lillian O., "Environmental Factors in Regulation of Growth and Development: Ecological Factors," *Plant Physiology: 5A,* Academic Press Inc., New York, 1969.

Wilkins, M. B. (ed.), *The Physiology of Plant Growth and Development.* McGraw-Hill Book Co., New York, 1969.

221

plants and the seasons;
triggering responses

TREES, SHRUBS, AND FLOWERS change constantly with the seasons and with the years. Through the ages they have been honored as vibrant calendars. Lyric voices have equated men's moods with the seasonal glories of foliage and flower.

Even the comic strip philosopher Charlie Brown fears the tree as a voracious predator of his kites in spring. And yet Charlie Brown shares a poignant kinship with that same tree's first lonely leaf to fall from its bough in autumn to presage a dreary winter.

Various kinds of plants germinate seeds, grow, flower, and fruit at different times in the year, each in its own season. Thus, some plants grow and flower in the spring, others in the summer, still others in autumn, and some even in winter in the more southern and subtropical climes.

In more northern gardens in autumn, many herbaceous plants stop growing and reproduce as seeds, tubers, or bulbs. And trees and shrubs in brilliant foliage stop growing and form overwintering buds, in apparent anticipation of winter and usually well before the weather turns cold.

Not only do plants reflect the seasons, more important, they are able to anticipate and foresee favorable as well as unfavorable periods in their life cycles. Their very survival depends upon their ability to predict and adapt to seasonal change.

Poets, philosophers, and plant husbandmen appreciated plant response to the seasons long before scientists understood the reasons. It is not plant psyche but rather imperative signals from the environment that are the pendulums in plants' diverse seasonal clocks. The plant scientist has begun to understand and control and manipulate these signals.

We emphasize that the striking feature of the seasonal adaptation is the sensing of a favorable or an unfavorable season before it comes. Some of the possible seasonal signals of the environment you might think of are the daily cycles of day and night, changes of light intensity, variations in food supply, temperature and its fluctuations, and differences in water supply.

Possibly less evident to you are the lengths of day and night and their systematic, gradual change with the season.

Your first guess would probably be that temperature is the paramount environmental control, with perhaps water supply a close second. However, a few warm days in mid-winter, or a cold, wet spring, or a hot, dry summer are poor omens indeed by which to live.

Think, then, about the long spring day that portends the summer and the shortening days of mid-summer that warn of the coming autumn. This systematically changing daylength—the scientist will more correctly advise you it is the converse nightlength—is the most consistent feature of a plant's environment and, in general, a major transmitter of its seasonal signals.

The signals are often amplified, or sometimes muted, by nutrition, water, temperature and, more recently, by manmade chemicals or by artificial light manipulation.

Author HENRY M. CATHEY is Leader, Ornamentals Investigations, Plant Science Research Division, Agricultural Research Service.

Coauthor A. A. PIRINGER is Assistant Director, U.S. National Arboretum, Plant Science Research Division.

At any one place, regardless of climate, the daylength will be the same each year on a given date. For example, in St. Paul, Minn., on each June 21, the daylength is always 15¾ hours, and on Dec. 21, it is always 8½ hours.

Along the equator, daylength is 12 hours every day. As you go north from the equator, the days are longer in mid-summer and shorter in mid-winter. The longest summer days, as well as the shortest winter days, occur in the Northern States. Seattle's longest mid-summer day, on June 21, is more than 2 hours longer than that at Miami on the same date. Seattle's shortest winter day, on Dec. 21, is 2 hours shorter than Miami on the same date.

What happens in your hometown? Here are some examples of the number of daylight hours on June 21 and December 21, the longest and shortest days of each year, respectively, for a selected number of U.S. cities from south to north: Miami, 13¾ and 10½; Dallas, 14½ and 10; San Francisco, 14¾ and 9¾; Washington, D.C., 15 and 9½; and Seattle, 16 and 8½.

Cities or towns in an easterly or westerly alignment with any of these cities will have similar daylengths. For example, Los Angeles will have a daylength similar to that of Dallas. But the climate in the two places varies and different plants are adapted to each place.

Although many tropical plants are daylength sensitive, temperature and rainfall appear to be more influential in controlling their growth and development, and dry and rainy seasons are recognized. However, in the more temperate regions, daylength tends to be highly influential when temperature and water are not limiting. Also, plant response to seasons tends to be more dramatic in northern latitudes because of more rapidly and widely changing daylength—and wide fluctuation in annual temperature and rainfall.

The morning-glory (*Ipomoea* species) is a good example of a cycle of plant seasonal responses. Morning-glory seeds germinate in spring and the young vines grow vigorously during early summer to bloom in late summer as the days shorten. Its showy flowers continue as the days cool and seeds mature. The seeds fall to the earth where they are kept in some way from germinating again until spring. Morning-glory is an annual plant with a relatively simple seasonal cycle.

Perennial plants are more complicated than annual plants because they must not only complete their yearly cycle of flowering but also must provide growth to carry the plant over from one season to the next.

Garden tulips (*Tulipa gesneriana*) form a bulb made up of telescoped storage scales. The bulbs at maturity contain stored material and a miniature growing point. Dry bulbs must be held at an optimum temperature of 68° F. for 3 to 4 weeks for the formation of a flower bud.

The tulip uses its innermost scale as a source of food to form the new flower, leaves, and stem. The flower bud forms but does not develop until the night temperature begins to cool during the fall months. Gardeners are usually urged to delay planting their bulbs until fall. Storage of the dry bulbs in a cool room over the summer is needed to prevent overheating which could damage the growing point.

Chilling requirement for most tulips is 12 weeks. By this time, and in the soil, the root system is formed and the flower bud has elongated to the top of the bulb.

Cold soil temperatures of winter repress flower development of tulips until the following spring. Optimum temperature for development of the flower bud is 48° F. Stem elongation and flowering occur with gradually warming temperatures the following spring. The plants turn green and develop colored flowers even in dim light.

The tulip bulb contains sufficient stored food to permit it to flower. The new bulb scale, however, begins to form at the base of the old flower stem and is dependent on the food translocated to it from the maturing leaves.

Tulips thus recycle themselves every

year to survive as a plant in the garden. Their flowering is primarily dependent on changes in temperatures through the seasons.

The rhododendron (*Rhododendron* 'Roseum Elegans') is a summer flowering shrub that forms large flower buds during the previous season of growth much like tulip bulbs. Growth, however, occurs in the air on the plant's branches. The yearly cycle begins with the dying of the current season's flower in early spring.

Beneath the dead flower is a cluster of dormant buds which immediately start to grow in response to the long days and warm temperatures of summer. The new rhododendron shoots do not grow continuously; they grow in a flush of stem and leaves and every 4 to 6 weeks a new flush of growth develops.

By the time the plant is starting to develop the third flush of growth, after 10 to 12 weeks, the environment has changed to gradually shortening days and cooler temperatures. Flower buds form as a result of the shortening days and cooler temperature.

Individual flowers within the bud develop slowly during the winter months. Without chilling, the rhododendron flower buds will never develop into fully expanded flowers.

On plants taken indoors during winter and given 8 weeks of chilling (50° F.) in a dimly lighted storage room, the buds expand to full-sized flowers 3 to 8 weeks later. The plants out of doors remain inactive until the gradually increasing daylength and the warming temperatures of the following spring. Growth for the new cycle of flowering commences with the fading of the current season's growth.

Tulips and rhododendrons are much alike in their seasonal requirements for growth and flowering, although one is a bulb and the other is a woody shrub.

The vegetative and the flower buds of rhododendron are induced to go dormant primarily due to the shortening daylength. Cooling temperatures intensify the depth of dormancy which preconditions the plant for survival under the extremely cold temperatures of winter. Curling of the rhododendron leaves in winter is good evidence of cold winter temperatures.

The following spring, all vegetative buds start to grow at the same time and give a great burst of new shoots all over the plant.

You can induce the characteristic spring growth on rhododendrons by shifting the growing plants to 8-hour days and growing them for at least 8 weeks, then chilling them for 8 weeks at 50° F. in a dimly lighted storage room. Return the plants to a warm (65° F.) greenhouse and expose them to long days. At any time of year, plants exposed to 8-hour days and followed by chilling always regrow with the characteristic growth of spring.

The fall-flowering chrysanthemum (*Chrysanthemum morifolium*) is an example of the adaptation of a herbaceous perennial to the seasons. Natural flowering occurs in fall. Shoots develop at the base of the plant, down under the leaves. The shoots look like asparagus tips appearing along the surface of the soil. Only the tips are erect and green.

If you dig up the plants and bring them into a heated greenhouse in fall, the shoots develop into rosettes of cabbage-like leaves. These plants will not flower. Other plants chilled for 6 weeks at 40° F. and returned to a heated greenhouse promptly elongate and immediately flower.

Meanwhile, the plants left outdoors make little growth and the green tips do not emerge above the soil line. The increasing daylength and temperatures of the following spring promote stem elongation and delay flowering of the chrysanthemum. The plants continue to grow and to expand in size as long as the daylength increases and the temperature remains about 65° F.

The signal for prompt flower bud initiation and subsequent flower development is triggered by autumn's gradually shortening daylength and cooling temperatures. Periods of natural heat or cold alter the time of flowering, but most years, it occurs at about the same time.

Foxglove (*Digitalis purpurea*), usually grown as a biennial, flowers during an extended period in late spring and early summertime. Mature seed, open flowers, and immature flower buds are often present on the flowering stalk at the same time.

The fine seeds fall to the ground and germinate within 2 or 3 weeks. Seedlings develop during summer into large clumps of broad, downy leaves by fall. The large leaves help insulate the growing point during the winter months.

Following 3 to 4 months of winter chilling, foxglove plants come into flower in response to lengthening days and warming temperatures.

If the flower stalk is removed at the end of flowering, the plants often produce side shoots and survive from year to year as perennials. If seed stalks are not removed, the seeds must be planted each year to have flowering plants the following season.

Planting seeds too late in the first growing season and severe damage during the winter will prevent foxglove from flowering the following year.

The variety and type of seasonal display vary with each kind of plant species. Winged spindle-shrub (*Euonymus alata*), a deciduous shrub, turns crimson almost overnight in New England gardens. Shortening days signal the plant to change its foliage to crimson, but cool temperatures also signal a darker crimson color, and adequate moisture keeps the brilliant leaves on longer.

In a Maryland garden, bluebeard (*Caryopteris incana*), another deciduous shrub, always opens its blossoms precisely in mid-August, but the shade of blue of the blossom is temperature influenced. If August is hot, the flowers will be light blue. They will be dark blue if August is cool.

The environment exerts its effects by altering the metabolism of plants. Although the major constituents of carbohydrates, fats, and proteins may be

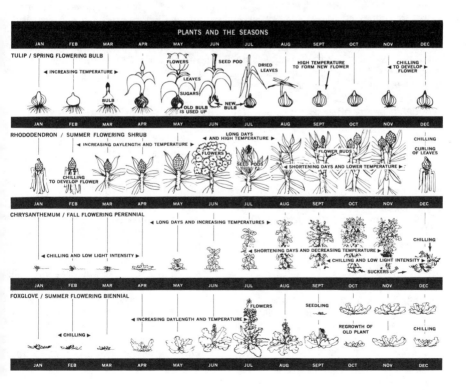

altered, their changes are thought to be the result of the triggering actions of plant growth regulators. These regulators are the organic compounds, other than nutrients, which in small amounts promote, inhibit, or otherwise modify any physiological process in plants.

The first discovered growth regulator, called auxin, was isolated from the tip of oat seedlings in 1928. The active agent, 3-indoleacetic acid (IAA), stimulated cell elongation just as it did when in the living tip. The first 25 years of growth regulator research were dominated by the auxins and auxin-like chemicals.

In the 1950's and 1960's many other naturally occurring growth regulators were detected, identified, and synthesized for reapplication to plants.

We now know that many chemicals are simultaneously interrelating, and trigger the plant responses. We also have become aware that many synthetic chemicals can block, enhance, or otherwise alter the priming action of the naturally occurring growth regulators.

Four types of natural growth regulators are believed present in all green plants at varying levels throughout the plant's life. These are auxins, gibberellins, abscisic acid, and cytokinins. Each type of regulator occurs in more than one chemical structure, each with varying degrees of activity. There are undoubtedly many other as yet undetected growth regulating substances. All constituents are present in every cell, constantly interacting, to regulate plant growth.

Auxins and auxin-like compounds promote elongation, stimulate rooting of cuttings and tissue growth, and induce the development of fruit without fertilization.

Gibberellins stimulate many developmental processes. They can reverse the dwarfing of plants, end dormancy in various plant organs, induce flowering of plants requiring long days, and promote plant development usually regarded as responses to daylength and chilling.

Abscisic acid stimulates the flowering of several short-day plants and in-

hibits flowering of some long-day plants. It also induces the cessation of growth of long-day plants.

Cytokinins are necessary for cell growth and differentiation. They also inhibit the degreening of leaves, and stimulate leaf enlargement, stem elongation, and bud formation.

Man has learned to make synthetically, or to produce large amounts of, the naturally occurring regulators as pure chemicals for reapplication to plants. Although many experimental uses have been found for pure chemicals, few wide-scale uses have been developed. This is due, in part, to the difficulties of timing the application and determining the dosage for optimum plant responses.

Three types of synthetic chemical growth regulators have been found which are widely used to regulate seasonal changes in the plant.

Growth inhibitors are found in plants at all stages of growth. The most common naturally occurring ones are aromatic organic compounds. Synthetic chemical inhibitors have also been found which suppress growth of leaf, stem, root, and flower. These chemicals permanently alter growth and persist throughout the life of the plant.

Growth retardants, eight families of chemicals, permit the scaling of many plants to any size. Treated plants are more compact, with dark green foliage. The growth of woody plants also slows and flower buds are formed. Many other characteristics of the plant are altered: Drought and salt resistance are increased, water loss decreased, sensitivity to air pollution decreased, number and rate of development of roots on cuttings enhanced, and storage problems of harvested fruit and plants reduced.

Ethylene is a unique chemical in that it can imitate the action of almost all the other types of regulators. It causes leaf drop, the rapid aging of many plant parts, and the immediate initiation of flowers on vegetative plants of the pineapple and morning-glory families.

The season of flowering of tulips, rhododendrons, chrysanthemums, and foxglove may be shifted by manipulating the environment and (except for tulips) by the use of chemical growth regulators.

Tulips may be dug and immediately stored dry at 31° F. for up to 6 months. The bulbs are then exposed to temperatures of 75° to 80° F. for several weeks to permit the bulb to form flowers. The bulbs are chilled at 40° for 12 weeks and then returned to a growing area for flowering 6 to 8 weeks later.

Since the bulb completely seals over the growing point, applications of the chemical growth regulators to tulips have been unsuccessful.

All aspects of the growth of rhododendron may be controlled with growth regulators. One may use auxins to promote rooting of the cuttings. Abscisic acid may be applied at frequent intervals to induce dormancy of plants growing on long days. Growth retardants slow the growth of plants and promote early initiation of flower buds.

Gibberellins, applied as a drop in a wound at the base of a rhododendron's flower bud, cause the immediate development of non-chilled flower buds. Cytokinins prolong the life of the green leaves. Ethylene promotes yellowing and early aging of leaves.

Chrysanthemum plants, in contrast, flower only in response to proper manipulation of daylength and temperature. Chemicals may modify their responses but, thus far, have never overcome the environmental control for flowering. Chemicals, however, can be used to promote rooting, regulate stem elongation, flower color, branching, and aging.

On foxglove, gibberellins properly used will promote flowering and growth retardants will increase resistance to frost.

As we learn more on how the seasons regulate growth, plants will more easily be lifted out of seasonal control and become man regulated. Such manipulation will require that the horticulturist identify the most responsive varieties of a plant to use.

Horticulturists must then mesh together light, temperature, atmosphere, and mineral nutrition to signal and set the patterns of growth.

Finally, the horticulturist will apply chemical growth regulators to modify growth for desired qualities of flowering, size, shape, stress, and aging.

Plants and their seasonal identities will ultimately give way to programmed, tailored plants with maximum utility, appearance, and persistence.

making the most of soil and water; sound practices for the garden

A GOOD SOIL is one that encourages good plant root and top growth by providing the right amount of nutrients, water, and air throughout the growing season. You may not have this kind of soil around your home, but with some knowledge and effort you can develop it.

The average homeowner has little control over the quality of the soil on which his house is built. The soil around your home may be very different from the soil of the general area. Extensive grading or filling may have removed or buried the fertile topsoil. Also, the heavy construction equipment may have compacted the soil so that water infiltration and movement in the soil is restricted.

Thus, poor soil conditions may be limiting plant growth in your garden or lawn.

What is soil? In simple terms, it is the thin covering of a mixture of weathered rock and organic matter on the earth's surface that supports all land plants. It is continually changing.

Mechanical disintegration of rock is brought about by frost action, plant roots, temperature changes, and erosion. Water, oxygen, and carbon dioxide produce chemical changes. The soil is alive with untold millions of microorganisms which decompose organic residues and convert them into humus.

When the remains of plants and animals are deposited under water, organic soils called peats and mucks are formed.

Chemical and physical properties of the entire soil profile must be considered in assessing the potential use of soils. This is extremely important in plantings around a home or in a small garden because the normal profile may have been destroyed by construction.

Roots of many plants grow several feet into the soil. If rock, cement, or other construction debris have been buried, they may interfere with normal root development. If these materials are abundant, they should be removed. Also, compacted subsoil should be loosened to permit water movement.

A soil contains different sizes of particles. The particles are classified as sand, silt, or clay—clay being the smallest and sand the largest. Soil texture is determined by the relative amounts of the sand, silt, and clay fractions.

A loamy soil is an ideal balance of these. It is a mixture containing from 7 to 27 percent clay, 28 to 50 percent silt, and less than 52 percent sand. As the composition changes we may move into a silt loam, clay loam, or sandy loam, all of which are good garden soils.

Author W. E. LARSON is a Soil Scientist in the Corn Belt Branch, Soil and Water Conservation Research Division, Agricultural Research Service (ARS), St. Paul, Minn.

Coauthor H. L. BARROWS is Chief of the Northeast Branch, Soil and Water Conservation Research Division, ARS, at Beltsville, Md.

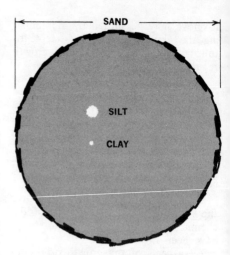

RELATIVE SIZES OF SAND, SILT, AND CLAY FRACTIONS.

The key to good soil texture rests in the word "balance". If there is too much clay, the size and connections among the pores are insufficient for adequate water movement and aeration. With too much sand, the soil loses the ability to store adequate water and nutrients.

Although a laboratory analysis is required to determine accurately the textural class, the homeowner can estimate the texture by feeling the moist soil. A soil with considerable sand feels gritty. A moist clay soil has a smooth plastic feel and will hold its shape. Intermediate mixtures of sand, silt, and clay will be less gritty or less plastic.

On small areas where soil conditions are not desirable they can be changed by adding sand, clay, or synthetic materials. For flowerbeds it may be desirable to remove the existing soil and replace it with a mixture of two parts loam, one part sand or perlite, and one part peat.

Structure of a soil is directly related to its texture. Moist soil materials will bond together to form porous aggregates. A desirable structure is one that contains aggregates of about one-eighth to one-fourth inch. The larger pores between aggregates provide for the drainage of excess water, while the many fine pores within the aggregates retain water for plant use.

A good structured soil will contain about 50 percent solid material, 25 percent water, and 25 percent air by volume. Most plants will not grow in very compacted soils.

Roots may not be able to penetrate the compacted zone, and because of the reduced air volume, those that do enter may not survive. Plant roots give off carbon dioxide and absorb oxygen during respiration. Either too little oxygen or too much carbon dioxide in the soil can slow or kill plant growth. Since oxygen moves into the soil and carbon dioxide moves out by diffusion, the rate of diffusion is critical and is reduced in compacted zones.

Clay and organic matter are the two most common soil constituents that bind particles. Too much clay favors large, hard clods when dry; too little clay results in a single-grained structure that cannot retain adequate amounts of nutrients and water. The clay content cannot be changed easily, but the homeowner may improve the soil structure by adding organic matter.

Presence of organic matter in a soil is the essential difference between a productive surface soil and a mass of rock fragments.

A good garden soil contains 4 to 5 percent of organic matter which is intimately associated with the mineral particles. To maintain this, fresh organic materials—either plant residues or manure—must be added to the soil periodically. The added organic material not only serves as an energy source for soil micro-organisms and soil fauna (such as earthworms) but also furnishes nutrients that become available to plants as the organic material decays.

Soluble nutrients added to a soil would leach or wash below the root zone if there were not some mechanism for retaining them. Fortunately,

A cloddy soil (left) can be improved by additions of organic matter and careful tillage (right).

both organic matter and clay retain most nutrients and release them to the plant roots as needed. This process is called cation exchange.

Since clay particles are negatively charged, they attract and hold positively charged ions (cations) such as calcium, magnesium, potassium, and ammonium. As these cations are removed from clay by plant roots, they are exchanged with hydrogen.

If most of the exchange sites are occupied by hydrogen, the soil is acid or sour. On the other hand, when most of the sites are occupied by bases (calcium, magnesium, potassium, or sodium) the soil will be neutral or basic. Generally speaking, soils in the Eastern United States must be amended periodically with lime to bring the pH (the measure of acidity) up to the neutral range.

Many plants can grow in the range

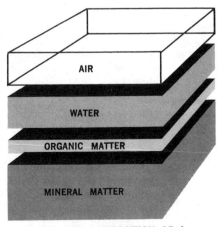

RELATIVE COMPOSITION OF A
SOIL WITH GOOD STRUCTURE

AIR

WATER

ORGANIC MATTER

MINERAL MATTER

pH 4 (highly acidic) to pH 9 (highly alkaline), but most plants grow best when the pH is between 6.0 to 7.5. Soil pH can be tested easily with test kits or indicator solutions. The pH can be raised by adding lime, and lowered by adding either elemental sulfur, iron sulfate, or aluminum sulfate.

Earlier in this chapter we referred to the water-holding capacity of soils. All soil water is not available to plant roots. During a soaking rain or irrigation, water moves into the soil pores by gravity and capillary attraction. By the end of the day following the rain, water has drained from the larger pores. The soil is then at field capacity.

When plants have removed water until they permanently wilt, the soil is said to be at the wilting point. The amount of water in the soil between field capacity and the wilting point is the available water holding capacity.

The soil structure, texture, and organic matter content determine the available water holding capacity of a soil. Sandy soils hold the least total water, and clays hold the most. However, the intermediate textures (loams) retain the most available water. Most garden soils can store from 1 to 2 inches of available soil water per foot of depth.

Gardens and lawns, when actively growing, usually require about 1 inch of water per week. If rainfall does not furnish this, supplemental watering is needed. Watering should be started when about a third to half of the available water has been removed by plants, and should be continued until the soil in the root zone is thoroughly wet. One good soaking per week is much better than more frequent light sprinkles.

Most lawn and garden sprinklers apply about a quarter of an inch per hour. This can easily be checked. Place one or more tin cans or other containers with straight sides in the area to be sprinkled and measure the amount collected.

Drainage of excess water from the root zone is just as important for gardens and lawns as is too little water. Inadequate drainage occurs in clay soils, soils with compacted subsoils, and soils with other impeding layers.

Where necessary, drainage may be increased by sloping the surface toward a drainageway, by providing furrows, by tiling, by deep loosening, or by a combination of these.

Soil will often settle around a house so that excess water will flow toward the foundation. If so, the area should be filled so that the slope is away from the house.

Furrows to prevent excess surface water from running onto a garden or lawn or to lead excess water off are often helpful.

If subsoils have been compacted during construction, loosening of the soil to several feet is desirable. For special plantings in high clay soils, it is best to replace the subsoil with a sandy or loamy soil.

A hole much larger than the initial root system should be made when planting shrubs or trees.

Some plantings are extremely sensitive to excess water during establishment. On larger areas, tiling may be desirable. Usually the design of a tile system requires technical assistance. For help contact your county agricultural extension office, soil conservation office, or a drainage contractor.

Although the practice of no-tillage on farms is becoming more prevalent, some tilling of the home garden is desirable. This is usually done in late fall or early spring with a motorized tiller or by spading. Tilling incorporates organic residues into the soil, loosens up compacted areas, and provides the home gardener with the nostalgic odor of freshly turned earth.

The desirable depth of tillage varies. Soils high in organic matter and with good structure need only shallow tilling, perhaps only enough to cover the plant residues. Soils that have infertile subsoils and compacted layers should be tilled as deep as practical while incorporating ample amounts of plant residues, manure, and fertilizer. This insures a deep root zone for storage of water and nutrients, and it will probably pay in reduced costs of watering.

Above, organic matter may be incorporated and a seedbed prepared by rototilling. Left, a hand rake is a good tool for final seedbed preparation.

When establishing a new lawn or garden, the soil should be tested for lime and fertilizer needs. On soils needing lime and phosphate, ample quantities should be worked in as deep as practical. Working ample phosphate into the soil will meet the needs of plants for several years and will insure that the phosphate does not enrich run-off waters.

Moisture content of the soil at tillage is critical, particularly on soils with relatively large amounts of clay. Tilling a clay loam or finer textured soil when too wet or too dry often results in large clods.

At an intermediate water content the soil can usually be broken without destroying the natural aggregate structure. The proper moisture content can be determined very easily. Dig up a handful of the soil. Squeeze it. If it crumbles, the moisture is right for tillage. If it remains in a tight ball, it is too wet.

Fall tillage is usually desirable in areas where the soil freezes. Exposure of the clods to freezing and thawing helps to promote natural granulation. By leaving the surface rough, water can enter more freely and the soil will warm more quickly in the spring.

231

Where wind and water erosion is a hazard, soils should not be fall-tilled unless the surface is protected with a cover crop or mulch.

Tilling for weed control should always be shallow. Deep tillage, especially close to the rows, damages plant roots. On many soils a shallow tillage to break soil crusts may be desirable even if weeds are not present. Breaking the crust will enhance water intake.

In this short discussion we have not gone into all of the soil and water problems facing the home gardener. We have mentioned those that probably have the greatest influence on the success or failure of the garden.

Fertilizers and mulches are also very important but are covered in the next two chapters.

For specific information about managing garden and lawn soils in your locality, contact your local county extension office, Soil Conservation Service office, State university, or a local garden or landscape dealer.

 # supplementing plant nutrients with fertilizer and lime

A SUCCESSFUL GARDENER who grows beautiful flowers, lovely lawns, and luscious vegetables has a fertile soil. If the soil is not naturally fertile, a successful gardener will make it fertile.

What is a fertile soil? It is one that provides a balanced supply of nitrogen, phosphorus, potassium, calcium, magnesium, sulfur, and a host of micronutrients for optimum plant growth.

Supplementing the soil's supply of available plant nutrients to meet plant needs through the judicious and wise use of fertilizer materials and lime is a major part of being a successful gardener. Of course, a soil's physical properties and soil water, as discussed in the previous chapter, must be considered if full value from fertilizer and lime is to be achieved.

Scientists concerned with plants' growth have established that at least 17 of the earth's elements are essential for growth and reproduction of plants. These are carbon, oxygen, hydrogen, nitrogen, phosphorus, potassium, calcium, magnesium, sulfur, iron, manganese, copper, zinc, boron, molybdenum, chlorine, and cobalt.

Plants take carbon and oxygen from the air, hydrogen from soil water, and the other 14 elements from soil.

Nitrogen, phosphorus, and potassium are known as the primary plant nutrients because over the years farmers and gardeners have found them to be present in soils in the lowest quantities relative to plant needs.

Thus the custom was established that a fertilizer which contained all three of these nutrients was and is called a complete fertilizer. A fertilizer bag labeled 10–10–10 contains 10 percent nitrogen, 10 percent available phosphoric acid, and 10 percent potash.

Calcium, magnesium, and sulfur have become known as the secondary plant nutrients, not because of secondary importance, but because the need to add them to soils is generally less than for the primary nutrients. Iron, manganese, etc., are known as trace elements or micronutrients because they are required by plants in very, very small quantities.

When soil scientists speak of plant nutrients in soil, they use the expression "available plant nutrients." For example, the soil in an azalea garden may

Author R. STANLEY DYAL is Assistant to Director, Soil and Water Conservation Research Division, Agricultural Research Service.

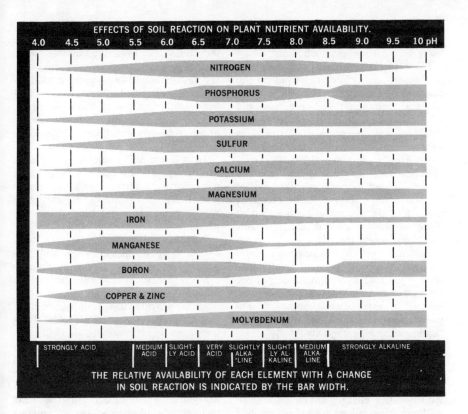

EFFECTS OF SOIL REACTION ON PLANT NUTRIENT AVAILABILITY.

| 4.0 | 4.5 | 5.0 | 5.5 | 6.0 | 6.5 | 7.0 | 7.5 | 8.0 | 8.5 | 9.0 | 9.5 | 10 pH |

NITROGEN
PHOSPHORUS
POTASSIUM
SULFUR
CALCIUM
MAGNESIUM
IRON
MANGANESE
BORON
COPPER & ZINC
MOLYBDENUM

| STRONGLY ACID | MEDIUM ACID | SLIGHT-LY ACID | VERY ACID | SLIGHTLY ALKA-·LINE | SLIGHT-LY AL-KALINE | MEDIUM ALKA-LINE | STRONGLY ALKALINE |

THE RELATIVE AVAILABILITY OF EACH ELEMENT WITH A CHANGE IN SOIL REACTION IS INDICATED BY THE BAR WIDTH.

contain many thousands of pounds of iron, yet the iron is not in a form that azalea roots can absorb. Thus, the iron is not available for use by the azaleas.

The soil property that most affects nutrient availability is soil reaction, that is, whether the soil is acid or alkaline. Acidity or alkalinity of every water solution or mixture of soil and water is determined by its content of hydrogen ions or hydroxyl ions. Water molecules break up, or in chemical language, ionize into two parts—hydrogen ions and hydroxyl ions. A solution with more hydrogen ions than hydroxyl ions is said to be acid. When there are more hydroxyl ions than hydrogen ions, the solution is alkaline.

Scientists use the term pH to express the concentration of hydrogen and hydroxyl ions in solution. A pH of 7 means the hydrogen and hydroxyl ions are equal and the solution is said to be neutral. A pH below 7 means the solution contains more hydrogen ions than

hydroxyl ions, and is said to be acid. Similarly, a pH above 7 means the solution contains more hydroxyl ions and is alkaline.

Whether the soil solution is acid or alkaline in reaction greatly influences nutrient availability to plant roots. The relationship between soil reaction and nutrient availability for 11 of the essential elements is shown in the graph.

Soil acidity, as such, is seldom toxic to plants. But in soils with pH values below 5.5 certain elements, such as aluminum or manganese, often become soluble to levels toxic to plant growth.

Many subsoils in the Southeast are below pH 5.5 and thus restrict or prevent root growth. Such a restriction reduces the volume of soil from which plant roots may absorb nutrients and water. These soils are usually low in subsoil phosphorus reserves as well.

Since calcium and magnesium, as well as phosphorus, tend to remain in soil areas where placed, gardeners should work limestone and phosphatic fertilizers deeply into such soils before lawn and garden establishment.

Plant species differ in their response to the soil acidity. For most plants, the conditions of nutrient availability, without toxic amounts, are best near pH 6.5. But certain plants—such as rhododendron, azaleas, pines, and camellias—grow best in soils of about pH 5.5. They are "acid-loving plants."

Sulfur and agricultural lime are the materials used most frequently to alter the soil reaction or pH. Lime increases the pH or decreases the acidity. Sulfur is converted to sulfuric acid in soils and then lowers the pH.

Another extremely important soil property affecting nutrient availability is the soil's ability to hold and store up nutrients until they are needed by plants. A part of this ability is expressed by soil scientists in terms of "cation exchange capacity."

When fertilizer salts are dissolved in water they break up or ionize into two electrically charged parts. Ions with positive charges are called cations; those with negative charges are called anions.

When ammonium nitrate is applied to a soil, it ionizes, yielding positively charged ammonium ions (cations) and negatively charged nitrate ions (anions).

Many of the ammonium ions will be held (adsorbed) on the soil particle surfaces.

When lime is added to acid soil, the calcium in the lime replaces or exchanges with the hydrogen adsorbed on the soil particles. This process of interchange of cations is known as cation exchange.

The cation exchange capacity of sandy soils is low, while that of clay soils is high. Thus, sandy soils are not as fertile as clay soils. Because of this soil property, the cationic plant nutrients—calcium, magnesium, potassium, and ammonia—are held in a form available for plant root absorption yet less subject to losses by leaching than are the anions.

Nitrate, chloride, sulfates, and phosphates are the most prevalent nutrient anions in soils.

Even though phosphates occur as anions, they are held in soils because they may be fixed by soluble iron, aluminum, and manganese ions that are usually found in strongly acid mineral soils. Phosphates may also be fixed by insoluble oxides of these elements.

Under moderately acid conditions, phosphates may react with the soluble clay minerals.

In alkaline soils, soluble phosphates are precipitated by calcium ions. Thus, phosphorus fertilizers tend to remain near the point of application except in sandy soils where leaching may take place.

Nitrate, chloride, and sulfate tend to move up or down in the soil, depending on the direction of water movement. Thus, these nutrients may move out of the plant rooting zone.

In improving soil fertility, organic matter plays several vital roles. It is important in determining the soil's cation exchange capacity which tends to regulate the soil's acidity, within limits, when acids or alkalies are applied to the soil. On decomposition, it releases plant nutrients. As discussed in the next chapter, the addition of organic matter to soils improves soil structure and water-holding capacity.

The gardener is faced with two fertilizer problems: (1) where to get the needed plant nutrients, and (2) determining how much is needed and how to fertilize.

Man has long sought to conserve animal manures and other organic materials, largely for their nitrogen content. Today, these sources are still used, but now fertilizer technology through industrial nitrogen-fixation processes provides more than 90 percent of the fertilizer nitrogen. By far the most important process is the combination of nitrogen gas with hydrogen to form ammonia. The ammonia may be used as a fertilizer material or converted into a number of fertilizer materials as listed in the table at the top of page 235 under "Chemical."

When properly manufactured and applied, the different chemical nitrogen sources are equally effective. Urea, when

Common Sources of Fertilizer Nitrogen for Gardens

Name	Grade	Nitrogen
Chemical		*Percent*
Ammonium nitrate...33–0–0		33.5
Ammonium sulfate...21–0–0		21
Sodium nitrate.......16–0–0		16
Urea 45–0–0		45
Urea formaldehyde...46–0–0		46
Organic		
Dried blood.........11–0–0		13.3
Castor pomace...... 5–2–1		5.5
Cottonseed meal..... 6–3–0		7.0
Dried manure....... varies		varies
Activated sewage sludge 6–3–0		varies

applied to the soil surface or on plants, may break down into ammonium carbonate and lose ammonia to the atmosphere. This reaction is speeded up by the enzyme urease found in most soils and plants. However, these nitrogen losses can be prevented by incorporating the urea into the soil. The use of the nitrogen fertilizers, especially ammonium sulfate, leads to increased soil acidity. The careful gardener in humid regions periodically checks the need for lime.

Urea formaldehyde (unlike the other chemical fertilizers), and the organic sources of nitrogen listed in the first table, will not burn plants. These materials are slow-release nitrogen carriers in that the nitrogen is released by microbiological action. Other slow-release nitrogen sources are floranid, magnesium ammonium phosphate, and conventional fertilizers coated with waxes, acrylic resins, or elemental sulfur. Costs are higher but the gardener may find the slow-release property worth the extra cost.

Some people contend that the nutritional quality of foods produced with organic fertilizers is superior to that of foods produced with chemical fertilizers. However, this contention has never been substantiated.

Plants have been grown for generation after generation in nutrient solutions to which only inorganic chemicals have been added, thus demonstrating that plants, unlike animals, have the capacity to synthesize all organic compounds required for their growth.

For the most part, the nutrients essential for a plant's growth enter the plant in the inorganic form. This means that the nitrogen in the organic matter in the soil or organic materials added to soils, such as animal manure or compost, must be decomposed by the soil organisms before the nutrients are available to plants. The source of plant nutrients, whether from chemical fertilizers or natural materials, makes no difference to plants.

A number of important materials are available for phosphorus fertilizer use by the gardener as listed in the table that appears below.

Rock phosphate, after fine grinding, may be applied as a fertilizer. However, because its solubility is exceedingly low in most soils, its effectiveness in improving plant growth may be nil. On highly acid soils it is more soluble, and thus its phophorus is more available.

Reaction of ground rock phosphate with sulfuric acid converts the rock phosphate into normal superphosphate. The production of normal superphosphate by this means started in England in the 1840's and was the beginning

Common Sources of Phosphate for Gardens

Material	Grade	Available phosphoric acid
		Percent
Rock phosphate	—	
Normal superphosphate .	0–20–0	20
Triple superphosphate .	0–45–0	45
Ammonium phosphate	variable [1]	14 – 53
Steamed bonemeal	2–27–0 [2]	18 – 34

[1] 11–48–0, 13–29–0, 16–20–0, 21–53–0, and 27–14–0.

[2] Averaged values from State fertilizer control officials.

Material	Grade	Potash
		Percent
Muriate of potash..0–0–60		60 – 63
Sulfate of potash...0–0–50		50 – 53
Sulfate of potash-		
magnesia 0–0–22		22 – 23
Nitrate of potash...13–0–44		44 – 46

of today's commercial fertilizer industry. Triple superphosphate is manufactured by treating rock phosphate with phosphoric acid. Its effectiveness as a phosphorus source is equal to that of normal superphosphate, and, because of its higher phosphate content, handling costs are less.

Ammonium phosphates are used principally in the West South-Central, Mountain, and Pacific States.

The plentiful natural deposits of potassium chloride (muriate of potash) require only mining and purification to produce a low-cost, high-analysis, and highly available plant nutrient. Though there has been little need or incentive to develop other potassium fertilizer materials, those listed in the table at the top of this page are available.

The term "soil amendment" is used in the fertilizer trade to refer to material such as lime, sulfur, or gypsum that are used to alter some physical and chemical soil properties. In addition they may supply certain of the plant nutrients—calcium, magnesium, and sulfur.

Calcium and magnesium are usually applied as lime. Agriculturally, "lime" refers to any calcium-bearing material capable of reducing soil acidity, such as ground limestone, quicklime, hydrated lime, chalk, marl, and seashells. Ground limestone is generally preferred to quicklime or hydrated lime because it costs less and requires less care in handling and applying.

The best material is finely ground dolomitic limestone. It contains magnesium and calcium carbonate. Many soils needing lime, particularly on the eastern seaboard, are likely to be deficient in both magnesium and calcium.

Furthermore, the danger of overliming is greatly reduced by using dolomitic limestone because this reacts relatively slowly in soils.

Sulfur additions in rain and snowfall range from about 2 pounds in certain rural areas to over 100 pounds per acre near industrial centers. Also, much sulfur is applied as sulfate in such fertilizers as superphosphate and ammonium sulfate. However, the use of high-analysis fertilizers which contain little or no sulfur and the transition to sulfur-free fuels for heating and to generate electrical power have resulted in increased sulfur deficiency of crops in recent years.

Soil amendments used to supply sulfur are elemental sulfur and gypsum.

The micronutrient fertilizers of copper, zinc, manganese, and iron are usually applied as the sulfate; boron as borax; and molybdenum as sodium molybdate. Iron and sometimes zinc may be applied as a chelate.

The gardener wishing to select the proper and most economical fertilizer must select from a wide choice of fertilizers. They may be purchased and applied to the soil as separate materials. This may result in savings in fertilizer costs, particularly where the gardener uses animal manures that need to be supplemented with phosphorus and potassium for a balanced plant nutrient supply. Separate materials may be advantageous for side dressing vegetables, particularly sweet corn, and for top dressing lawns.

The three primary nutrients—nitrogen, phosphorus, and potassium—tend to balance, support, and to supplement not only each other but the other plant nutrients as well. Mixed fertilizers, manufactured by combining fertilizer materials to furnish the desired fertilizer nutrient ratio, provide this balance. Furthermore, the three fertilizer nutrients may be added in one application.

Pulverized fertilizer, though usually lowest in price, often is dusty, may become damp and cake, and may "burn" plant leaves, especially if not promptly washed off the leaves. Granular mixed fertilizers are produced by agglomeration of the ingredients in a moist state followed by heat drying and screening during manufacture. Their improved physical condition, resistance to caking, reduction in segregation of ingredients, relative lack of dust, and reduction in danger of leaf burn are usually worth the additional cost.

Handling costs per ton are about the same for all fertilizer grades. Therefore, unit costs for plant nutrients—especially in mixed fertilizers—are lower for the higher grades.

An important point to remember is the fertilizer grade ratio. A 5–10–5 fertilizer grade has a ratio of 1–2–1 as does a 10–20–10. From the standpoint of economy, the 10–20–10 furnishes more nutrients per dollar. To prevent overfertilization, however, greater care must be exercised in applying the 10–20–10 since it contains twice the fertilizer nutrients of the 5–10–5.

Specialty fertilizers are available for growing ornamental plants, lawns, and house plants. Costs per unit of plant nutrient of such fertilizers are usually higher than farm fertilizers. The added costs may not be of as much concern for the gardener as they are for the farmer who uses fertilizers that are the most economical for his particular situation.

A pulverized farm fertilizer made with soluble nitrogen sources may be used on a lawn, but it should not be applied when the grass is damp and must be washed off the grass to prevent leaf burn. Additional fertilizer applications may be needed during the season.

A specialty fertilizer formulated for use on turf usually contains nonburning, slow-release nitrogen sources. One application should last the season. Specialty fertilizers are formulated to meet plant needs completely, while the ideal fertilizer should meet plant needs by supplementing the soil's supply of available plant nutrients.

States have passed laws, rules, and regulations requiring that the guaranteed chemical content of the fertilizer be clearly labeled on the bag, on a tag attached to the bag, or, for bulk fertilizer, on the invoice. The grade of a complete fertilizer must be prominently labeled in the form of three hyphenated numbers, such as 10–6–4. These values refer to the percentages of nitrogen (N), available phosphoric acid (P_2O_5), and water-soluble potash (K_2O) in the fertilizer.

In addition, the net weight; name, brand, or trademark; potential acidity in terms of pounds of calcium carbonate per ton; and name and address of manufacturer must be printed on the bag, on a tag, or on the invoice in case of bulk blends.

Plants display symptoms characteristic of nutrient deficiencies. These sometimes are called "hunger signs." Plants may be stunted without displaying any symptoms—often called "hidden hunger"—which on casual observation may detract only slightly from the plant's utility. Those wishing information on nutrient deficiency symptoms should see the books by Wallace and Sprague that are listed at the end of this chapter.

Although plant symptoms are a useful guide to the need for nutrients, they must be interpreted carefully. Furthermore, by the time nutrient deficiency symptoms are clearly evident, much damage has been done. The trick is to determine nutrient needs before plant injury.

Through continuous experimentation and observation. State and Federal agricultural research agencies know which soils are likely to be deficient in one or more plant nutrients. This information is the basis on which fertilizer recommendations for ornamental plants are made by the cooperative extension service of the various State agricultural experiment stations.

The cooperative extension services maintain county offices—they may be listed in the telephone directory under Cooperative Extension Service, Extension Service, the name of the county agricultural agent, or the name of the county farm advisor—usually at the county seat. The extension service prefers to make fertilizer recommendations based on soil tests.

Rapid soil tests made routinely by 48 State agricultural stations, and by

How a soil test is made. Left, soil samples are put in containers and forms filled out by a home gardener or project grounds-keeper. Below, at soil testing lab, samples are crushed and sieved. Lower left, portion of sample is placed in container, then mixed with solution to extract plant nutrients. Bottom, mixture is filtered.

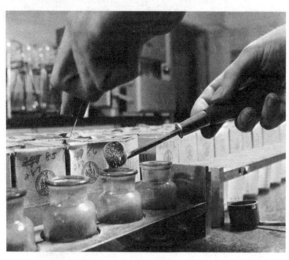

Above, soil extract ready for chemical testing. Many labs, such as University of Maryland lab shown in this photo story, use automated equipment to test for several plant nutrients simultaneously. Below left, soil pH is determined electronically. Below right, interpreting soil test results and making proper lime and fertilizer recommendations is a job for a qualified scientist.

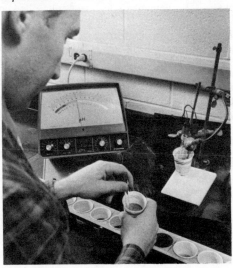

commercial laboratories and many fertilizer companies, are most helpful in determining fertilizer requirements. But these tests are valuable guides only if (1) the sample is representative of the garden soil, and (2) if other factors which influence nutrient availability—such as soil physical conditions, water, and the plant nutrient requirements—are considered.

The county agent's office or the commercial agency should be contacted before samples are selected as they will have sampling instructions and usually a container for shipping.

Several States and private companies are offering plant analysis as a means of finding out what's wrong with abnormal plants and as a check on how well a fertility program is working. But plant analysis is not expected to replace soil testing.

Soil test data are valuable as a guide only when properly interpreted by a technically trained, experienced person. State agricultural experiment stations have conducted many studies to correlate soil test data with crop response in the field. They have also observed the results of farm and garden fertilization as a guide to future fertilizer recommendations. And they know the nutrient requirements of many different plants. Individuals should keep these facts in mind when considering purchase of a commercial soil-testing kit.

Fertilizer and lime recommendations are generally in the form of so many pounds for a specific area. The gardener must then decide which fertilizer or liming material to use.

Plant characteristics and the climatic region determine the proper time to apply fertilizers. As an example, in the Washington (D. C.) area, the bulk of the fertilizer should be applied to cool-season grasses in the early fall, with smaller amounts as needed during the spring. Warm-season grasses should be fertilized in late spring or summer.

By contrast, in North Dakota one application of fertilizer in the spring is recommended. Late summer or early fall fertilization, especially with nitrogen fertilizers, must be carefully timed or avoided so plants will not be growing vigorously and thereby fall prey to fall frost injury or winterkill.

The gardener may apply the selected fertilizer to a flower or vegetable garden in one or more ways. Sometimes, combinations of these methods are used.

Thus, fertilizer may be: (1) applied to a green manure or cover crop grown before the garden is planted, (2) spread upon the surface and plowed or spaded into the soil, (3) spread upon the soil after plowing or spading, (4) placed in bands 2 to 3 inches away from the seed row and at least 2 inches below the surface at time of planting, (5) used as starter solutions when transplanting, (6) put on the soil surface as a top dressing after plants are established, (7) applied in a solution or in the irrigation water, or (8) used as a spray on plant leaves.

Spreading the fertilizer and plowing in is most convenient. However, increased weed growth and increased soil fixation of phosphorus usually follow. Band fertilizer placement, more difficult for the gardener without suitable machinery, may be more expedient because of reduced weeding.

The preferred method of fertilizing shade trees is to put the fertilizer in holes at regular intervals within the outer half of the branch-spread zone. These holes should extend well into the upper subsoil.

Movement of fertilizer salts plays an important role in determining where to place the fertilizer. Soluble chemical nitrogen fertilizers readily move into the soil and then move up or down depending upon the direction of water movement. After biological action the nitrogen in nitrogenous organic fertilizers is changed to soluble chemical forms that move in the same pattern.

Phosphorus fertilizers and lime tend to remain in place. Potassium tends to move up or down in the soil but at a slower rate than nitrogen.

To reduce seedling injury by nitrogen and potassium fertilizers and to reduce soil phosphorus fixation when you plant in rows, it is well to place the fertilizer in bands beside the seed row.

240

As each gardener adds to the beauty of the place where he lives and works by improving the soil fertility through proper and wise use of fertilizers, he adds immeasurably to the improvement of the Nation's environmental quality.

By providing plant nutrients essential to grow vegetative cover for erosion control in both urban and rural areas, fertilizers reduce pollution of the Nation's surface waters by sediment. This is particularly true of areas disturbed during construction of highways, roads, buildings, and homes.

However, the gardener should be careful when spreading fertilizer to keep it off any area from which it may be easily transported in runoff to storm sewers and thence to streams and thereby increase the rate of nutrient enrichment (called eutrophication) of surface waters.

For further reading:

Chapman, H. D. (ed.), *Diagnostic Criteria for Plants and Soils.* University of California, Berkeley, 1966.

Childers, N. F. (ed.), *Nutrition of Fruit Crops—Tropical, Sub-Tropical, Temperate Tree and Small Fruit.* Horticultural Publications, Rutgers—The State University, New Brunswick, N. J., 1966.

McVickar, M. H., and others (ed.), *Fertilizer Technology and Usage.* Soil Science Society of America, Madison, Wis., 1963.

Nelson, Lewis B., "Advances in Fertilizers," *Advances in Agronomy,* A. G. Norman, (ed.), Vol. 17, Academic Press Inc., New York, 1965.

Sauchelli, V. (ed.), *Technology of Fertilizers.* ACS Monograph No. 148, Reinhold Publishing Corp., New York, 1960.

Sprague, H. B. (ed.), *Hunger Signs in Crops—a Symposium.* David McKay Company, Inc., New York, 1964.

U.S. Department of Agriculture, *Soil, the Yearbook of Agriculture.* Washington, D. C. 20250, 1957.

————, *Selecting Fertilizers for Lawns and Gardens.* Home and Garden Bulletin 89, Washington, D.C. 20250, 1971.

————, *How Much Fertilizer Shall I Use? A Gardener's Guide for Converting Tons or Pounds Per Acre into Pints, Cups, Tablespoons, or Teaspoons per Row or Plant.* Leaflet 307, Washington, D.C. 20250, 1958.

Wallace, T., *Diagnosis of Mineral Deficiencies in Plants by Visual Symptoms.* Chemical Publishing Co., New York, 1953.

 using composts and mulches, keys to good gardening

MOST HOMEOWNERS have little choice in selecting soils for gardens and ornamental plantings. More often than not, the original surface soil has been disturbed or is of poor quality. So you must build a soil to suit the plantings you want.

Composts and mulches are very important in soil building. Compost is the partially decomposed remains of plant materials. Worked into soil, compost loosens the soil for easier penetration of plant roots, water and air, and increases the soil water-holding capacity. Mulches are surface coverings applied to soil to prevent moisture loss, increase water in-take, and moderate soil temperature. Compost may be used as a mulch, but many other materials are also good for this purpose.

Composting of organic refuse for use on home gardens is a time-honored practice, beneficial to the soil, satisfying to the gardener, and helpful in preserving environmental quality. Basically, the process consists of the partial rotting of organic materials, mostly of plant origin, by bacteria, fungi, and other soil organisms.

During composting, the most readily decomposed organic constituents are consumed, leaving a crumbly product

241

that is relatively stable in the soil and which contains many of the mineral elements needed for plant growth.

A proper operating compost pile heats up, by bacterial action, to 120° to 160° F., a temperature sufficiently high to kill most weed seeds and plant or animal disease organisms that may be present. Thus, composting is a clean, safe, and beneficial way to recycle garden wastes.

Many municipalities are turning to composting, not only for leaves, prunings, etc., but even for some parts of city garbage. These commercial composts are becoming generally available to the homeowner, either on a free, help-yourself basis or for a modest price.

Advantages of commercial compost are that the product is quite uniform in composition; it is usually dried, screened, and bagged for convenient use; and its plant nutrient content is fairly well specified. Compost can, however, be easily made by the homeowner willing to spend a small amount of time and effort.

Home production of compost is considered an art by many gardeners, and you will find many different procedures recommended in gardening journals and textbooks. The choice of methods to use or types of compost pile to build is a matter of taste or tradition.

You can compost almost any plant waste material from around the garden, provided it is in small enough pieces to rot in a reasonable time. For those who have compost shredders, larger prunings can be used. Otherwise, brushy stems thicker than a lead pencil should be excluded.

The bulk of a compost will usually be autumn leaves supplemented with dead annual plants, small prunings, and lawn clippings. You can include saw-

dust and small wood chips from the home workhop. And you can safely add fireplace ashes and dust from the vacuum cleaner.

Materials not suitable for composting include rags, bones, paper, plastic, grease, paint, oil, and kitchen garbage. Evergreen prunings, holly leaves, or other spiny plant materials do not break down very rapidly, and may be a nuisance in the handling of the finished compost.

The site for the compost pile should be an out-of-the-way corner of the garden, screened from the view of both owner and neighbors. You can make a satisfactory compost pile without any retaining structure, but some type of box or frame is helpful.

One simple solution is to make a 4- to 5-foot diameter cylinder of heavy wire fencing 3 to 4 feet high in which to build the compost pile. A compost pit is also satisfactory if there is free drainage from the bottom. More elaborate frames can be made from cement blocks, brick or railroad ties. In all cases, the most important point is to have free drainage and aeration at the bottom.

Home compost is usually built up as the plant material becomes available. The result is that the bottom of the pile is composted before the more recent additions have broken down. This means you must fork off the top to remove the finished compost, then replace the part that is not yet ready. This mixing is beneficial, since it aerates the rotting material and helps break it up. In fact, turning the compost once a year is recommended for more uniform and faster composting.

Plant refuse is generally too low in nitrogen to break down rapidly, so some fertilizer should be added. The amount is not critical and cannot be stated exactly because of the unknown composition of the compost material.

A reasonable guide is to add 1 quart measure of 5–10–5 or 1 pint of 10–6–4 mixed fertilizer per square yard of composting material, packed 6 inches deep.

In building the compost, add the

Author J. D. MENZIES is a Research Microbiologist at the U.S. Soils Laboratory, Soil and Water Conservation Research Division, Agricultural Research Service.

Coauthor W. D. KEMPER is a Soil Physicist and Director of the Laboratory.

leaves, clippings, etc., and tramp them down. When a packed layer 6 inches deep has accumulated, spread fertilizer on the top and water the layer thoroughly. Repeat the process for additional layers.

In areas where the soils are acidic, limestone, gypsum, or hydrated lime added at a rate of ½ pint per square yard per 6-inch layer of compost will benefit most plants. However, this material should be omitted if you are going posting when the inside compost is used.

It is probably helpful to poke aeration holes down into the pile occasionally, using a stake or rod. Leaves and lawn clippings should be mixed with coarser plant wastes to prevent formation of wet, compacted layers.

Adding top soil to compost is sometimes recommended as a way of inoculating the compost with bacteria needed for decomposition. This is not

One or more circles of rectangular wire fencing can make containers for composting leaves and garden waste around the home.

to use the compost for acid-loving plants like azaleas and rhododendrons.

Most of the added chemical fertilizer will be converted to organic forms in the composting process, but organic fertilizer can be used at equivalent rates.

Two key conditions for good composting are moisture and aeration. You should keep the compost moist but not soggy. If it gets too wet, it will become anaerobic (without oxygen) because too much water prevents air movement through the pile. Anaerobic compost will not decompose as fast nor heat properly. If too dry, microbial breakdown will stop. Portions of the organic material on the sides and top of the compost pile which have not decomposed may be set aside for further com-

necessary and may actually form layers that restrict aeration and drainage. The plant material itself has abundant microbial inoculation. Special inoculant cultures are not needed.

The composting process will take from 1 to 2 years to complete, depending on the climate, amount of mixing, and other conditions. A compost built in the fall and not turned over during the following year may be sufficiently decomposed in 1 year to use as a mulch for the winter, but will be better for garden use if left until spring.

The finished compost can be spread on the garden area 1 to 2 inches deep and forked in; it can be placed on the soil surface around perennial plantings as a mulch; and it can be used to mix with sand and good garden soil for potting plants. The homeowner who regularly composts his leaves and garden waste can expect the satisfactions of a thriftier garden, neater premises, and a less polluted environment.

Mulches have important functions, and one of the most important is to conserve soil water for plant use. Water supplied to the garden by rain or irrigation is lost by runoff, transpiration through plant leaves, evaporation from the soil surface, and by percolation through the soil. You can use mulches to reduce losses from surface runoff and evaporation, thus making more water available for plant needs.

Water droplets, falling on soil, often destroy the surface structure and eliminate the large pores that allow rapid infiltration of water. This, in turn, results in water being lost by surface runoff with accompanying soil erosion.

When placed on open soil, a mulch absorbs the impact of falling rain, the water seeps gently into the soil, there is no sealing of the soil surface, and runoff seldom occurs.

After water enters the soil, some of it is normally drawn back to the surface, there to be lost by evaporation. Mulches act as a one-way valve, allowing water to enter the soil rapidly but reducing later evaporation.

When the air becomes dry and has the capacity to absorb water from a wet surface, mulches generally dry quickly, since they contain only small amounts of water. When dry, they no longer act as capillary conductors carrying water to the top of the mulch. They shield the soil surface from air currents and consequently greatly retard further evaporation.

A mulch of 2 inches of pea gravel may reduce annual evaporation from the soil surface by 75 percent. Generally, sand or larger gravel are less effective. Organic mulches derived from various plant materials are often more readily available than gravel or coarse sand. They all reduce evaporation appreciably, especially in situations where the soil surface is open to sun.

In shady locations, as under dense shrubbery, the primary benefits of a mulch will be improved water intake rather than reduced evaporation. To get maximum benefits from mulches for water infiltration, you should work up the soil surface before you add the mulch.

A good mulch can often double the length of time that a flowerbed can go between waterings. This benefit is particularly attractive to busy homeowners with little time for garden work and to vacationers who may wish to leave home for 1 or 2 weeks with the assurance that their plants will survive. The actual time for which the water can be adequate will depend on water-holding capacity of the soil, depth of rooting, spacing of plants, and the weather conditions during the period.

In establishing new grass seedlings, you can use to good advantage the ability of mulches to reduce evaporation, runoff, and erosion. A sparse cover of straw, peat, or other mulch is often necessary, particularly when seeding during the hot days of summer.

The mulch helps keep the soil surface from drying, shades the young seedlings, and reduces soil washing from sprinklers or summer rainstorms. One bale of wheat straw per 1,000 square feet of new seeding is usually adequate.

Mulches may also have surprisingly large effects upon soil temperature, especially during the spring months when there is less vegetative cover on the soil. They are also valuable as winter protection for roots and crowns of tender perennial plants and shrubs.

Organic mulches act as insulators because of low heat conducting properties, whereas gravel is a good heat conductor. Therefore, dark gravel mulches will tend to warm light colored soils and organic mulches tend to keep soil cool. This principle can be used to slow down or speed up plant growth in the spring.

Organic mulches decrease weed seed germination, and the few weeds that do emerge can be easily pulled and left to form part of the mulch. Mulches are favorable habitats for insects, slugs, and

Plant materials for garden mulches. From top to bottom, finished compost, partially composted oak leaves, pruning chips, and shredded oak bark.

cutworms, but this fact also attracts wild birds who generally keep the pests under control.

Mulched plantings in the home garden can be more attractive than unmulched plantings. Modern landscaping takes advantage of the color and texture values of mulches to point up the beauty of the plantings, especially in formal settings. Dark colored mulches widen the pupil of the eye, allowing more of the sensible light from flowers to enter the eye. Consequently, these dark mulches give plantings a more attractive appearance.

Another advantage of mulches is that they reduce the splashing of mud onto flowers and foliage. Besides being unsightly, mud splatterings may also favor disease development. This is especially true for low-growing fruits like tomatoes and strawberries.

You will find a wide variety of organic mulching materials for sale in garden stores, or available from farmers, industrial plants and municipal sources. In making a selection consider cost, durability, appearance, and the use you have in mind.

Wood and bark products are generally long-lasting mulches available from garden stores. You can find tanbark, shredded wood and bark, fine bark mulch, or coarse bark chips. From sawmills you can obtain sawdust (preferably old and partially rotted) or wood shavings. Municipal maintenance departments often have pruning chips or shredded leaves available for the asking. You may be able to find unusual waste materials from processing plants that make good mulches.

Home and farm mulch materials will include compost, dry shredded leaves, fresh lawn clippings, and whole or chopped grain straw. Straw is not a long-lasting mulch and needs to be applied heavily to obtain much effect. It also may contain too many grain or

PLASTIC MULCH FOR FLOWER BEDS

STEPS IN PLANTING

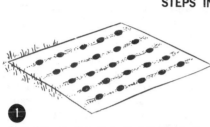

1 Prepare the planting site in the fall. Dig planting holes 4 to 6 inches wider and deeper than the plant root ball. Mix peat moss and organic matter in the planting holes. Space plants evenly over the site.

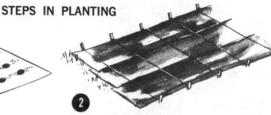

2 Place rolls of black plastic over the area to shade out weeds and retard water loss. Use three or four wide strips slightly overlapping. Tie down the plastic with rocks, wires, or stakes. You may cover the area with a mulch of organic matter instead of using plastic if you wish. Keep the mulch moist to keep it in place.

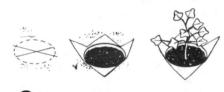

3 Cut an X slit in the plastic over each planting hole. Enlarge the slits to the proper size hole and set the plants through them.

4 Set the plants at the same level they were growing before they were transplanted. Fill the hole with good soil and pack the soil firmly around the roots. Leave a slight basin at the top to hold water. Water thoroughly after planting.

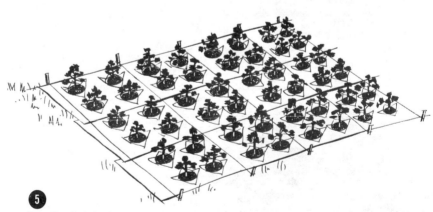

5 Keep the plants in place with an organic mulch over the plastic until the plants are established. Use a mulch of pine bark, wood chips, or hulls. Pull weeds by hand if they grow.

weed seeds. Farm manures can be applied as surface mulches with the advantage of adding plant nutrients. Manures, however, may lead to odors or insects.

In recent years the relatively low cost of polyethylene sheeting has led to its use as a mulch for melons and for other low-growing, high-value crops. Holes punched in the plastic when the seeds are planted allow the stems to grow through the plastic. The plastic also acts to prevent weeds, to keep the fruit clean, and to decrease evaporation. Before laying the plastic, shape the soil surface in furrows and slot the plastic at the bottom of the furrows to allow water intake.

Disadvantages of plastic for ground cover are that water collects on it in puddles, it is not very attractive, and leaves and litter are more obvious. You cannot walk on it and it ends up as a non-biodegradable waste.

One of man's long-standing desires has been to control his climate. He has done this in his home, his office, and his car for his own comfort. His efforts to control the outdoor climate have not generally been successful.

However, by using mulches wisely, a gardener can cause major modifications in soil water, soil temperature, and radiation reaching plant leaves—three of the most important climatic features affecting plant growth.

 ## your garden's little climates and how to manage them

EVERY GARDENER has the problem of selecting plants that will grow well in his soil and local climate. Yet many gardeners want to modify their soils, and even their local climates, in order to grow plants that they love but that are not entirely adapted to their soils and climates.

Although science can help, gardening is mainly an art. A gardener must know what kinds of soils and climates he has and what kinds of soils and climates are demanded by the plants.

A gardener can select plants that fit the soil and climate he has or make changes so that he can grow the plants he especially admires. Most of us do some of both: Yet most of us also try plants difficult to grow. We try them in different places in our garden in various soils and climates. We may be fortunate enough to find a proper place for the plant. If after a few tries the plants still grow poorly, we select them out.

As a gardener, you can get a fairly good general view of the climate from the local summaries made by the Weather Bureau. You can determine the total rainfall and its approximate distribution through the season, the probable intensity of heavy storms, if any, the approximate dates of the last frost in spring and of the first frost in autumn, the range in velocity of the winds, and so on.

Within and around the normal homesites in the area, however, the local climate varies quite a bit from the general statement for a given community. For example, the house itself produces some dead shade during certain parts of the day. In those places the amount of light received is low and so is the temperature. Also there are many interactions between local temperature and moisture and the character of the soil.

By management, you can actually alter these little climates, or "microclimates." You can do this through the plantings themselves and by use of mulches and other practices, such as those for water control.

Through careful selection of the site

for a garden, kinds of plants to grow, and management practices, you can modify air drainage, local wind currents, sun and shade, humidity, the water both on and within the soil, and soil temperature.

Cold air is heavier than warm air. If your garden is near the top of a slope, it may miss some late spring frosts or early autumn frosts because cold air tends to slide down the slope and settle in depressions. If your garden is in a depression, the total frost-free season there could be shorter than the average for your area. On gentle slopes, a tight fence, hedgerow, or vine-covered fence will block some of the air flow. Thus, the advantage of air drainage is lost.

Strong winds are a handicap to some tender plants. Such plants are injured by cold winds and frequently they are blown over. Around the house and garden there are many little swirls of wind and some quiet places. Tight hedges reduce wind velocity considerably. If the wind strikes a wall, it may swirl vigorously around the corner of a house. You can identify these spots of low and high wind by observing where snow or dry leaves are blown away and where they accumulate.

In my own garden there are some spots where I cannot put the kinds of plants that are hurt by winds. Practically every garden is unique in this respect. One of the functions of both low and high evergreens is to help buffer the wind for other plants.

Generally speaking, temperature is a bit higher in areas where a high proportion of the space is used for streets and sidewalks. The temperature is generally higher on the sunny side of walls—facing south and southwest—and near unshaded walks. Many people make gardens in areas which already have plantings of trees and hedges. Partly for temperature and for other reasons, some of these old plantings may need to be removed.

Generally, the local temperature near

Author CHARLES E. KELLOGG retired as Deputy Administrator for Soil Survey, Soil Conservation Service, in 1971.

a south-facing wall is warmer than the surrounding area. Many gardeners have south-facing stonewalls or brickwalls on which they train fruit trees or other plants to grow flat against the wall. That is, all of the branches that grow out from the wall are pruned away. A great many gardens in northwestern Europe grow peaches and other fruits this way. It is called espalier training.

In Alaska it helps to grow tender plants against a southwest-facing white wall. Cucumbers and strawberries grow faster out of doors if planted in soil-filled oil drums setting on top of the ground. The sun warms the soil and the plants grow faster. At Circle Hot Springs tomatoes can be grown well in soils warmed through irrigation with the hot water.

Similarly, in areas with *very* cold winters, apples are trained with stakes to grow only 12 to 18 inches above the ground. Grown in this manner, they have snow protection during winter. This is comparable to espalier training but done horizontally on the ground instead of vertically on a wall.

Other gardeners train fruit trees and vines on strong wires attached to strong posts. The plant area is 8 to 12 inches thick and 5 to 6 feet high. The plants get good light, and all of the pruning, spraying, and picking can be done easily. This is called "cordon" training.

Tender plants can be covered with lightweight sheets, held down by stakes or stones, to avoid an anticipated late spring or early autumn frost. To those who love their plants, this is a common practice. To others it may be too much of a job. Some gardeners use such light coverings to protect tender plants from sleet.

Snow also can destroy azaleas and other fine shrubs with brittle branches. As the snow accumulates, the plants can be saved by gentle strokes of the branches from beneath with a broom to remove the load of snow.

Some plants do best in partial shade. However, there are two kinds of shade. They are: (1.) the dead shade of a solid wall or building; and (2.) the moving shade of trees.

Generally azaleas do not do well in the dead shade of a solid wall. But the aucuba does well there. Neither azaleas nor aucuba will do well in open sun.

Many kinds of ornamental plants do best in moving shade. As the sun bears down through deciduous trees, there are alternating spots of sun and shade on the plants during the summer and very little shade during the wintertime. Most rhododendrons and azaleas like this kind of shade. Satsuki azaleas like some winter sun and summer moving shade. Many gardeners make plantings of other shrubs and trees mainly to give their azaleas or rhododendrons moving shade.

Roses do not like much of any kind of shade. It is best to find a sunny place for them or make a sunny place by pruning or removing trees.

Once started, English ivy does well in either sun or shade. However, it is most easily started in the shade. You can provide shade for the young plants with shingles pressed into the soil until the plants are well rooted. This same method can be employed for many vegetable and ornamental plants when first set into the garden from the cold-frame or greenhouse. Tomatoes, peppers, and begonias are good examples.

Besides shade, a higher than normal humidity is needed for some plants. For example, for starting cuttings of azaleas, holly, and other plants, a higher humidity can be provided by inverting a jar over the plant. The jars must be staked so squirrels and other animals cannot push them over.

For bigger plants you can make large jars from old glass jugs. Fill the jug with water up to the point where it curves inward when seated on a level place. Soak a string in gasoline and tie it around the jug on exactly that line. Set fire to the string and the jug will break evenly. (Handle such jars cautiously, preferably with leather gloves, because of the sharp edges.)

You can increase humidity in other ways, too. You can use a good mulch, even a sponge mulch, that holds water and gives a little higher humidity for the plant.

The ideal garden soil is pervious to water. A good deal of water should soak into the soil and any excess should drain away beneath. Yet many times we want to make gardens on soils lacking this ideal situation. But, it is necessary to avoid places that are too wet and too dry for certain kinds of plants.

How do you know if a place is too wet or too dry? Here is a practical way. Say you want to plant azaleas, roses, or most vegetables. You can dig a hole 12 to 18 inches deep and fill it with water. If the water does not drain away easily in 5 to 10 hours, you will know that you cannot expect good results from plants requiring both air and moisture in the rooting zone. Their root zones must not become waterlogged.

You can go to the expense of tile drainage or you can bring in new soil and use raised beds with stone borders to get a satisfactory rooting zone.

Yet there are plants that tolerate wetness. Many ferns do. Some kinds like shade and others take sun. In moist shady places, you can use mosses. But unless you keep weed plants out, the moss cover will not be complete.

It is more difficult to avoid dryness on slowly permeable sloping soils. When the rains fall heavily, most of the water runs off and, unless the soil is protected, the runoff takes some of the soil with it.

There are several devices for preventing loss of soil. You can make earth terraces, for example. The terraces need to be at a slight angle to the contour so that any excess water that does not soak into the soil runs off slowly into a suitable outlet. By moving slowly, more of the water soaks into the soil. But earthern terraces are a bit unsightly in decorative gardens near the home where stones are better.

In my own garden I use little stone terraces for making nearly level beds. Depending on the degree of slope, I may use stones about 8 inches long with 4 inches in the soil, or stones 36 inches long with about 12 inches in the soil. I prefer somewhat irregular quarried stones. Others use brick and the like, but for small walls these will become unsightly with any settling unless one goes to the trouble of making a concrete base as solid as that for a house wall.

Infiltration of water is very greatly improved by mixing compost into the upper soil so that water enters easily. Then too, earthworms, if given compost and grass clippings on the surface for food, help enormously to improve the permeability of the soil. Even so, the stones need to protrude somewhat above the upper level so that the water from heavy rains can gradually seep down the slope.

The roots of some plants do not thrive in soils of high temperature. The wisteria and clematis vine are two examples. A good mulch of sawdust or compost helps to keep the soil cool. In fact, in places with high summer temperatures and a good deal of sun, most garden plants respond to a mulch cover.

If the soil is deficient in organic matter, a 2-inch sawdust layer covered by tanbark or compost is helpful. Since the sawdust has some carbohydrates in it, which furnish energy for microorganisms, it is helpful to add about one cupful of ammonium sulphate or three cupfuls of cottonseed meal for each bushel of sawdust. Otherwise, the stimulated micro-organisms compete with the plant roots for nitrogen.

Some plants that need mulching in summer should not have much mulch in the winter where there is danger of sudden cold snaps. Some of the azaleas and other tender plants fall in this class. With a sudden freezing cold, the only source of heat for the lower branches and the main stem is that coming up from the soil. Little heat can come up through a mulch. The mulch acts very much like the material in the wall of a refrigerator.

So, for those kinds of plants, I remove the mulch around the stem in late autumn. Also I wrap the stems of the tender ones up to 2 or 3 feet with masking tape. This helps prevent freezing and cracking and if freezing does occur, the tape prevents the movement of moisture out of the plant so the crack may heal later.

In fact, it is a good idea in planting a dogwood, or any young tree, to wrap the whole stem with masking tape and keep it on until its roots are well established. Many young trees are inclined to dry and crack or freeze and crack. You may wrap the stem with cloth but, if you forget to take it off, it may girdle the tree whereas the masking tape cracks automatically.

Some plants grow well together. For example, oak trees and azaleas are suited to each other. The reason is that most oak roots are fairly deep and most azaleas are fairly shallow. Yet azaleas rarely grow well, if at all, near a red maple, tulip-poplar, or other shallow-rooted tree. The tree gets all the available moisture and nutrients.

If you want to have a general garden with annuals, perennials, and shrubs, you cannot expect to have success under shallow-rooted trees. Even though weeping willows, red maples, and most of the poplars can be fine for a wild garden, they tend to ruin the soil and the climate for most ordinary garden plants. Between them you may have daffodils, violets, and other hardy things, including some plants that might be regarded as weeds in other than a wild setting.

Actual experience with plants will give the best results in your garden. The eye of the observant gardener, who takes notes as he goes along, is the best guide.

"Nature seldom gives us the very best; for that we must have recourse to art." (Gracián).

For further reading:

Kellogg, Charles E., *Our Garden Soils*, MacMillan, New York, 1952. See appendix for soil and climate requirements of many garden plants.

**PLANTS
IN
ACTION**

youth gardens sprouting, with community support

THE JOY OF PLANNING a garden, and planting a seed, and watching the wonder of nature turn a dry kernel into an abundance of flowers and vegetables has opened up to thousands of children over the country. A vacant lot in a crumbling neighborhood, a bit of earth between two outdoor volleyball courts, or, as if in answer to a dream, a full-fledged demonstration garden large enough to accommodate dozens of individual plots, all qualify for the title—Youth Garden!

Started much like a seed itself, a relatively new idea has blossomed out across the land and has brought the delight of gardening to children and places never thought possible.

In Washington, D.C., over a thousand children between the ages of 9 and 14 tend gardens which range in size from single 3-foot rows to 5- by 14-foot plots.

While there are a number of similar programs around the country, these Washington gardens have received wide national attention because they are located in the Nation's Capital and have become the subject of a concentrated effort to "spread the word." A well-organized operation now boasting over 45 gardening locations and a large demonstration garden complete with a headquarters building and greenhouse, the D.C. program can well serve as a model for the rest of the Nation.

Wherever they exist, there is only one key to youth gardening—a dedicated group of interested citizens who believe that "If you give a child seeds, tools, a plot of ground, and a little help, he will make a garden."

The Washington program, which began in 1962, sprouted from a seed brought to Washington from New York City by a community-minded woman who had started a similar program there. In Washington, she soon gathered around her a group of like-minded individuals who were quick to see that such a project would not only benefit the children involved but would help the entire community.

Funds for the program, which originally came only from contributions of private citizens and groups, now are supplemented by an appropriation from the city government.

A Cleveland, Ohio, program that stimulates "home" gardening is not only supported by the Cleveland school system but can be part of a student's curriculum. The students even compete for certificates and cash prizes. Children in elementary schools and in junior and senior high schools participate in the program.

The school gardening program in Cleveland and the Brooklyn Botanic Garden Program are probably the oldest in the United States, dating back to the early 1900's. These two programs served as forerunners of efforts as ambitious as the victory garden program during World War II.

Hilltop, located on the campus of the Indiana University, serves both as a very successful youth garden and as a research laboratory that has trained hundreds of leaders who are spreading the message. It is a leisure science program for the youth of Bloomington and a teacher education outdoor laboratory. This gardening program is sponsored

Author ROBERT F. LEDERER is Executive Vice President of the American Association of Nurserymen. He is currently Chairman of the Washington Youth Garden Council.

by the city department of parks and recreation, the university, and the Bloomington Garden Club in order to "give every boy and girl an opportunity to better understand the living world around him by actively working with it."

Indeed, Hilltop, which was initiated in 1947 as a Leadership Training Center to teach university level students the idea of gardening for youth, might be singled out as the most important factor in the current expanding interest in youth gardening. Literally hundreds of Indiana University men and women have left the Hilltop Center with a strong desire to spread the ideas and knowledge gained there.

In Whittier, Calif., youth gardening takes the form of a group known as the Junior Hummingbirds, who maintain a municipal park by keeping it weed- and litter-free. Each spring the Hummingbirds plant annual flowers in downtown Whittier in large tubs that contain street trees. These tubs are their year-round responsibility and a weed doesn't have a chance!

This youth gardening group also has an herb garden that it maintains and periodically expands. Adjacent to the municipal park, it can be enjoyed by park visitors.

Probably one of the most unusual gardens of all is at the C. Melvin Sharpe Health School in Washington, D.C.'s, inner city. Some children attending the school are multiple-handicapped, but their personal difficulties seem to make them all the more enthusiastic in their gardening.

Besides having successfully landscaped their own school, each of the Sharpe Health students who participate in the youth gardening program has a short row to tend which is all his own. The gardens are located in a protected area within the school, made possible by a "courtyard" type of construction which allows four classrooms to have windows opening on a common court.

The sheer joy apparent in the face of a paraplegic child hanging on to his wheel chair with one strong hand while tending his garden with the other convinces even the most skeptical of the power of putting a child, soil, and seed together.

Regardless of which successful youth gardening program is examined, one key ingredient is soon obvious: organization. The overall program of fundraising and the day-to-day activities of the participating children must be carefully planned and operated. Neither has ever proven successful without superior organization.

Particularly important is direct and constant supervision of the gardening activities. Nothing has proven more frustrating to the children and more destructive to individual programs than lack of a definite schedule of instruction and garden work. Hence, it is extremely important that qualified adult gardening leaders be found before starting any program.

The Washington program early in its development hired a full-time director and in 1970 added an assistant. They hope a second team of director and assistant will be appointed. This would make it possible to more than double the number of children participating, currently 1,000.

Leadership for youth gardening in South Bend and Mishawaka, Ind., comes from various garden clubs and the Urban League, all guided by the county agricultural extension service, the South Bend Redevelopment Department, and experts from Hilltop at Indiana University.

A budding program in Toledo, Ohio, is completely endorsed by the city government and is operated by the Division of Recreation and Forestry. A twice-a-week schedule of planned and well-supervised activities begun in 1970 shows every sign of becoming a permanent part of growing up for lucky Toledo children.

Surely, it does not take much imagination to develop a never-ending list of potential Youth Garden leaders from the great number of those with a knowledge of gardening and a conviction that children, too, can grow in a garden. Some sources to be explored are teachers, housewives, businessmen, retired persons, nurserymen, playground directors, recreation personnel, Boy Scouts, Girl Scouts, and 4-H Clubs.

When youth gardening is organized and supported by individual citizens or organizations, it is necessary to include those who are not necessarily experienced gardeners but who are not afraid to lick stamps, make phone calls, and work hard to obtain assistance and money. (Always keep in mind that a major ingredient of every youth gardening program is *money*—for supplies, transportation, seeds and plants, and even rent if free gardening land is not available.)

In 1970, the President of the General Federation of Women's Clubs made spreading the word of youth gardening her personal project. All 14,000 of the Federation's clubs were furnished details in hopes that some would create programs for their own areas.

In that year more than 2,000 clubs asked for more information as a step toward developing gardens, and Federation officers expect that more clubs each year will adopt youth gardening as their own. The program has been added to those suggested to clubs by the Federation's Conservation Department as an opportunity to help children develop "sensitivity toward the world about them."

Youth Gardening creates the opportunity for all kinds of public performances that provide an occasion for the children to perform and to show the fruits of their labors. Perhaps just as important, these performances serve as a "show place" for the gardens too.

In Washington, youth gardeners have formed their own Dutch Dancing group which performs in public each year during their Spring Festival, wooden shoes and all! Part of this group's activities is the sewing and the maintenance of their own colorful costumes. Such dignitaries as members of the President's Cabinet, Senators and Congressmen, the Mayor, and many other officials have participated in the festival, as well as the Fall Harvest Awards program.

Because a large part of the money that makes the Washington program possible must be approved by both the city and the Federal governments, it has proved to be an absolute necessity to bring the children, along with their accomplishments, together with those who handle the purse strings.

In the fall of 1970 the Mayor and members of both the Senate and the House of Representatives participated in presentation of the many awards won by individual young gardeners or gardening groups.

One 12-year-old had been singled out to receive the Mayor's Award for the Most Enthusiastic Gardener. After accepting, he very shyly said he was not accustomed to speaking in public. Then he proceeded to deliver a beautiful five-minute speech to the more than 300 fellow gardeners and dignitaries gathered in the Caucus Room of the House Office Building on Capitol Hill.

On display and of great interest to reporters, television cameramen, and visitors were all manner of vegetables and flowers. There was even a nearly 10-foot-tall stalk of sugar cane grown by one ambitious young lady after she was told it couldn't be done as far north as Washington, D.C.!

Recognizing the need to reward young gardeners for their efforts, most program planners include public ceremonies along these lines, complete with awards.

Toledo holds an Honors Day to give and receive awards, a City Festival to show the wonders produced in individual gardens, and a Watermelon Feast so the young participants can really enjoy the rewards of gardening!

In 1971, the Cleveland public school system celebrated its 36th Annual School Garden Awards program. Individual presentations were made to outstanding junior gardeners from among the more than 20,000 who took part in that city's program.

Hilltop pays for one special event with another. Its Spring Plant and Bake Sale held in late spring helps pay for Honor Day in late fall. The continuing theme of Honor Day at

Participants in Washington (D.C.) youth garden program show fruits of their labors.

255

A parent's permission is required before a child is allowed to participate in gardening after school hours. When this permission is requested an additional question is often included: "What kinds of vegetables would you like to have your child grow?" One of the worst things that can happen to a sprouting young gardener is to take his production home, proudly anticipating a taste of the fruits of his labor, only to find that his parents are not familiar with the particular vegetable that he grew.

With the rule that each gardener is working for himself and keeps his own production, provision must also be made that enough of each vegetable grown is produced to feed a family of four or five.

Hilltop is, "I pledge to do a little bit more than my share."

But regardless of the program—the Massachusetts Horticultural Society's school gardening programs, the Pennsylvania Horticultural Society's day camp gardens, Philadelphia neighborhood gardening, or the Beloit, Wis., Youth Gardens—the word is simply: plan, plant, harvest, and *reward!*

While gardening has proved almost universally acceptable to every age and economic group, the total program must be interesting enough to attract and hold children. Most of them need guidance every step of the way. Once a garden program is established, active recruitment of the children who will participate is necessary. After the first year the word is passed on.

Major recruitment in most existing programs takes place in schools. In Washington, the director visits grades three to five in nearby schools. These classes are composed of children 8 to 12 years old. Those under 8 are usually not developed physically to the point where they can handle gardening equipment. Recruitment efforts always seem to end up with the difficult task of deciding which children can participate. Generally, there are many more candidates than gardens.

Even a youth gardener can lose interest in his project during hot summer months. The cure is simple—get up early and do the tough part before old man sun sends you looking for shade. Many garden programs follow a twice-a-week schedule of gardening from 10 a.m. to noon; lunch from noon to 1 p.m. (at home); return to the garden for craft activities; and then a hike or supervised game to end the day at 3 to 3:30 p.m.

When possible, the day should start with all children together for a nature study session. These sessions, always employing graphic materials, can be involved with touching and seeing some facet of nature: earthworms and what they do for us; the life cycle of some insects who share the garden with us; or a lecture on parts of flowers and what they do to help us garden.

Perhaps one of the more important aspects of a full gardening program is that it must never be restricted to the growing season alone. Children who have come to include gardening as a part of their life should be kept together in the off season by carefully supervised off-season projects.

Outdoor gardening itself can be part of this year-round activity. Spring is for planting, summer for tending, fall for harvesting, and winter for planning.

Nursery catalogs can serve as winter sunshine to children as they plan and dream of spring fun in the garden.

In areas of the country where winter is severe, garden-related projects should be included in the program. Some of these are growing plants from cuttings, bulb forcing, dish and terrarium gardening, splatter painting, and indoor gardening with sweetpotatoes, pineapples, avocados, and various citrus plants. Even carpentry has proved to be part of gardening as the children build window boxes and bird houses and feeders.

Garden craft activities should also relate to the subject at hand: weed and flower pressing, nature painting, and bird identification are all worthwhile subjects. If backed up with illustrative material, they will usually prove hits. The idea must always be to keep your young gardeners involved all the time they are in the garden, whether during the active gardening season or, for instance, just before Christmas when wreathmaking with natural materials is the business of the day.

And never forget: be it a vacant lot in Indianapolis or the edge of a playground in Los Angeles, "If you give a child seeds, tools, a plot of ground, and a little help, he will make a garden."

schoolyards have class as outdoor laboratories

A THIRD GRADE CLASS in Nevada looked out their classroom window one day and watched a small whirlwind spiral a column of dust into the air.

Instead of trying to answer the rush of questions from the children, the teacher seized the moment to take the class outdoors to observe the blowing dust. Soon one youngster put the class reaction into words, "That's our schoolyard blowing away!"

As the group continued the walk and discussion, a sharp-eyed girl noticed that no dust was blowing from a near-by cemetery, so the teacher led the class on for further investigation.

They soon came up with their own conclusion; it was the grass that made the difference. From this the teacher and her students went on to examine the root structure of the grass and how the roots helped hold the soil.

Learning to control soil erosion on a Tennessee school site means shaping and seeding the slope to appropriate grass seed mixtures to protect the soil from water runoff.

Later on, the class planted grass on a portion of the schoolyard. Each stage of the project was accompanied by animated discussions of how and why, and finally the class agreed on a summary of their experience: "Seeds grow best in good soil, and they need water and sunshine. When the seeds grow into plants, the blades of grass catch the rain or water from the sprinkler and help it soak into the soil. The plants hold the soil—and everything works together."

When the teacher opened the door to the blowing dust and growing grass, the

Author KATHARINE N. MERGEN is head of the Educational Relations Section, Information Division, Soil Conservation Service (SCS).

Coauthor CARL H. THOMAS is Regional Biologist for the Caribbean Area and the 15 Northeastern States serviced by the Regional Technical Service Center, SCS, headquartered at Upper Darby, Pa.

youngsters quickly grasped the difference in learning *about* soil, water, and plants from textbook studies and learning *from* the growing plants, living soil, and running water in the out of doors.

Much too often, students spend their time reading endlessly about environmental problems and natural resources without ever having a chance to find out how to protect soil from erosion or measure pollution in a stream.

This is a little like trying to teach youngsters how to ski by handing them a diagram of the ski slope and all the best books on the techniques of running a slalom course or schussing a hill without ever getting out in the snow.

Conservation studies confined to the conventionally structured classroom situation sometimes bring forth unexpected reactions from children who are far removed from outdoor learning opportunities.

A conservationist once brought several abandoned bird nests and a birdhouse to a first grade class for a talk on how birds live. One little boy examined all the bird homes with great interest and then inquired, "How do the birds make these wooden houses?"

Still more traumatic to the adult was the experience of the man who provided a first grade class with study skins and stuffed birds to examine while he told stories of the many kinds of birds he knew. The lecture was interrupted by a small girl who asked in outraged tones, "Who killed the birds?"

By using the schoolyard as an outdoor classroom, children in kindergarten and first grade can begin to recognize colors, shapes, textures, and sounds in their natural setting, and to see how insects, birds, squirrels, and other small animals live in the natural environment they share with people.

For the older students, the outdoor classroom enables them to carry on day-to-day study projects through continuing observations of changes within the environment. The student begins to make decisions in problem solving projects, and learns to evaluate some of the results of various kinds of resource management. But most important, he is finding out that most environmental problems have no quick and easy solutions; there is no such thing as instant conservation.

Nearly all schools have at least one small corner of the schoolyard that can be developed into an outdoor classroom. Imagination and ingenuity can do much with a tree in a tub, a patch of grass, and a little bare soil. Even mosses on walls, grass in the cracks of the sidewalk, and the ubiquitous dandelion can be great teachers. Grasshoppers, ants, crickets, butterflies, and worms are found everywhere, and each has its own lifestyle and its own environmental needs.

On a very small site, one tree may represent a forest, and every shrub and vine will be chosen because it can teach many things—how plants hold the soil, how insects and wildlife find food and shelter, how to add beauty to the schoolyard. Plants and trees native to the area provide a link with the history of the community as children learn how Indians and pioneers made use of resources, and how the economic development of the community may have been related to natural resources of the area.

An outdoor classroom on a city site may be no more than a few feet of soil beyond the blacktopped playground.

One enterprising elementary teacher found a small space beneath the fire escape where the children could plant things and study them as they grew.

Another teacher marked off with paints of various colors a complete watershed on the uneven surface of a paved playground, outlining the ridges, valleys, and river drainage. On rainy days the class gathered outside to watch the water follow the contours of their watershed.

By comparing the runoff from the paved area with that from a lawn or grassy slope, the students could estimate roughly the increased amount of runoff that occurs when rain falls on city streets and rooftops, or on the paved surface of large shopping centers and airports.

Outdoor experiences with the small watershed can be extended to local watersheds and then to the drainage areas of large rivers by making use of maps, and by researching the influences of watersheds and drainage areas on the water resources that are available for people.

Schools with limited space for outdoor studies have also made use of one of the oldest techniques in agriculture—terraces on steep slopes to hold the soil in place and to increase the planting surface. Here the students can grow a variety of grasses, flowers, small shrubs, and other vegetation.

Even lawns can be used to study plant-soil-water relationships and to observe the life cycle of many insects and small creatures. Lawns in themselves make a good example of a perennial grass stage that survives through the management and protection provided by people.

Paths worn across the schoolyard

lawn are fine examples of overuse by too many pounding feet, and the resulting erosion is much like that which occurs on overgrazed rangelands where too many cattle or sheep have destroyed soil-holding vegetation. Wildlife areas crowded beyond the carrying capacity of the land may exhibit similar kinds of resource damage.

With an area of lawn assigned to each student, or to small groups, the youngsters can use this study area to observe the living creatures on and in the soil. These are listed, classified, and described in daily records kept over a period of time. One youngster regularly listed the large black and white dog that visited him each day.

Teacher explains root structure to center-city students in Washington, D.C., before the children start a planting project in their outdoor classroom. Scotch pine seedlings placed on a slope will add beauty to the school and later will help hold the soil in place.

Examining organisms within the soil opens up a new and unexplored world for children. They learn how each of these small creatures, ranging in size from microscopic bacteria and protozoa to earthworms and beetles, fills its own ecological niche.

And the experience of calculating the quantities of these organisms—sometimes more than a billion in a 4-inch cube of soil—helps to show that rock particles are not soil until living creatures are a part of the soil materials.

A single acorn from an oak tree on the schoolyard can be used to show in miniature the process of interdependence. The acorn grows because the tree makes use of soil, water, air, and sunlight. When it ripens and falls to the ground, along with many other acorns, it may be chewed on by insects or gathered up by a squirrel.

If the squirrel eats the acorn, it has served one purpose in the energy cycle; if the acorn is gradually returned to the soil by insects, fungi, and bacteria, it helps enrich the soil for the next generation of acorns. If it is the rare acorn that succeeds in becoming a seedling, it has entered still another cycle, and if it is not eaten by a rabbit or trampled by careless feet, it will complete this cycle and produce more acorns.

One of the prime values of the outdoor classroom is its intimate relationship to the local community and its resources. No two learning areas are identical in size, shape, and variety of natural resources, but they will reflect pretty accurately the local conservation needs and opportunities.

Even when the initial ideas for outdoor classroom developments are strikingly similar, the results will be far different. In New Jersey, for example, an elementary school developed a miniature version of the major plant communities of the State. In Colorado, teachers and students had the same idea, but instead of pine barrens and marsh areas with skunk cabbage, there are shadscale, mountain mahogany, and high-country evergreens on the Western school site.

Opportunities for creative teaching are literally endless in the outdoor classroom. In addition to ecological studies and conservation practices developed by a Michigan school on a site with a great variety of resources, teachers there have emphasized creativity and originality through designs, murals, and sketches based on the natural environment.

Conservation education and the outdoor classroom program, as an integral part of the school curriculum at all grade levels and in all disciplines, is in many respects attitude education. It adds a dimension of personal involvement and individual responsibility. The student learns to look at his own community with a more discerning eye and to assess the decisions made by people in the protection and use of resources.

The story of an outdoor classroom development in a small west coast town in Washington illustrates very well how the conservation program has woven into the curriculum a consciousness of history, an understanding of the ecological principles that underlie good resource use, and a sensitivity to esthetics and enjoyment of the out of doors.

Wahkiakum County is named for an Indian chief and lies in the tall timber country not far from the Pacific Ocean. Most of the youngsters in the county go to school in the town of Cathlamet. They have a hundred acres of outdoor classroom where some kind of study is going on every day.

Kindergarten and first grade children use the mini-trail just outside of the elementary school for their projects. Second graders have learned plant identification on the mini-trail, but they like to make up their own names,

Cathlamet (Wash.) third graders release tadpoles raised in schoolroom.

and now the ferns are known as "hairy fans," holly is labeled "Stickly Bush," and the fir cones are addressed as "Mr. and Mrs. Pointer."

A third grade class, inspired by a 450-year-old fir tree in the center of the outdoor classroom, wrote a narrative poem about "Father Fir" and his children and grandchildren now growing up around him on land formerly cleared for pasture. The music teacher set the poem to music.

Third grade students also did a study of soil, water, and plant relationships in the outdoor classroom, sectioning off areas of land for detailed investigations that were recorded by the students.

By the fifth grade, the youngsters are carrying on comprehensive environmental studies, and they are already familiar with the principles of diversity, and change, and interdependence in nature.

Historical links with the past involve children in learning about the Cathlamet Indian tribe that once lived where their school now stands. Chief Wahkiakum is buried in the little pioneer cemetery next to the schoolyard.

The economic impact of natural resource use on the community is readily understood as students learn that Cathlamet started as a fur-trading post early in the 19th century. Timber resources are still a major factor in the county's prosperity.

Elementary students researched information on Indian shelters and came up with a design for the outdoor classroom shelter that was built by the boys in the vocational agriculture class.

High school biology classes have a hundred-acre laboratory for experiments and demonstrations as they study biotic communities within the forest environment. And the high school's speech class prepared a half-hour TV program on the outdoor classroom.

Development of the outdoor classroom began in 1969; 2 years later the school won national recognition and a first place award from the Association of Classroom Teachers for the project.

Much of the success of the Wahkiakum outdoor classroom development is the result of careful planning on the part of teachers and administrators who recognized the need for sound educational objectives and wide community involvement.

The school also made use of the conservationists and resource specialists from the Soil Conservation Service, the State department of natural resources, and other agencies. The teachers were given special training in the use of the outdoor learning areas. The science department of the school developed workbooks that were geared to the conservation studies program.

Cost to local taxpayers was very little. The school received an $1,800 Federal grant, and another $300 was donated by the State soil and water conservation committee. Community help, with skills and materials, has been generous. Students have done most of the work.

An advisory committee—made up of students, teachers, administrators, and citizens of the community—continues to give leadership in developing the long-range plans for the program. The resource specialists serve on this committee.

Vocational agriculture classes helped lay out and clear the four loop trails, each of which is designed to provide specific learning opportunities. The boys also volunteered to take on the job of trail maintenance—no small task in this area of abundant rainfall and rapidly growing ferns, shrubs, and bushes. The Vo-Ag group also built the soil study pits and a series of small ponds to be used for water-related learning projects.

Wahkiakum, like many other school site outdoor classrooms, is a learning experience without end; there will always be another problem to solve, another tree to plant, and another poem to write.

The marker placed by the students at the beginning of the learning trail sums up their feeling for the outdoor classroom: "May there grow here the rack of the buck, the reach of the pine, the mind of a child, and the heart of a man."

kids go to the environment to learn about it first-hand

BUTCH, A FIFTH GRADER from Eugene, Oreg., was doing a study of comparative sizes and ages of trees in one of his classes in the forest environment. He discovered that the trees with the most space around them grew the fastest. In summarizing the results of his investigation, Butch said: "You know, people living in crowded cities don't grow too well, either."

In many places around the country, kids like Butch, teachers, community groups, and resource agency people are going to school in different environments. They are studying in such places as the forest, the seashore, the desert, the inner city, the farm, the shopping center, and sometimes even the local dump!

According to one teacher, "Too long we've neglected the learning opportunities that exist in the outdoor environment, one of the few places where total involvement in the learning processes takes place."

Would Butch have made his analogy about the need for growing space if his teacher had kept him inside the four walls of the classroom?

Learning in different environments gives people the opportunity to develop awareness and understanding about the world in which they live. They also learn skills and techniques of investigation which can lead them to changes in attitudes and values about their environment.

Butch was spending a week at school in the forest. He and his classmates were busy setting up experiments and investigations to observe, collect, interpret, and communicate data about how organisms and environmental elements are interrelated in a forest community. Understandings about ecological concepts of adaptation, change, and interdependence were being discovered by the students themselves, rather than having the teacher lecture about them.

Butch's classmates declare: "We like being able to find out things for ourselves, without always being told."

Butch and his classmates were reacting to a teaching situation which encourages the student to get directly involved in the learning process.

To insure a greater interaction between a child and his environment, teachers are being encouraged and trained to recognize and use environments other than the classroom to apply the basic learning skills.

As part of its environmental education program, the U.S. Department of Agriculture's Forest Service is sponsoring training courses for teachers and resource people. The basis for this type of training is to put participants in situations where skills and techniques are developed through their own involvement in the learning process, rather than have them sitting back, passively listening, as in a lecture situation.

Teachers report that discovery and involvement approaches to environmental learning result in student-initiated investigations that apply the basic learning skills to real situations. Each student contributes his own participation to the investigations and there seems to be more of a feeling of "belonging" in the learning experience.

One process of involving partici-

Author ERNEST C. MCDONALD is the Environmental Education Officer, Pacific Northwest Region, U.S. Forest Service, Portland, Oreg.

Coauthor CHARLINE MCDONALD is an Environmental Education Consultant in Portland.

pants in a land use decision-making situation is through simulation games. Taking a local land-use problem that requires a decision, the participants assume the roles of different interest groups who might be concerned with the problem.

For example, in one simulation game each group proposed possible uses for an unused area of city land. They analyzed consequences of using the land for a sewage treatment plant, industrial park, a recreation complex, and a housing development. Each proposal was evaluated based on needs of the land, and needs of people in the city.

Real life environmental issues involving conflicts of interest groups can be examined through these simulation gaming techniques so that students themselves discover cause-effect relationships, discuss all sides of the issue, and suggest solutions to the problem.

In order to make a more intelligent analysis, students might study the land by collecting and recording observable soil characteristics (such as color, feel, structure, depth, acidity or alkalinity), and constructing a model of the soil profile. Using land capability charts and soil limitation criteria to interpret this data, students can then evaluate potential uses of the land.

Teachers who were involved in a similar activity at an environmental education training course remarked:

"Learning by doing gives you a surprising awareness of how the kids would feel doing it. I especially liked how we related the scientific data we collected in the field to the discussion of social and political implications later."

Environmental learning experiences should relate not only to regional and worldwide problems, but to problems where we live. Eight-year-old Mike learned how to use a soil-testing kit to determine acidity and alkalinity in the soil. Now his services are in demand in his community, and he makes the rounds of the yards of his neighbors, testing soil and giving advice about which plants and flowers can grow best in different places in their yards.

But what about the child who doesn't even have a yard, who spends most or all of his time in the inner city environment? Children can become involved in setting up a variety of problem-solving activities on their own schoolyards, such as determining what effect the blacktop has on the environment (that's known as "blacktop ecology"), or by learning to make a map with a cardboard box plane table. Students can then analyze the land-use pattern on their schoolyard, discuss the alternative uses of different areas, and plan for more efficient use of available schoolyard space.

Sometimes children, through simple words, offer unique insights into their feelings about the spaces around them.

From her classroom window, Mary made these observations about her schoolyard:

> *Walls*
> *Big, small*
> *Fences—brick, wood*
> *Some things that keep*
> *one thing from another*
> *Tall*

On Mary's schoolyard there were, indeed, "walls" in every direction. Even the tree in the middle of the blacktop had a fence around it.

Planning for better use of spaces on their schoolyard led Mary's class to visit other streets, buildings, and neighborhoods around their school, to see how the planners and builders employed structure, texture, design, and color to create pleasant or unpleasant spaces for people. Mary's class is now taking longer field trips to observe the effects of land use changes in their community.

Remember making that homemade barometer and wind gage when you were studying weather in school? One group of fourth graders not only learned about weather, but constructed their own air pollution index chart based on observable daily weather conditions. The Regional Air Pollution Control Authority has agreed to establish an official air pollution recording station on their schoolyard. The chil-

dren are not only increasing their understanding of air pollution problems, but are at the same time contributing valuable data to management of the environment.

One third grade teacher provided language and visual arts experiences for his students when he instituted a study of pollution. The children went through the community, taking photographs of visual pollution which they believed could be corrected. A slide show, composed of photographs from each child, and narrated by the students, was presented to the rest of the school, the Parent-Teachers Association and various community groups, to enlist their support in community improvement projects already initiated by the third graders.

Environmental learning enables people to accept a responsibility for the quality management of their environment. Education in the environment must also give people the tools and the skills to make intelligent social and political decisions about the world in

Top, life cycles in a rotten log—birth, growth, death, decay. Above, interpreting the landscape by reading tree rings.

265

which they live. Involving young people in environmental experiences that develop attitudes and values sometimes results in action-involvement in unexpected projects.

For several years students from one school had used a nearby pond as an environmental study area. When a proposed freeway threatened to eliminate their outdoor classroom, the students collected and interpreted data about the value of the pond to their community. They compiled a report and presented a plan to the planning commission for relocation of the proposed freeway. The freeway route has been changed, and the students feel that their report contributed to the decision.

A demolition project threatening some of the city's finest architectural examples caused one group of youngsters to take action in a way that would make their views heard—personal letters to the local newspaper.

DEAR MR. EDITOR:
It is utterly absurd to knock down all those beautiful houses. I think we should restore them so we, and our children, and our children's children, etc., can have a nice place to see some old houses which should really be a part of our state's history.
Please publish this so the people who wish to knock them down might reconsider.
Your friend,
CRYSTAL
Age 13, Grade 8

Behavior changes take place within and between people as they learn in the environment. High school students interacting with teachers and principals at resident outdoor schools begin reassessing their goals in life. "What contributions can I make to improve the quality of educational experiences?" they ask.

One high school student at a week-long resident outdoor school on the Oregon coast expressed his feelings in this way:

"There's so much to learn
So much I don't know,
How can I
Learn to teach others
So they too might

Wonder at the sea of knowledge.
Like the rolling ocean
There is always more to learn,
More to experience.

"If I could but make others
See this,
I will have profited.

"Show me a way
To reach others,
And know what they are feeling,
And I shall not ask for more."

Trained in the skills of group interaction and the teaching-learning process, these high school students assume roles as teaching technicians with elementary students, helping teachers set up investigations for younger children to interact with their environment. For example:

• An experiment in tree competition can develop an understanding of why we need to thin certain tree stands to increase the amount of usable wood fiber per acre.

• Collecting and interpreting soil data can help people better understand the need for increasing productivity of the soil.

• Inventorying a stream contributes to an understanding of the need for clean water for a healthy fisheries resource.

• Measuring the amount of park land in an urban area can develop an awareness of the need for open spaces in cities.

One teacher had this to say: *"Real learning takes place by actual experiences and not just teaching facts and having the children parrot them back."*

Learning in the environment, using the senses, offers an opportunity to observe the "tiny happenings", things we normally pass by and fail to notice. The following "events" were observed by children and teachers in a creative writing class on the schoolyard:

The tiniest sound in the world is . . .
"The slurp of a slug as he samples a morsel while moving his foot, always leaving a part of himself behind . . ."
"The explosion that results when a dandelion is blown apart . . ."
"A busy ant, carrying home the groceries . . ."

"That still, small voice of rightness that comes to my consciousness and says, 'be encouraged, you can do more' ..."

Another class spent time in the park across the street from the school, looking for different shapes of things. Some kids liked the "tree with the big hole in the side shaped like an upside-down pear."

When Jimmy returned to the classroom, he wrote one of the first voluntary papers in his school career:

"It's a tree at the end of the park.

"It's real bushy and green and round and it's got stickers all over it and it has red berries.

"I chose that tree because it's round—no other trees are, they're always spreaded out.

"When I went over there by myself it was quiet—nobody came over to bother me."

We hear a lot of talk about education in, for, and about the environment. Education must be a comprehensive experience that helps a person take all the skills learned in school and apply them to an interaction with the environment.

For example, using a simple process in measurement, children can discuss and explore cause-and-effect relationships of one of the most complex social and political problems facing us today—supply and demand of water. Measuring the average width, depth, and velocity of a stream gives children basic data needed to calculate the total volume of water in the stream, and how many people could live off the water in that stream. This is exactly what scientists are doing to determine if we have surplus water in some of our major rivers to send to other parts of the nation. Students involved in stream studies begin asking these questions:

Should my area supply water to another part of the country to grow more food to ship back to us to buy?

Should we irrigate more land here and just ship the food to the other area in the first place?

Does the water in this river belong to our State? To the region? To the Nation? To the western hemisphere?

What constitutes surplus water, anyway? And for whom?

This type of investigation provides opportunities for people to relate what they hear about managing our water resources to the personal experience they had in measuring the stream.

At a workshop session on Interpreting the Landscape, teachers went on observational searches to find evidence of past events, then pooled their findings for a group interpretation. They reconstructed the cultural and natural history of the area by listing past events by both man and nature.

Using this same technique of investigation, teachers helped their students inventory their own community to reconstruct its cultural and natural history. They found the answers to these questions:

Which streets are oldest? Which houses? How can we tell?

Where is the original "downtown business area" of our community?

What landforms give clues to geologic history?

How has the shape of our community changed since it began?

Other urban investigations included:

• Comparing a downtown city block with a suburban block.

• Investigating the effect of various building materials upon temperature variations on streets.

• Inventorying the plants in a blacktop environment.

Quality environmental learning requires total involvement. One way to encourage this involvement is by establishing local environmental education committees, where people from all the segments of the community—parents, teachers, administrators, representatives of resource agencies and community organizations—can work together to better understand and to improve the quality of living in their community.

Community people and resource agency personnel receive training in environmental investigation techniques, similar to the teachers, that help them initiate back-home action plans.

Examples of the action plans that are developed at these training sessions include:
• Planning of environmental study areas.
• Supporting the local environmental education programs.
• Promoting of citizen involvement in environmental management decision making.

Ultimate impact of these action plans will be community behavior that demonstrates personal commitment.

If we provide environmental problem-solving experiences for school children, we can help them to become thoughtful decision makers with concern about the complex interrelationships of the web of life. And hopefully, then, they will have both the motivation and the skills to make positive contributions to the management of a quality environment.

For further reading:

U.S. Department of Agriculture, *People, Cities and Trees.* Program Aid 958, Superintendent of Documents, U.S. Government Printing Office, Washington, D.C. 20402, 1970. 10¢.

U.S. Forest Service, *Materials to Help Teach Forest Conservation.* FS–28, Washington, D.C. 20250, 1970.

——————, *Watersheds.* FS–15, Washington, D.C. 20250, 1966.

giving handicaps the heave-ho: braille trails and lion tales

THE WORLD OF NATURE is simply too fascinating for anyone to lose out on its wonders due to physical limitations.

Robert Lewis, an educator in Aspen, had long had a dream for visually handicapped people to enjoy nature—life size.

His idea for a nature trail for the blind found support in the U.S. Department of Agriculture's Forest Service. And today his dream is coming true all across the country.

The action started in 1967. An area was found not far from Aspen that contained many interesting natural features. Plans were drawn up by the Forest Service, and several organizations—including the Colorado Highway Department and the Lions Club—agreed to lend their services to assure success for the project.

The result was the Roaring Fork Braille Trail in the White River National Forest. That trail proved so popular that other interpretive nature trails for the handicapped have since been built in National Forests in various parts of the country. In 1971 the Lion's Tale, the ninth trail created by the Forest Service, was dedicated in the George Washington National Forest in Virginia.

Other public and private agencies have also begun to provide similar outdoor opportunities for the handicapped. At present, there are more than 25 special nature trails throughout the country.

A good example of what has been done in a densely populated urban area is the "Touch and See" Nature Trail at the National Arboretum in Washington, D.C. It was built by the Agricultural Research Service, U.S. Department of Agriculture, with guidance and signs provided by the Columbia Lighthouse for the Blind. The 24 stations, each bearing a sign in Braille and in large print, are connected along the third-of-a-mile length by hemp rope.

The trail is open to the handicapped and sighted alike. Here the "nature" story is told in a simple way to visitors

Author RICHARD F. DROEGE is Deputy Chief of the Forest Service.

268

who may have no contact with forests because they live in urban areas or have physical disabilities.

In Montana, the State Federation of Women's Clubs established a Braille Garden and Trail at the School for the Deaf and Blind at Great Falls, Mont. The members provided guide ropes and mounted Braille plaques. The school was delighted and has incorporated the plan with existing plantings and with an adjoining area to be developed with new construction. The State federation sought and obtained technical advice and assistance from the Soil Conservation Service, the State forestry department, and the extension horticulturist.

The project, interestingly, had special side benefits. Boys at the Swan River Youth Camp—part of a corrective industrial institution—transplanted native materials and prepared posts for the Braille signs. They gained self-esteem in doing something for others.

Tucson, Ariz., Albuquerque, N. Mex., Wyckoff and Port Monmouth, N.J., Manchester, Pa., Arvada, Colo., and the Brooklyn Botanical Gardens, Brooklyn, N.Y., are among the areas that now have Braille Trails—all designed to give special pleasures to those among us who cannot see the bright flowers and vivid greens of the plant world.

In South Carolina, Dr. T. L. Senn, Chairman of the Department of Horticulture at Clemson University, has built a nature trail for the blind—with guide ropes and special markers—within a large colonial garden. This garden, planned and planted by the Horticulture Department, features a colonial cabin, plants popular in colonial days, and some historically interesting artifacts. The blind are invited to "touch" and the signs, prepared with the help of a young blind teenager, provide descriptions which have meaning for the unsighted.

At Roaring Fork Braille Trail in the White River National Forest, the Job Corps from a nearby camp cleared a safe trail leading to 22 selected stations where natural objects could be experienced by senses other than sight. The corpsmen erected Braille signs and large-lettered signs for the partially sighted. Teachers and students of the Colorado School for the Deaf and Blind helped in the Braille translations of the nature messages. A turnoff from the main road, a small parking lot, and easy access to the trail were provided.

This short trail starts at a wooden footbridge, winds through a forest of spruce and fir, then proceeds over a glacial moraine down to the edge of a shallow mountain stream and across a small meadow—all this within an area equal to about one city block.

Visually handicapped visitors are encouraged to come into contact with nature through their other senses—to touch ferns and lichen, running stream water, and the growth rings of tree stumps; to smell the balsam aroma of handcrushed needles and the multitude of other odors in a forest environment; to listen to the stream, and the sounds of birds, small animals, and the wind in the trees.

Dwain Jackson studies a tree trunk with his fingers while Philippe Maggio reads from a large print and Braille marker on the "Touch and See" Nature Trail at the National Arboretum in Washington, D.C.

Reaching out to nature with all available senses, and reading the explanatory messages on the markers, can give one a "sense" for natural things often more intense or vivid than through sight alone.

Although the Roaring Fork Braille Trail served as a prototype for later special trails, the others had their innovations. Specific nature trails were made to accommodate not only the handicapped but anyone who wants to use them.

Low pole rails rather than nylon ropes were installed along La Pasada Encantada (The Enchanted Way) in the Lincoln National Forest in New Mexico. Paved trails were introduced to make the going easier for people in wheelchairs.

Mounted animals in their natural setting and relief maps were installed on the Catalina Desert Trail in the Coronado National Forest in Arizona where they could be studied through the sense of touch.

"Sniffing" boxes with the odors of local plants and a rotating tree finder (for the sighted) to help in tree identification were placed on Discovery Way in the George Washington National Forest in Virginia.

One of the most heartwarming features in building special facilities for the handicapped in National Forests is the way that everyone wants to pitch in and help. The General Federation of Women's Clubs, the Lighthouse for the Blind, the Braille Service of New Mexico, Lions Clubs, and the San Bernadino City School are among those who give active help to the Forest Service in these projects.

In addition to trails, the Forest Service has designed two recreation areas especially for the handicapped and their families. One is the Shady Rest Campground near Mammoth Lakes, a heavily used, year-round recreation area in the Inyo National Forest in east-central California. The other is the Trout Pond Recreation Area in the Apalachicola National Forest in western Florida.

These special areas provide accommodations for persons in wheelchairs.

Paved trails and paths are wide and slope gently. Picnic tables have spaces for wheelchairs. Water fountains are low. Guard rails offer protection on the fishing piers. Restrooms have ramps and handrails, sufficient space to maneuver wheelchairs, and special clothes-changing spaces.

Shady Rest, completed in 1970, has room for 17 families and three groups. A self-guiding and paved trail nearby called "Adventure Walk" runs 900 feet and has 11 stops. At each stop, a push-button tape player tells about the plant and animal life, land features, and the historical background of the region.

Five miles northwest of the campground, a fishing pier and small picnic area—specifically for the handicapped —have been constructed at Twin Lakes.

Shady Rest was a community project involving the Lions Club and other citizens of Mammoth Lakes. The Lions collected donations of materials and money from other civic organizations, industry, and individuals throughout the West. Most labor and equipment were contributed locally. The Forest Service planned and designed these facilities.

Trout Pond Recreation Area, about 13 miles south of Tallahassee, Fla., was suggested by the Tallahassee Handicapped Club. The area includes 3,500 feet of paved paths; modified restrooms; picnic area; fishing pier with benches; a swimming pool with a ramp to allow easy access to the water; and low, flat steps for the arthritic and the elderly. A spray area is available for those who are unable to go into the pool.

The paths have a white line painted along the pavement for the partially sighted and wooden signs at hand height with large, cutout letters. The signs direct the visitor to the picnic areas, pool, fishing pier, and shelter. Plastic plates imbedded in the path and slightly raised above ground level guide the blind visitor, through his cane, to the location of signs. Overnight camping facilities for the handicapped are expected to be added later.

Besides the special trails described,

there are many self-guiding trails throughout the National Forest system that can be traversed by partially handicapped persons. The Forest Service plans to adapt many other recreation areas so that the handicapped can use them.

Opening the wide and fascinating world of nature to the blind and the handicapped in our society has barely begun. There is much that has to be done, and it need not be expensive. It is often possible, for instance, to adapt portions of an existing trail in a public park or woodland, or even in a privately owned wooded area if the owner consents, without too great an outlay of money or labor.

To get a project started in your area, a local service club could pool its efforts with a public park or forest resource agency and with organizations concerned with the handicapped. Service clubs have been largely instrumental in raising funds for trail projects and have, in many instances, provided the labor of members and others in the community to get the job done.

When your project has been agreed upon, there are certain guidelines that should be followed:

Choose an area with a variety of interesting natural features, away from industrial or urban noises and from air and water pollution, if possible.

Make the trail self-guiding. It bolsters the handicapped person's self-confidence if he knows he can walk along the trail with little or no help.

Seek guidance from the blind and handicapped to assure that you are meeting their needs.

If possible, include a running stream within easy reach of the trail and natural objects that can be felt, heard, or smelled as well as seen. Contrast open, sunny areas with those that are forested or shady. Also, vary the trail surface from a forest floor of soil and leaves or shredded bark to fine gravel or pavement.

Make the going easy—smooth surface, gentle slopes, with no obstacles in the way for any of the handicapped or elderly.

Provide a guide rope, preferably of nylon or some other synthetic material, about 30 inches high along the trail length. Run the rope through eyelets in posts set 15 or 20 feet apart. If a manila rope is used, allow for rope shrinkage in wet weather. If log rails are used instead of ropes, set them low enough to serve as resting spots.

Install sturdy signs, slanted slightly to allow rain runoff, on wood or metal stands 30 to 36 inches high so that everyone can read them easily, including people in wheelchairs.

The message on each sign should be in Braille for the blind, and in large printed type for others. Raised letters may be used instead of Braille. National or local organizations for the blind will be glad to furnish assistance with the Braille printing.

Messages on the signs should be short and simple, giving a brief description of the plant or object, its characteristics, and the site where it is growing or lying.

Trails should not be so long as to be tiring. The usual length is about 800 to 1,200 feet. The width is about 4 to 6 feet, if the trail is built in a circle or loop, so that the visitor returns to the starting point. If not built in a circle or loop, the width should be sufficient to allow two wheelchairs to pass with at least a foot to spare.

The number of signs and their distances from each other will depend on the length of the trail and the number of points of interest.

The cost can be as little as $100 (or even less), if the trail is included in an existing park or public garden. The cash outlay will depend on the extent of the project and on the amount of materials and labor donated by volunteers and cooperating agencies. Some that are more elaborate may run into thousands of dollars.

Don't judge the value by the cost. The handicapped, particularly those who live in urban areas, gain new perspectives and, in many cases, a new excitement about life from their "own parks." Understanding and enjoying an outdoor environment can add to the quality of life for them. These special nature trails add to the quality of the Nation's environment.

Listen to this bit of advice from a perceptive young woman who is blind and who has visited some of the nature trails for the blind:

"Emphasis should be placed on the educational value and beauty of the trail for both blind and sighted people. With the exception of braille signs and guided ropes, the trail should not possess any special feature for the blind.

"'A sniff box for the blind' to smell a variety of wood fragrances should not be a special attraction . . . . A sighted person . . . thinks it would not be worthwhile for him . . . The blind person, on the other hand, feels that this special exhibit makes him different from his sighted peers, and . . . he may resent and avoid it.

"A sniff box could be a valuable feature of a trail, if it is not limited . . . to the blind. The sense of smell is for each of us only one of several ways to make one aware of his natural environment.

"A trail designed for the blind and physically handicapped should . . . uphold the same objective as that maintained by other trails—to develop a growing knowledge and awareness of mankind's natural environment. In actuality, this special trail is not really so special after all, for it possesses only two distinctive features: guide ropes and braille and large print markers. If planners and designers were to keep this fact in mind, their finished product would probably be very successful and appreciated by blind and sighted visitors alike."

More special trails and facilities for the handicapped are being planned in the National Forests. As the idea spreads, the number of trails on public lands, including city parks and even some private lands, will grow. The 25 or so existing trails today on all lands will likely appear a small number indeed when we look back to 1971 from the end of the next few decades.

 # green fingers help reshape troubled neighborhoods

BUSY FINGERS indicate something is being done. Sometimes the fingers stray from acceptable paths to engage in less than honorable activity, but when the active fingers are guided along productive lines they generally create something for which a community and even an entire city can be proud. This was the case in Portland, Oreg., where an idea became a reality in 1968 and grew throughout the State and Nation to help troubled neighborhoods solve their own problems with pride.

Portland differs little from any city in the United States except that its size offers more problems than a wayside town, but it has fewer problems than the largest cities in the Nation. There are the days with smog, bulging schools, a river splitting the city and too few bridges to handle the traffic during rush hours. Its people can resemble any city cross section, anywhere, and some of them find themselves with problems they can't handle until shown a way.

An area of Portland known as Albina was a depressed and almost forgotten tract of land on the east side of the Willamette River. The residents were predominantly Black and could speak about little else but joblessness, crime among adults and juveniles, inadequate nutrition, broken homes, needy dependents, and the indifference of absentee landlords to substandard housing conditions.

Something had to be done that money could not provide alone. A new attitude and spirit was needed, but a simple, worthwhile project to bring it about had not been found. Travel away from Albina was difficult and few could participate in activities that were not within walking distance of their homes. Youngsters had been able to participate to a limited extent in scouting, church outings and 4-H Club programs, but again the problem of going away from the community prevented participation by more than a mere handful.

Three things happened early that spring that were to give Albina a new spark of hope. An imaginative member of the Oregon Federation of Garden Clubs (Mrs. Frances Mathews) had gotten the idea for her organization to sponsor a vegetable gardening project. She had discussed this with her friend, Mrs. Viviane Barnett, a Black real-estate broker who lived and conducted her business in Albina. Mrs. Barnett combined her enthusiasm with personal energy and drive to start the project moving.

The final event was the U.S. Government funding of special work to involve depressed areas in programs that were similar to or a direct part of 4-H Club work.

Mrs. Barnett found herself engaged in many meetings and campaigns to get information to the children and parents of the Albina area. Handbills, press releases, radio and television announcements all contributed to the gathering of interested but cautious persons who believed that the empty lots and backyards were meant for something better than growing weeds to hide the collection of refuse, rusting junk, and abandoned automobiles. Once cleared of debris, the fertile soil could be tilled and planted to vegetables and even

Author WILBUR BURKHART is Area Extension Agent for the North Willamette Valley, Oregon. His office is in Portland.

Coauthor GRAY THOMPSON is Extension Agent, 4-H Club Work, who supervises youth programs for Oregon State University from his Portland office.

flowers to brighten the neighborhood, as well as offer the participating families a better variety of fresh produce for daily meals.

Committee action followed under the tireless Negro leader who knew the end of the day only by the time all work at hand was done. The project name, "Green Fingers," was born and was to identify all future efforts directed towards making the project a success.

Idle land under control of the State Highway Commission was given to the project free of charge for a 2-year period. This consisted of several city blocks or portions of blocks to be used for new highway construction some time after the 2-year period had passed.

Once the obstacles to use of the land had been cleared, the cleanup operations never wanted for volunteer help, trucks and other equipment to carry out the ground breaking and soil tilling operations. National Guard equipment use was donated to getting the garden tracts cleared, graded, and broken so tilling operations could be done on schedule. By this time 50 families had involved 200 persons in the hand tool work of final soil preparation.

Seeds, fertilizer, pesticides, and small equipment were needed to start the action on the newly-tilled gardens. Two other persons with several years' experience each in guiding of youth work through 4-H Club programs, Gray Thompson and Willard Lighty, gave help to locate seed from firms that had excess supplies. The firms made outright donations when they learned of the project goals.

Fertilizer manufacturers, pesticide formulators, and civic clubs turned their attention to the vegetable gardens of Albina. Equipment was loaned or donated for the safe and effective application of fertilizer, insect killers, and irrigation water.

The agri-business organizations had only to learn of a need and they provided the answer—because "Green Fingers" was no longer a strange word in Portland.

Seeds were packaged from the bulk supplies and a variety assortment given

273

each participant along with the appropriate Oregon State University vegetable garden bulletins. Many had never before planted a seed or watched a small plant grow from the series of operations they were about to perform. More joined the program as churches and schools learned of the project and urged family participation.

Some of the more militant groups of black people endorsed the operation and gave active support in many ways because of the visible progress that was being made.

Water for summer irrigation is not always plentiful in "rainy" Oregon where clouds can suddenly disappear one day early in June to stay hidden until late fall. When water is available, it must be metered to and paid for by the user without exception.

A civic organization noted for its hilarity in getting worthwhile jobs done is the Portland Rainmakers who had launched a sales campaign to sell "Watered" and "Uncommon" stock at every opportunity, including an occasion when a member visited the floor of the United States Senate. Proceeds of the stock sales went to pay for the irrigation water used to keep gardens moving along.

Fear of vandalism was short-lived due to the number of persons involved in making the project a success. Some damage was done to the gardens by carelessness but the spirit and attitude of persons in the community provided both volunteer watches and a feeling of respect for the gardens which by this time had given a new life and hope to the community.

Everyone who could lend a helping hand was already working or asked if he could be involved.

One individual became the "watermaster" in order to insure against any garden dying from lack of water when it was time to start the sprinklers. Waste of water too was a concern and this role of watermaster proved important since the individual was able to exert his friendly push towards some youngster who was not quite working up to capacity.

Success in one location proved to generate a competitive spirit and teamwork approach. Comparisons of one group's success to another group's efforts identified the need for saying thank you to all the participants and project supporters. Mrs. Barnett already had the plans made for a harvest festival where vegetables were exhibited and judged.

The event again was a huge success, and concluded with a soul-dinner picnic where the leaders and participants expressed gratitude for the help they had received.

Onlookers saw many ways to adapt this project to their own communities to provide a productive learning experience in their backyards and vacant lots.

The project had proven itself to be without an age limit as all from tiny toddlers to retired grandfathers took some kind of active part.

Young couples saw it as a way to stretch inadequate food budgets and provide themselves with a more nutritious diet.

Produce was used fresh, or stored and preserved by freezing and canning to provide vegetables for the gardenless winter months.

Albina no longer claims title to being the only or the largest home garden center in Portland. Its original 3 acres of vegetables have grown in size to the point where the leaders are not sure how large the aggregate of all plantings might be.

Other school units and churches have followed in the same path to utilize idle tracts of land which would otherwise collect junk partially hidden by weeds.

Today the count has risen into the thousands of persons throughout the country who find new adventure and learn new lessons as they help themselves. The numbers of idle and mischievous fingers are reduced as the younger generation beams with pride while showing visitors its accomplishments. The many leaders like Mrs. Barnett wear smiles of satisfaction in knowing their efforts have helped a group of "Green Fingers" build a better America.

274

inner city neighborhood gardens
create new community spirit

IT HAS BEEN SAID, "Beauty and blight are infectious; inoculate a neighborhood with either and it will spread." Cities such as Philadelphia and Los Angeles, Baltimore and Boston have found inner-city residents interested in improving their environment with projects of neighborhood gardens. Some efforts are sparked by metropolitan housing authorities. More often the local garden clubs initiate projects through their federation.

In Washington, D.C., an elementary school program became the motivating force behind a neighborhood improvement effort.

In the spring of 1970, Mrs. Sylvia Shugrue, a science teacher in the D.C. public schools, set out to teach her pupils something about the way things grew in the United States.

The school's only bit of earth was a badly eroded bank supporting a completely black-topped playground. With the help of Thomas Ayres, a retired soil conservationist, she and several of the school's staff supervised the youngsters' efforts to stabilize the bank.

At the suggestion of David Karaker of the National Park Service, the school lot was divided into four parcels, each designated to be typical of a major growing area of the United States. Cooperation of the Park Service made it possible to plant the "forest" area with saplings of maple, black locust, mulberry, and oak. The "cropland" area was planted with summer squash, tomatoes, collards, and corn, providing several families with fresh vegetables. The "desert" area's unfamiliar barrenness stood out against the lushness of the surrounding parcels. The fourth area, planted as "grassland," was indeed a very mini-prairie.

Children have a natural affinity for soil, and being able to play in it on schooltime makes it all the more fun. They also have enormous natural curiosity, and watching tiny seeds sprout into growing plants that can only exist with adequate care makes youngsters develop a sense of responsibility to living things. It frequently converts them into lifelong gardeners.

But curiosity isn't a trait solely confined to children. The constant outdoor activity at the school brought neighbors together to watch the progress of the small garden.

With the instincts of a good teacher, Mrs. Shugrue realized she had created an atmosphere for learning outside the classroom as well as inside the brick walls of the schoolhouse. She began to give away the extra plants to neighbors who just came by to watch and chat.

Front yards started to bloom and flourish with attentiveness and tender loving care. Sidewalk tree boxes were cleaned up and planted with summer-flowering annuals. By summer vacation, the entire area was awash with green and blooming plants. Together, the children and the neighbors celebrated the completion of the ecological landscaping at a dedication which coincided with Earth Day.

"Our Block of Earth" had demonstrated what cooperative effort could do to improve immediate surroundings. But this was not to be the end. Good ideas have a way of growing.

Author AILEEN LUBIN is Editor of *The Green World,* a segment of Panorama produced by WTTG-TV, Metromedia Broadcasting, Washington, D.C. *The Green World* reports on gardening, ecology, and the environment.

Supported by a grant from the Society for a More Beautiful Capital, the neighbors of Madison School cared for the children's gardens all summer long. They watered and kept a watchful eye to prevent damage from vandalism. When September came and the children returned to school, their garden was intact.

It was at this point I first came across the project, then in the throes of bulb planting for the coming spring bloom. Knowing how successful the community gardening efforts had been in Philadelphia, I approached Mrs. Shugrue with the idea of forming a Neighborhood Garden Association in Washington.

The Neighborhood Garden Association (NGA) of Philadelphia was organized in 1953, and currently has over 500 city blocks participating in a gardening program. An application to become a garden block is made either by an individual or a group to the NGA. Eighty percent of the families on the applying block must agree to participate. A block leader is designated.

Window boxes are built and planted. The project in Philadelphia is the oldest of its kind in the country, and has been the basis of many parallel efforts in the United States and abroad.

Contributions from the American Association of Nurserymen, the Society of American Florists, the Floral Telegraph Delivery Association, and the American Society of Landscape Architects had made it possible for the Washington group to take a bus trip to Philadelphia. There they could see for themselves what had been accomplished in neighborhood gardening programs in that city.

December was hardly a month for viewing gardens, and the weather was anything but ideal. Despite the cold drizzle, our hosts walked us through their demonstration gardens and in and out of narrow inner-city streets to show us vest pocket parks and window box gardens which held the only living green things in a background of brick and cement.

A tour of the association's head-quarters adjacent to the demonstration garden showed the Madison School neighbors how the Philadelphia program functioned all year long. The headquarters provided space for meetings, workshops, and a library.

The chatter by our group of about 30 adults and children on the way back to Washington indicated that seed had been sown on fertile ground. The Madison community had dreams of accomplishing as much, and perhaps even more, in their own neighborhood.

Meetings continued to be held at the school with the cooperation of the principal, Mrs. Dolores Zucker, and her pupil personnel staff, Mrs. Frances Boldin and Mrs. Janet Davis. The new neighborhood garden group was formally named the Community Environmental Improvement Association, an appropriate name as concern for the environment spread beyond their gardening efforts.

Cooperation of the Department of Sanitation was enlisted in refuse removal. Teams cleared trash and litter from front yards of empty houses, and cleaned up street accumulations. People began to paint and fix-up. Negotiations were started for permission to use an empty house lot across from the school as a demonstration garden.

The lot was small and in all but an impossible condition for growing anything. Foundation rubble had been pounded into the ground, which was more like concrete than soil. Children had used the open space as a play area for years. It seemed an insurmountable task to prepare it for a garden.

Trial efforts at pickaxing were futile, but no one was defeated. As in all community efforts, pooling talents and contacts is the answer to getting things done.

Someone secured the use of a backhoe and the worst of the building rubble was removed. It was decided to build a small retaining wall of railroad ties and fill the lot with fresh topsoil. Again, this was accomplished by contacting someone who could help.

The Society for a More Beautiful Capital pitched in to help with the purchase of a new fence. The labor to erect it was supplied by the community.

While spring preparation for the demonstration garden got underway, other neighbors continued the effort to spread community interest. Staff personnel at Madison School joined neighbors in approaching people with the idea of block gardening.

The summer of 1971 saw 10 surrounding blocks organized and planted. Although community gardening groups in other cities have sponsors for a few seasons, the Community Environmental Improvement Association of Washington, D.C., has financed this effort themselves. White elephant and bake sales have been organized; plans for block parties and plant sales are underway.

Ralph Waldo Emerson said, "It is one of the most beautiful compensations in this life that no man can sincerely try to help another without helping himself."

If gardening together can be the means to the full realization of "community," then no city should be without such an effort. Not all social ills can be cured by such projects, but where the garden projects have been established there has been a marked improvement in respect for private property, decreases in neighborhood crime and vice, and a concern for each other that previously was nonexistent.

Whether initiated by local government, the garden clubs, or settlement houses, we must try to see more neighborhood garden efforts established in the United States.

public housing gardens— landscapes for the soul

WE DO NOT usually associate agriculture with the depressed central city areas, and yet it is here that a new role has emerged for a specific agricultural discipline: horticulture. In public housing where clusters of multistoried buildings dwarf the individual resident, participation in gardening has led to self-realization and a fuller appreciation of life's potential. Growing flowers has become a means of communicating deeper values in living to people whose environment is hostile to such values.

I have reached these conclusions after 9 years of working with the New York City Housing Authority, Tenant Flower Garden Competition. The contest, devised originally to develop more favorable relationships between the authority and its 600,000 tenants, has grown from 105 entries in 1961 to 283 entries in 1971, involving 3,000 tenants.

Much of the success of the program has been due to the energetic leadership provided by the Tenant Program division, which also develops programs of sports, arts and crafts, etc. They are assisted by a Staff Garden Committee of the managers and superintendents of projects, and also a Tenant Garden Committee—the leaders of the previous year's winning gardens.

Operation of the contest is quite simple. In March, groups of residents wishing to participate fill out an entry form and are assigned plots of ground (not to exceed 300 square feet) at their project on which to grow gardens. The full gamut of associations is represented, including children's day care centers, Scouts, ethnic societies, senior citizens clubs, handicapped workers, and youth groups.

Author CHARLES A. LEWIS is Director of Sterling Forest Gardens, Tuxedo, N.Y. For 9 years he has served as judge and advisor to the New York City Housing Authority Flower Contest. He has been consultant to large beautification projects in Washington, D.C., and in New York City.

Jamaica Day Nursery sign says "We planted corn, zinnias, petunias, marigold, lima beans, snap dragon, morning glory."

The authority provides instruction programs on growing plants, utilizing the services of local botanical gardens and horticultural groups. Slides of previous years' gardens, available to all groups, provide clues to desirable design concepts.

The authority has developed a manual covering design, preparation of soil, use of fertilizer, planting, and growing plants from seeds. A large portion is devoted to descriptions of various plants and the conditions required for each, with blank spaces provided for inserting plant pictures. Each garden entry receives an allowance of $25 for purchase of seeds, plants, fertilizers, and other gardening necessities.

Each group is responsible for its own garden design, including the choice of plants. Some start with seeds and cuttings grown in milk cartons on window sills, while others prefer to purchase started plants. The gardens are cultivated and watered all summer by the contestants, aiming for perfection in August, when a panel of judges—horticulturists, landscape architects, and garden writers (three per borough)—view the entries and select the best gardens in each borough.

Awards are made to the winners at a gala meeting in late August, with city officials in attendance and an audience composed of participants from all five boroughs. Excitement runs high as the slides of the winning gardens are shown, each group loudly acclaiming its entry as it flashes on the screen. Finally the awards, silver bowls, and testimonial scrolls are given to representatives of the winning groups.

At first glance one would assume gardening in public housing projects is a rather innocuous beautification activity. This was my attitude as I approached my first judging experience during the contest in 1962. However, in talking to the contestants about their gardens, I became aware of a much deeper involvement, beyond the obvious esthetics of a flowerbed.

The contestants expressed themselves in letters to the authority, ". . . but what is more important, is everyone getting to know each other. Everyone smiles and discusses our garden. They worry over too much rain, not enough rain. . . . They're all so pleased that the children are interested in caring, not destroying. From early morning till late evening you can see neighbors leaning on the garden fence. It has become a center spot in our court, where everyone is a friend."

From another letter, ". . . the boys really suprised me the most in their tender handling of the plants. They watch the plants like hawks, and woe betide anyone who comes near with mischief in mind."

One project in a devastated part of Brooklyn had seven entries in time to start the contest, plus 10 more gardens started by the tenants even though they were too late to qualify. They used their own money to produce these gardens.

The manager, tremendously enthusiastic, said the children who usually trampled grass were now cultivating and watering. Gardens bloomed in areas where grass had not been able to survive in the past 10 years.

He said that where there were gardens, people no longer threw debris out of the windows. He believed the gardens were an effective deterrent to vandalism.

It is interesting to note that even though this project had entered the contest for the past 6 years and had never won a prize, in 1971 it had more entries than before plus the 10 spontaneous noncontest gardens. Perhaps this is a cumulative effect of the previous years of gardening activity.

In several other projects we found tenants had also contributed funds to expand their gardens, including tulips for spring.

Tenants told how the gardens had become a new focal point for their project, being used as a setting for graduation and wedding pictures. It became the place where neighbors sat to enjoy the flowers and talk.

At one project the groundsman, on his own time, created a large garden full of choice blooms in an area that had been reserved for trash collection. He said he believed people should see flowers rather than old mattresses, and thought that gardens created public disapproval of vandalism. He was well respected by both young and old in the project. In the fall he propagates four hundred cuttings and gives them to the tenants for winter house plants.

With vandalism prevalent, the gardeners developed some interesting methods for cooperative protection of the gardens. One woman on the East Side said she expects no vandalism in the garden because "all the rotten kids are in the contest this year." Often the gardeners would seek out the troublemakers and assign to *them* the task of guarding the plantings.

Neighborliness at Drew-Hamilton Houses.

279

At another garden we were told of lookouts, one with binoculars, in each of the adjoining tall project apartment buildings, who would sound the alarm if anyone tried to pick the flowers. Often the children were given the job of guarding the flowers, each with a specific time of day when he was on duty.

After the program had been in existence for several years the housing authority became aware of unexpected benefits stemming from the tenant gardens. Vandalism of trees and shrubs planted by the authority was reduced where there were gardens. More surprisingly, vandalism inside the buildings was also reduced.

Tenants began to request the authority for permission to help with the landscaping of the buildings—the very antithesis of vandalism! The authority is now looking for ways to continue the program into the winter with perhaps indoor window gardens and also artificial light gardens.

In some projects, garden clubs have been started and tenants wish to have planters, which they would maintain themselves, placed in the lobbies. The gardens are providing an opportunity for dialogue between tenant and administration concerning beauty, rather than the usual complaints and enforcement of regulations.

A number of other communities have reported flower contests and gardening programs. The Norfolk (Va.) Redevelopment and Housing Authority boasts three beautification contests each year for residents of public housing: a cleanup campaign in the spring; a beautiful yards contest in the summer; and a doorway decoration competition during the December holidays. In Middletown, N.Y., gardens bloom at housing projects as the result of a contest inspired by a garden club.

Another type of garden activity in low-income private areas has blossomed in Philadelphia where 500 blocks now participate in a voluntary window box project under the guidance of the Neighborhood Garden Association of Philadelphia.

The flower boxes acted as a catalyst for spontaneous neighborhood improvement. Streets were cleaned, vacant lots cleared, houses painted and repaired, and people on the same block met each other as neighbors, often for the first time. The cultivation of plants had led to a new appreciation of the neighborhood.

It should be apparent that growing flowers can produce profound changes in residents of depressed areas. What is there in this activity of gardening that imparts feelings of dignity and worth, bringing participants to a heightened self-image?

When a group of people join together to plan a garden, they create a common cause whose aim is beauty. Each can express his unique individuality in selection of plants and design of the garden. During months of gardening, the city dweller directs his thoughts and efforts toward the creation of something good and beautiful, often in surroundings that are not conducive to these expressions.

Growing flowers is essentially a one to one activity; the gardener building a direct relationship with his plants. He learns day by day, at a rate dictated by the growth of plants (a different rhythm than found in daily activity). He is involved in a long-term project which cannot be speeded by additional effort, but with patience rewards bountifully.

In the garden he can express himself without fear of rebuke. Plants are nonthreatening, offering their reward without discrimination as regards age, race, language, sex, or social status. A certain amount of knowledge and skill is required, but plants will blossom predictably if given proper care.

The city gardener discovers in his work new life-enhancing values. Growing plants suggests to him the possibility of beauty and order in his life; it is a bridge to a new basis of communication with fellow residents.

As the plants start to bloom, he finds, often unexpectedly, that his private effort is generously providing a pleasure for others. Through this medium, he can find new avenues for

Plantings at Edenwald Houses.

relationships with his neighbors, a heightened expression of his individuality in monolithic apartment complexes.

All of these positive values are developed during the months of tending the garden plot.

Sociologists have defined some of the deficiencies of distressed urban areas as: a need for stimulation to break the monotony of daily life; a need for that sense of community which emerges, not because people are forced to live together, but rather from spontaneous actions; a need for mastery of the environment, so that a person knows he has some degree of control over what happens around him, and is not a helpless cog in the overwhelming machinery of living. The flower projects speak to all these needs.

At a time of despair in core cities across the Nation, here is a vital new challenge—urban horticulture. It can bring to the city values that have been enjoyed by gardeners of all ages: a sense of order, beauty, and self-esteem. Horticulture therapy is used in hospitals and prisons, a full 4-year curriculum is of-

fered at the college level. Why should it not be a part of the treatment of urban ills?

Our increasing population will cause greater concentrations of people to live together. But provide these people with the opportunity to learn from growing plants and perhaps there will emerge a better way of life in the city.

The flower garden technique can be a key to the release of aspirations long denied by the ghetto. Beautification has two faces, the obvious outward physical improvement of an environment, and, perhaps more importantly, the potential for a personal spiritual awakening.

There is much talk about ecology today in terms of the effects of pollution on water, air, soil; the destruction of species; and overpopulation. We try to understand the delicate interaction of minute biological systems which create the dynamic balance of the whole biosphere. How concerned are we about pollution of one of the most important of these systems—the human spirit?

Walter Hickel recently called for a "personal kind of ecology—call it

281

ecology of the mind and spirit of man." He said, "There is a mystery attached to the variety and perfection of nature, a mystery which stirs wonder in a child and gives a grown man perspective. If we help refresh the inner man, we would begin to answer such real problems as those of the inner city."

In the ecology of the human spirit, the microclimate of a flower box or a flowerbed can contain a tremendous healing force.

Horticulture has a new and a vital challenge—to nurture and bring to fruition this potential for human good, which finds life in city gardens.

For further reading:

Bush-Brown, Louise, *Garden Blocks for Urban America.* Scribners, 1969.

New York City Housing Authority, *Annual Flower Garden Competition Manual.* N.Y.C. Housing Authority, Department of Information, Tenant Program, 250 Broadway, New York, N.Y. 10007.

career training in horticulture
for handicapped young folks

"I used to be retarded."

BOB'S WORDS show the transformation in attitude that takes place within a few weeks after retarded young people start their training at the Melwood Horticultural Training Center which is in Upper Marlboro, Md.

The words were a part of Bob's enthusiastic welcome to a newcomer to the center, which is devoted exclusively to mentally retarded boys and girls. Bob was showing the newcomer around the grounds, and wanted him to know that he, too, could find a new life there.

The first step in the transformation takes place when the young person checks in. A young man who arrives at the Center as "little Jimmie," even though he may be 17 or 18 years old, is introduced to the other trainees as Jim. He is told he will be treated as a man, and that he will be expected to act like one. As often happens when a person knows he is expected to behave a certain way, Jim accepts his changed status and responds like a young man.

At the Melwood Horticultural Training Center, new ground is being broken in the lives of the mentally retarded— in the greenhouses, potting sheds, and classrooms—to provide career opportunities that most of the handicapped, and their families, had never dreamed possible.

Melwood was established in 1963 by a group of parents who believed that a plant-growing environment would be an ideal one in which to develop job responsibility, basic work skills, and employability in mentally limited young people. The convictions of these parents were strong; some were professional horticulturists as well as the parents of mentally retarded children.

Starting with a tent on 7 acres of land, Melwood has grown to include a complex of greenhouses, classrooms, a floral shop, and bed after bed of nursery stock to be used in landscaping jobs. This impressive growth is a direct result of a strong community involvement, especially through Lions Clubs that have actually built and financed much of the center's physical facilities.

A 100-acre tract in another part of the State has been acquired. This is being developed as a Horticultural Training-Residential Facility, a happy extension of the center.

The center now earns approximately

Author EARL COPUS, JR., is Director, Melwood Horticultural Training Center for the Retarded, Upper Marlboro, Md.

Trainees with coleus plants in potting shed.

40 percent of its total income. It is otherwise supported by funds from the State, county, private organizations, and dedicated citizens. The center's earnings come from the sale of trees, shrubs and house plants, many of which are grown on the grounds and in the greenhouses; from services in landscaping public and private grounds and in erecting playground equipment; and from the work of the trainees in community cleanup drives.

By late 1971, some 60 trainees were enrolled, 40 boys and 20 girls, in the regular daytime program. Their I.Q.'s vary from a low of 40 to a high of 100, with an average of 60-70. There are also enrichment classes at night in driver education, crafts, cooking, and other subjects for both the Melwood students and alumni. The staff is balanced between those trained in horticulture and those with a sociological background.

We try to keep the newer boys close to the center until they get to know a little about working with the plants and learn some self-sufficiency. They are always keen, though, to go out on the truck with the experienced boys who work in the field during the spring and autumn on some of our maintenance contracts.

The center's primary aim is to prepare these trainees for community employment—to go just as far as possible toward making an otherwise "unemployable" into a self-supporting adult. The training structure goes far beyond the natural therapeutic benefits of working with one's hands in soil. It is a combination of community on-the-job training supported with academic, social, and recreational activities.

Trainees are assigned either to "vocational" or "work experience" courses. For young men, the vocational program is directed to on-the-job landscaping, plus grounds maintenance, playground equipment erection (at public parks

283

and schools), and environmental clean-up projects in the community.

Young women in vocational training participate in a program emphasizing greenhouse and floral design skills, both at the center and in the community. The center's own floral shop provides valuable contacts with customers as well as vocational experience.

The work experience program is designed for the person who requires an extensive personal and vocational adjustment. It is like the vocational program except that it is much more individualized.

To see how Melwood's training program gets started and works, let's go back to Jim.

For the first few weeks, Jim is placed in a variety of work tasks so that we can gage his personal adjustment needs, his demonstrated abilities, and his general interests. He is closely supervised . . . and given individualized instruction in how and when to water plants, what tools to use with what jobs . . . rake, hoe, shovels . . . and some of the simpler chores in the greenhouse.

During this time, one of the teachers assesses Jim's math and reading competence, since many of the trainees who come to us cannot read or write. This helps us avoid putting Jim in any embarrassing situations. Eventually, we can help create new motivations for him to learn to count, tell time, or to prepare and manage a simple personal or family budget.

One of Jim's first learning experiences is related to transportation. The center provides transportation only from certain central community pickup points. Jim's family—with the help of his instructor—teaches him to use public transportation to and from this pickup point.

When Jim achieves a certain stability within his new environment—with most boys this takes 6 to 8 weeks—he goes on a small community work crew, or he is assigned to a prevocational unit remaining at the center as part of the work experience program.

Throughout his stay, Jim is surrounded by a learning environment, which is not restricted to the four walls of the classroom. In fact, the "little red schoolhouse" (built by trainees and local Lions Clubs) serves only as a center for teachers and trainees. The learning occurs everywhere . . . in the greenhouses, tool shed, photo lab, the production of the monthly newspaper (written primarily by the trainees), the floral design shop, in community sales, and social trips.

The learning speed is completely geared to help Jim with his work tasks. Teachers go with his work crew to the field, and teach basic academic and social skills as they apply to the work.

After 4 to 6 weeks, Jim is sufficiently motivated to attend every day, although he may have difficulty in adjusting to the schedule of work 8 hours a day, 5 days a week, and 12 months a year.

The length of Jim's stay is flexible, depending entirely on his needs and achievements. Eighteen months is the average.

During his stay, Jim is paid according to his level of productivity and his

Summer staff aide shows trainee how to use cash register in Melwood floral shop.

Instructor (center) explains how to operate power mower.

attitude. He soon learns that he will get paid only if he helps to earn the money. By the time he begins to earn money, he understands why he is at Melwood, and he is interested in working towards community job placement.

Melwood's past history with all of its "Jims" and "Janes" has proved the value of the horticultural environment and vocational program. Through a balance of social and work assignments, the trainees learn to meet and conquer the stresses and demands of the work-a-day world.

It is such an environment that helped Marie, a young lady who spent 5 years in an institution where she was thought to be capable of only very limited training. All of her work had been routine —putting plastic spoons into plastic bags. At Melwood, the creative and motivating environment opened up new levels of productivity and self-respect to Marie. After a year at the center, she learned to make corsages and flower arrangements, a much more rewarding kind of work.

Approximately 20 to 30 trainees a year attain community employment. Graduates often earn between $2.25 and $3.00 an hour. The job responsibility and work habits they acquire at Melwood also qualify them for employment in other kinds of jobs as well— like stockroom helper, labor helper, and clerical aide.

Employers have been highly satisfied with graduates from Melwood because they are conscientious, steady, and anxious to please. Employers who have hired a trainee or two come back to ask for others.

For example, the National Arboretum—a horticultural showcase of the U.S. Department of Agriculture—has been a leader in hiring the mentally retarded graduates of Melwood. It has already put 7 of our graduates to work on its grounds, in its greenhouses, and its herbarium, and has plans for hiring others, including female trainees.

One of the graduates who went to work at the National Arboretum some time ago did so well that he soon saved more than enough money to buy a new car—for cash.

He was so pleased with his job at the arboretum, that he came back to Melwood for one of our "enrichment" evenings, bringing the Department's movie about the Arboretum, and told of his experiences there. He made quite a hit with the girls with his new car!

The garden shop of a large Washington chain store has hired a young lady graduate to do floral design work at $3.41 an hour. And the manager of a community park in Maryland wrote recently that the Melwood student he had hired is his best employee despite his handicap.

Pam and Debbie, two young trainees, described in the Melwood Newsletter their participation in a holiday plant sale sponsored by a USDA employee group:

"At the Department of Agriculture we sold plants, arrangements, wreaths, and wrappings. Every day for three days the crowds would get worse. We worked from 10:00 to 3:00 each day. We had to pick things out for people every day. We learned how to make change at the sale. We had a lot of fun at the Department of Agriculture. We met many people there. Everybody likes the things we made. The people there were very considerate. The Department of Agriculture was very big."

Melwood is proof that a horticultural environment opens training and career opportunities for the mentally limited. It has been so successful in its 9 years of existence that it has attracted national attention, and Melwood's format is being copied in other communities.

Melwood has also proved that a helping hand to the handicapped can provide practical help to an industry. There has long been a national shortage of trained workers in the floral and nursery industries. The shortage of trained horticultural workers in the Washington metropolitan area has been especially acute. Many workers, without physical or mental handicaps, prefer other types of work.

So the handicapped, trained and equipped by Melwood, offer a new source of labor to nurseries and florist shops. The employers are pleased to find that in helping a person achieve self-respect and employment, they are helping themselves. They have learned that Melwood has been taking the unemployable and making them good employees, taking people who might otherwise become a public responsibility and making responsible citizens of them.

Although Melwood is devoted to the mentally limited youth, the horticultural environment it has thrived upon has proved fitting as a training ground for other types of handicapped. Many successful and innovative programs, some predating Melwood, have widened the career potentials of other groups—including the blind and the deaf.

For instance, the Nation's forests are now being used as training camps for a variety of handicapped individuals. In Washington State, 100 disabled young men have taken part in a relatively new type of training-employment program. The men are physically strong but have varying handicaps such as deafness, mental retardation, and other obstacles to normal employment. But in the forests, they have helped in planting more than 4 million trees to aid the labor-short timber industry.

"Greenhouse and Nursery Training for the Blind" grew out of a shortage of job opportunities for blind and visually handicapped persons in rural communities. Set up in 1955, this project was sponsored jointly by the Office of Rehabilitation, U.S. Department of Health, Education and Welfare, and the Department of Education at the Georgia Academy for the Blind at Macon, Ga. It was their purpose to invent special techniques and provide special training to enable sight-handicapped persons to achieve the same horticultural objectives as persons with unimpaired sight.

The amazing thing about this project is that those sight-handicapped persons learned, physically and psychologically, to become useful employees for many of the usual tasks in greenhouses and nurseries. They learned that they would be competing with sighted persons, and could not expect preferential treatment. In less than 2 years, six adult trainees had been placed with commercial flower growers and nurserymen.

This pilot project proved that it could be done, and it has now become a continuing program for the young students of the Georgia Academy for the Blind. Besides, it serves as a model for other institutions wishing to offer courses leading to horticultural careers for the blind and partially sighted.

Jean Marie Fisher of Tuckerton, N.J., is also proof of the value of horticulture as a training environment. She is a 1949 graduate of the Marie H. Katzenbach School for the Deaf in Trenton, N.J., where she received her horticultural training. She began work for a commercial florist in the greenhouse, then moved on through work in retail shops as a designer, and now operates her own florist shop.

Miss Fisher is not the only success story from the Katzenbach School. Other graduates have found placements with universities, retirement villages, and other campus style industries. Some have been placed with large commercial growers.

Use of horticulture as training, career opportunity, and therapy for the handicapped is on the increase. The success so far has been great. The present trend must continue so that more handicapped are given the opportunity to achieve their career potentials through horticultural training.

older citizens bring young thumbs to a wide range of gardening

SOME RETIRED PERSONS are born gardeners; some learn gardening after they retire; still others have gardening thrust upon them.

No one knows how many million retirees dig and delve in everything from a window box to a half acre; to say nothing of the countless others past 55 who, although still employed, garden for a hobby. The 1970 census shows that 38,631,990 Americans are 55 or older.

Some of these senior-citizen gardeners work in groups; others go about it on their own.

Many retirees have moved to places where they must learn about new soils, new climates, and even new types of plants. For born gardeners the new environments present an interesting challenge.

Those who have never gardened before—or thought their gardening days were past—have become gardeners as the result of encouragement by neighbors, friends, or relatives. And then there are those who have had gardening thrust upon them; either as a way to pass the time, or because social pressure has demanded that they "keep the place looking nice."

If you asked these senior disciples of Demeter why they worship at her shrine, they would probably say because they like growing things, because gardening takes them out of doors and gives them exercise, or because it's just something to do.

Not all retired persons are affluent. In recent years many have been established in publicly supported housing centers. Public programs have been set up for retired persons on welfare or with low incomes.

One of these is the Golden Age Center of the Welfare Federation in a downtown Cleveland, Ohio, low-cost apartment house for the elderly.

Author CHARLES A. (AL) BOND resides at Panorama City, Wash. He formerly was Extension Editor at Washington State University.

Participants in Cleveland's Holden Arboretum project. Left, pruning privets for their roots, to be used as understock for lilacs. Right, working in the greenhouse.

In that center, a gardening program has continued for 16 years. This program has actually resulted in mutual benefits! The horticulturist of Cleveland's Holden Arboretum has supervised the garden project and in return the arboretum has received help from the senior citizens.

Two series of classes are conducted each year for members of the Cleveland Golden Age Club; one in the spring and one in the fall. Each series runs for 5 weeks.

Members of the local branch of the Garden Club of America furnish transportation to the Arboretum and give instruction in the greenhouses, and serve snacks to members of the gardening classes.

Eight ladies were included in the introductory group. As the idea caught on, attendance increased. Now there are 20 to 25 participants—both men and women—in each group. Ages range from 65 to 80. There are a few new people each time, but there are a number of repeaters and several members have participated for 5 years.

Class members are introduced to the many mysteries of garden culture. They learn about plant propagation, hybridization, making cuttings, and making plant labels, and they assist the horticulturist in his work. They tour the grounds of the arboretum where they can see the fruits of their greenhouse activities.

During their arboretum tours, class members are encouraged to collect crabapples, black walnuts and hickory nuts, wild grapes, and apples. All these they are free to keep, to eat, or to use in various types of handicrafts.

Some of their greatest satisfactions come from contributing something useful to the arboretum program. For instance, one arboretum program called for the collection of maple seeds to be sent to Poland. The Golden Age Center gardeners pitched in and in 10 minutes had completed what would have taken the short-handed arboretum staff a considerably longer time.

Another example is at Rockford, Ill. The local branch of the Men's Garden Club of America has sponsored a program for residents of three high-rise apartments for the elderly.

Of the 350 residents, about 50 take part in the "gardening under lights" program.

To get this program started required money, time, and approval of local and State housing authorities. The garden club put up $700 for installing tables, gardening lights, and materials. One club member with considerable indoor gardening experience volunteered to lead the project. He enlisted the help of fellow members. Housing authorities and apartment managers enthusiastically embraced the idea.

One first-floor room in each of the buildings was assigned as the "gardening under lights" room. There the lights and tables were installed. Advance notices were posted announcing that the program would get underway during Men's Garden Club week.

Residents were quick to enroll. Out of the 350 apartment occupants, some 50 participate. There has been some turnover, of course, but the number remains about constant.

Weekly one-hour classes are held to introduce new projects and to teach various aspects of plant culture. During the rest of the week, group members

may visit the room whenever they wish to care for their plantings. Each participant has a small "plot" on a table for his experiments.

When the program started in the fall of 1970, the immediate goal was to get something blooming fast. Therefore, they started in with slips from coleus, browellia, and impatiens. Later they planted miniature tree seeds. These plantings eventually were used in a study of the art of *bonsai*. The most popular project was the creation of terrariums in goldfish bowls.

In the spring of 1971, gardeners started seedlings which later on were moved outside to supplement plantings of the housing project's landscape gardeners.

To check acceptance of the program and to guide future development, the garden club distributed questionnaires to participants. They were invited to criticize the program. Sixty-three percent said the space was too small as against 37 percent who said that space was ample. Some said they would have liked more time for discussion, and others said the lessons were too short. On the whole, response was overwhelmingly favorable.

Members listed among their enjoyments: learning, planting, watching the plants grow, fellowship, good leadership, and working in the earth.

The Rockford Men's Garden Club is hopeful of starting similar programs elsewhere.

Another development for retirees which has been spreading throughout the country for a decade or so is the retirement community. Here individuals and families in the 50-plus bracket own or lease various types of dwellings. Frequently part of the agreement calls for some sort of landscape care by the community management. But many of the residents do not rest with that.

For instance, floriculture of one kind or another occupies a good deal of time

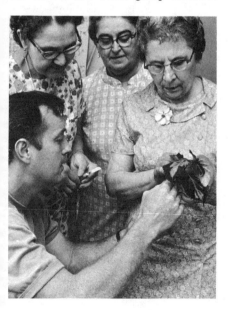

Residents of senior citizen housing learn about propagating plants at indoor gardening program sponsored by Rockford (Ill.) branch of Men's Garden Club of America.

for the majority of the 900 residents of Panorama City, near Olympia, Wash. Vegetable growing attracts about 50 of the 900.

Mild climate at the southern end of Puget Sound, coupled with ample rainfall (about 50 inches) and a loose, sandy loam, are all conducive to gardening. Many of the residents had engaged in gardening before moving to the community.

The corporation which manages Panorama City encourages residents to maintain flowers and shrubbery around their houses or their garden court apartments.

The corporation also provides a tract of sixty 20- by 40-foot plots for dedicated vegetable growers. Free water and a locked shed for tools and gardening supplies are furnished. Each gardener is assigned a plot by a committee. If all are not taken, some avid growers take on a second plot; or several gardeners might "farm" plots together, and at garden fairs sell the produce to nongardening residents. Proceeds are used to buy communally-owned tools of the trade.

They grow everything from Jerusalem artichoke to zucchini squash. One devotee claims a yield of a half-bucket of potatoes to the hill. Some also are growing strawberries, blackberries, and raspberries.

One slave of the spade is undaunted by a physical handicap. He trundles to his plot by wheel chair. Across its arms rests a saw horse. He deserts his wheels to mount the horse as he works his bit of earth.

The average gardener spends about 2 hours a day working at his plot. Many regularly spend more hours in discussing with colleagues the joys and sorrows of gardening.

Produce goes to the grower's table, to the family freezer, or to appreciative nongardening neighbors.

Many women residents participate in the gardening project.

Roses are favorites among specialists. A retired high school teacher has 65 varieties around his home and has show trophies to prove his expertise.

The broad-leaved evergreens such as rhododendrons are indigenous. Most bulbs do well. Chrysanthemums and asters make showy fall displays.

Another group of specialists totes native shrubs and flowers in from the wilds. Transplants include trilliums, manzanita, salal, Oregon grape, and wild currants.

A retired manufacturer of greenhouses brought one with him. In it he raises orchids and other exotics.

Each month some 60 to 70 persons gather at the community center for a garden forum. Sometimes an outside speaker appears. At other times residents swap garden talk or listen to words of wisdom from neighbors. Several are pros. One is a former State supervisor of horticulture, and one is a long-time commercial florist. There's a retired U.S. Department of Agriculture plant inspector and a retired State district horticulturist.

For 2 years this group has spearheaded a resident only, noncompetitive flower show. The 1971 show had more than double the first year's 250 entries. Visiting experts said displays rivaled many professional exhibits.

One of the larger retirement communities is Sun City, near Phoenix, Ariz. "City" is no exaggeration. The population in 1971 was 17,000.

The management corporation provides for the city's gardeners a 7-acre Agricultural Center enclosed by a 6-foot woven wire fence. The center is divided into 161 plots; some are 20 by 40 feet and some 40 by 60. The corporation provides free, piped irrigation water.

Activities are formally organized. Each of about 200 members of the Agricultural Club pays an annual membership fee of 50 cents. The club with elected officers meets monthly except in the three summer months. A secretary keeps minutes. Bylaws establish rules and regulations for orderly operation of the gardens. The club has been active since 1960. Most of the members garden.

About a third of the plots are worked by man-and-wife teams; some 12

Member of Agricultural Club hoes his crops at the Sun City retirement community in Arizona.

percent of the plots are tended by women alone. One of these lady gardeners is 93 years old and at the last report was going strong.

Some members reach their fields by car. Others use golf carts and bicycles. Some gardeners use power equipment such as roto-tillers and small tractors. Most of them, however, welcome the opportunity to exercise their muscles with shovel, hoe, and rake.

Gardening in Arizona is not without its unique problems and practices. Mother Nature has been lavish with sunshine but stingy with rain and other precipitation.

The trenching method of planting is used. Irrigation is by flooding rather than sprinkling because of the high rate of evaporation. The climate permits plantings in the spring, summer, and fall.

Some residents grow roses and other flowers. Other residents concentrate on vegetables. Some cultivate both flowers and vegetables.

Most of the common vegetables are grown, and some that are not so common in more northerly climes. Take, for example, okra, peanuts, and sweet-

potatoes. Melons are popular and are planted both in spring and summer. Cabbages are put out in the fall. Almost any season is harvest time for one or more crops.

Surplus produce above family needs finds a ready home among nongardening neighbors. None is sold.

One reason for the wire fence is an attempt to frustrate marauding rabbits. Success has been limited. The fence is no deterrent to birds. Consequently, in the spring and fall the plots are covered with nylon netting. Before the fence was built there was some pilfering by humans.

Arizona conditions may be foreign to "tenderfeet" from other parts of the country. Therefore, new club members are waited upon by a delegation of oldtimers. These elder statesmen brief the newcomer on soil preparation and other cultural practices. The new member is also presented with a packet of gardening publications from the University of Arizona Extension Service.

Extension specialists and county agents often appear as speakers at monthly Agricultural Club meetings.

Social scientists say oldsters with nothing to occupy their hands and minds tend to brood, to feel lonely, to believe they have nothing to live for. Planting and caring for growing things gives them a focus of interest and a sense of accomplishment.

As Karl Menninger, the renowned psychiatrist, said about one group gardening project: "I want to be on record as believing strongly in this program of training in Horticultural Therapy. It is one type of what we call adjunctive therapy which brings the individual close to the soil, close to Mother Nature, close to beauty, close to the mystery of growth and development. It is one of the simplest ways to make a cooperative deal with nature for a prompt reward."

Some of the literature on horticultural therapy for the elderly implies a volunteer service opportunity for professional and experienced amateur horticulturists, floriculturists, and flower arrangers. It makes the point that the shut-ins and patients in rest homes and convalescent hospitals take a new lease on life by becoming involved in helping set up indoor greenhouses, making seed collections, and watching the plants grow in a dish in which seeds have been set in a constantly moistened sponge. Others may be interested in growing herbs in a window box.

In *Therapy Through Horticulture,* Watson and Burlingame suggest many opportunities for volunteer help. However, they advise volunteers to approach homebound and infirm patients with caution and empathy. They prescribe advance consultation with hospital authorities and occupational therapists.

The authors point out that many patients have extremely limited strength and that others may resist help until rapport is established.

Plenty of oldsters will be on hand in the future to sow and reap. Bureau of the Census reports for 1970 show that 19 percent of the U.S. population is 55 years old or older. The highest projection figures forecast this percentage dipping to 18.8 percent in 1980 and rising to 19.8 in 1990. The total numbers are expected to rise appreciably; six million more in 1980 than in 1970 and another increase of three million in 1990.

No matter whether the retired gardener be hale and hearty or creaky in the joints, he or she can remain active within limits.

Younger people are wont to ask retirees "What do you do with your time?" A well-nigh ideal response is: "I grow flowers, shrubs, vegetables."

To lift a parody from the Sun City-Youngstown News-Sun—

"Old gardeners never die. They just spade away."

a bright new look for shopping— malls with planted areas

MAIN STREET U.S.A. is not like it was when our great-grandparents tied up at the hitching rail on Saturday mornings for their weekly shopping. That was a pleasant, bucolic, elm-shaded scene. Then came the automobile, the population explosion, the supermarket, suburban sprawl, the shopping center, freeways, and the decline of central cities.

There are still towns in the United States whose main streets look about as they did a century ago. But there are not many like that. Today we have these four basic types of shopping environments:

The commercial strip—in smaller towns this is still a few blocks on Main Street. In suburban areas and on the outer fringes of larger cities and metropolitan areas the strip expands and proliferates along most arterial streets and highways, sometimes many miles in length. It tends to form a large gridiron, particularly when encouraged by strip zoning, which dominates urban and suburban areas and creates a system of de facto neighborhoods.

This is the shopping environment most of us are familiar with: crowded streets, bright lights, a confusion of signs, buildings of all sizes, shapes, and styles lined up higgledy-piggledy, unpredictable and complicated parking arrangements, with little or no green vegetation.

The urban downtown—in the centers of cities and metropolitan areas the commercial strip tightens up, becomes continuous rows of buildings opening directly on the street, of any height from one to many stories. It becomes mixed with more business, entertainment, and light industrial uses, has much worse traffic and parking problems, and there is even less greenery. However, in many cities, such as Los Angeles, a high percentage of downtown area has been converted to parking lots through the tearing out of old buildings.

Suburban shopping centers, which have grown rapidly since World War II. These are not commercial strips, but rather are concentrated groups of stores, selected carefully for the anticipated market area, and surrounded by ample parking. Usually they are put together by one developer-architect team which assembles land, financing, buildings, and commercial leases to produce functioning centers.

The suburban shopping centers are far enough out from downtown areas to find adequate land at reasonable prices. They are made possible by freeway, highway, and/or rapid transit systems which make them easily accessible to many thousands of potential shoppers. Because of the convenience of one-stop shopping and ample parking, they present serious competitive problems to the commercial strips and downtown areas.

A small percentage of these suburban shopping centers goes beyond the bare minimum of grouped shops with adjacent parking space to provide more or less elaborate planting and pedestrian mall or garden spaces.

Downtown renewal areas—some downtown commercial areas have endeavored to meet the shopping center challenge by physical renewal programs. Parking districts have been formed to create adequate parking areas, either by clearing land or by building multi-level structures. Buildings have been renovated, rehabilitated, or replaced with newer and better structures. Sections of downtown, or entire centers, have been reconstructed as new shopping-business complexes. Downtown streets have been closed to auto

---

Author GARRETT ECKBO, a landscape architect, heads the San Francisco office of Eckbo, Dean, Austin & Williams.

traffic and converted into pedestrian malls.

All of this combined experience has made it possible now for us to decide, in any community, what kind of a shopping environment we would like to have, and how we might go about getting it. It is no longer a question of more parking, sign control, or decorating Main Street with hanging baskets of flowers, and trees in pebbly pots.

We now know how to study entire shopping areas, including both public rights-of-way and private commercial property. We can make plans for renovating, rehabilitating, redesigning, and/or redeveloping all or parts of them, as the owners, tenants, and city officials may agree.

All four types of shopping areas can be studied in this way—commercial strips, downtowns, the older shopping centers which may not be up to newer competition, and renewed downtowns whose programs may be incomplete, or not sufficiently advanced.

One fundamental decision must be made at some point in any such shopping area study: Is it enough to provide adequate shopping and parking space, or will the addition of planted pedestrian spaces increase the area's competitive potential?

For those of us who like plants and gardens the answer may seem obvious. But for many hard-headed merchants, developers, and marketing economists it must be proven that the addition of planted spaces will actually increase the business volume by attracting more customers.

As usual, figures can be used to prove both sides. High quality shopping centers with elegant pedestrian spaces have excellent business results. So too do poor quality centers with minimum pedestrian spaces, when they occupy strategic locations. Redeveloped downtown mall areas like Fresno and Burbank in California improve business. But old downtowns may also do well with more parking and with better merchandising.

Current environmental and ecological concerns are creating an atmosphere

293

in which the visual quality of shopping
areas may be considered important for
its own sake. If the other aspects of
shopping area planning receive proper
consideration, visual quality—including
planted pedestrian spaces—will certainly not be bad for business and probably will improve it. Nothing would
help the quality of life in urban and
suburban America more than if all
shopping areas of all types were to
become involved in serious competition
in order to provide quality shopping
environments.

What do we mean by a quality
shopping environment, including planted pedestrian spaces? We mean one
which has not only attractive and convenient buildings and adequate parking, but also high-quality circulation
spaces between them and connecting
all of them. By high quality we mean
some or all of the following:

—Ample walking space wherever we
want to go, without conflict with cars.

—Planting of trees, shrubs, vines,
flowering plants, grass to create a garden atmosphere.

—Spaces with comfortable seats, out
of the way of circulation, where we

may sit, relax, rest, recuperate, enjoy the shopping scene, and gather our forces for further participation.

—Integration of shopping activity with pedestrian space development, and with displays, exhibits, kiosks, and action programs.

—Integration of community activity with shopping development by means of art shows; social, political, and cultural events; communication centers; and spaces where groups may meet.

—Play areas for children.

—Integration of planting with circulation, social, and sitting spaces, and other garden elements like fountains, pools, canals, sculpture, mosaic, shelter, lighting, communication systems.

Following are some exciting California examples of quality shopping developments.

Fulton Mall in Fresno has exceeded all expectations in its social, economic, and esthetic success. Ten blocks of Fresno's downtown streets were cleared of all existing paving and curbs and completely redesigned in 1963.

The long, narrow, urban space, confined by buildings of irregular height in what had been a dying area, was rejuvenated with new sculptured landscape forms and water elements.

Fresno's hot summer climate demanded shade and coolness. For these qualities the designers provided pools, fountains, trees, plantings, and shelters, as well as sculpture and other art, lighting, music, and playgrounds.

Paving patterns, the forms of planting areas, and water elements were used to create a sense of leisurely movement throughout the mall while allowing access for emergency vehicles. All of these forms changed the scale of the space, making it seem shorter and wider.

Many art objects were donated by local groups and organizations. The mall became a community project and donations for construction of various mall elements came from a number of firms and individuals in Fresno. Cost of the Fulton Mall was $1.3 million.

Comprising a city-block-long addition to the existing Fulton Mall complex in Fresno, the Kern Mall extension was conceived as a part of the continuing effort to provide both a refreshing and viable pedestrian-oriented shopping environment in downtown Fresno. The newly completed extension, constructed over what was Kern Street, provides a vital link connecting restaurant and lodging facilities to the core of the marketing area, and will support the growing community as other extensions are joined to the mall system.

Major mall elements include a large open center, sierra boulders, a fountain with a stepped pool, and curved linear planting areas.

Riverside Mall, a four-block pedestrian mall with two minor cross malls, was completed in 1966 at a cost of approximately $800,000. Constructed on what had been a major thoroughfare in Riverside, the 100-foot width provides ample space for large planting elements and grade changes within the planting and seating space.

Two major water elements introduce sound and coolness, while planting, seating, and shelters afford rest and leisure for the shoppers. A kiosk shows directions to businesses located on the mall, and a play area is available for children's interest. The mall complements the graceful charm of several early California buildings, including historic Mission Inn.

San Fernando Boulevard in Burbank, once clogged with noisy traffic, is now a flower bedecked urban open space for strolling and shopping, thanks to the creation of Golden Mall. This six-block pedestrian mall with cross malls was constructed in 1968 at a cost of about $1 million.

Design for a grade change across the mall of about 1 foot to 1 foot 6 inches offered the opportunity to introduce steps, ramps, and retaining walls. Pavilions, pools, kiosks, and fountains are major mall elements. Restrooms, storage, and seating are also provided.

Preliminary plans for the Taaffe Street Mall, a 1,700-foot-long mall on Sunnyvale's main street, were completed in 1969. This vital part of the city's central business district was to be

Above, Riverside Mall in California. Right, Bay Fair Shopping Center, San Leandro, Calif. Below, Golden Mall at Burbank.

transformed into an integrated, unified complex of sculptural concrete forms and coordinated paving and planting areas, a pleasant place to shop, stroll, or sit in the shade for an hour.

The irregular geometric forms, which are the primary design elements on the Taaffe Mall, would support seating and serve as displays and as information panels. They would create, through their function as walls, variation and visual patterns, breaking up the long, narrow, confined "tunnel" effect created by the existing structures which line Taaffe Street.

Fountains offering coolness, sound, and motion would be emphasized by platforms serving as bridges and viewing points for the water elements. Tot lots and playground equipment, eating areas, a public address system, a space structure that shades the major pedestrian collection point, and corridors serving as focal points for the entire downtown area would make the mall a community center.

A traffic and pedestrian circulation and parking study for downtown Sunnyvale was made during the design phase for the Taaffe Mall. This study co-ordinated city activities with entrances and facilities on the mall.

Murphy Street, which parallels the Taaffe Mall, was the subject of a street beautification study.

Recommendations were made for enhancement of pedestrian areas and redesign of street parking patterns.

plants in action—changing blight to beauty, teaching ecology

THE SEVENTIES will be remembered as the decade in which urban and rural areas did an about-face—when they woke from torpor and neglect, and got busy trying to repair and protect the landscape.

It was about time, too, and everybody knew it. Although there were gaps of understanding between young and old, black and white, women and men, right and left, everybody seemed to agree on one thing in the seventies: the need for a balanced, beautiful environment; for healthier, handsomer cities and countrysides.

This about-face was heralded by a set of four commemorative postage stamps issued in the fall of 1970. All across the land they proclaimed, "Save Our Soil," "Save Our Water," "Save Our Air," and "Save Our Cities."

In previous decades we had just about decided we did not need natural beauty. We were so enthralled by the works of man in steel, concrete, and glass that plants became something very unsophisticated indeed. They could be of interest only to farmers and eccentric little old ladies.

But that line of thinking did not turn out too well, as we all know. Something inside us began to be dissatisfied with bleak stretches of road, cities which looked like asphalt deserts, and countrysides decorated with weeds and litter.

So we went to work. By "we" I mean everyone—the young people working on people's parks or city beautification projects; members of civic clubs, garden clubs, roadside councils, and chambers of commerce. All of us began putting plants into action to fight the blight, ugliness, waste, pollution, and the ecological imbalance which were threatening to engulf our planet.

"We" also includes the mayors, governors, and Federal administrators who put both money and clout behind the large, ambitious projects. Included, too, are Congress and the President who passed and signed into law the National Environmental Policy Act in 1969 and the Environmental Quality Improvement Act in 1970.

I am also thinking of the organized nationwide groups, often partially funded by business, such as the Environmental Improvement Program (EIP). Sponsored by the National Council of State Garden Clubs and Sears, Roebuck and Company, EIP is perhaps the best example of a comprehensive program aimed at encouraging people in their own communities to improve the quality of the environment.

Awards are offered at the district, State, and national level as an incentive

Author HUBERT B. OWENS is Dean of the School of Environmental Design, University of Georgia, Athens. He is a past president of the American Society of Landscape Architects.

Above, Alamo (Ga.) Garden Club members plant daylilies in City Park, as part of a Georgia Electric Membership Corp. program. Below, University of Georgia students participate in spring cleanup in Athens, Ga. Cleanup was sponsored by a bank.

to garden clubs to work on projects such as creating vest pocket parks, playlots, or roadside rests.

Sears is backing the program with well over $100,000.

Although all federated garden clubs in good standing are eligible to enter projects in the EIP competition, high school, intermediate, and junior gardeners are encouraged to participate and often do. In fact, the program encourages involvement of as many community groups as possible in projects which will restore quality and order to the environment.

The program has been extended over a 2-year period, from January 1971 to January 1973. But a great deal has already been accomplished. Let's take a closer look at some of the outstanding projects which have been carried out by ordinary citizens in all walks of life. The following large- and small-scale efforts were aimed mainly at transforming blight into beauty with the help of plants.

In Centerville, Tenn., members of the garden club and a church are turning a city dump into a park and recreation area. They began by filling more than 60 trucks with old stoves and refrigerators, cans, and trash of all kinds. The garden club ladies even operated the big machines which were used to clear the dump!

They then planted more than 13,000 white pine trees, and covered the rocks with moss, ferns, and lichens. Wild flowers were planted so that every wild flower in the State will soon be represented in the park.

In Sumter, S.C., a council of eight garden clubs transformed 38 blighted areas into mini-parks—a cooperative venture which has drawn on the help of other groups in Sumter and is by no means finished yet.

Each club selected a spot in a depressed area which had been turned into an eyesore by litter and neglect. Neighbors and other interested citizens helped club members clean up these lots and plant flowers, shrubs, and trees.

Benches and litter containers were placed in each mini-park.

Celosia—a plant which resembles the comb of a gamecock—was planted in each park because "Gamecock" was the nickname of General Thomas Sumter for whom the county itself was named.

The clubs received cooperation and moral support from civic organizations, city and county officials, and the local newspaper. Plans are already in the works for continuing and expanding the project. In fact, the idea has already spread to neighboring towns.

In Montclair, N.J., a similar cooperative effort resulted in creation of a vest pocket park in the downtown shopping area. Members of the garden club persuaded a bank to let its littered vacant lot be transformed into an oasis of beauty.

The land was cleared by a group of civic-minded young people. Scale drawings of the lot were donated by the Parks and Recreation Department, and plants were given by local florists.

Garden club members supervised the planting, as well as spearheading and coordinating the entire effort. Before it was all over, they had arranged to have a fountain, spotlights, benches, and trash containers provided by various community groups.

They have noticed, incidentally, that a park which was built with so much community cooperation has been maintained with great care and pride by all those who visit and enjoy it. Litter seems no problem here.

While some citizens were tackling small-scale problems of ugliness, members of the garden club in Greene, a small upstate New York village, made beautification of the entire community the focus of their efforts. Many of the trees in Greene had been felled by disease and the construction of sewage and water lines, which also ruined the town's main street.

To repair the damage, the garden club launched "Project Pride." The entire community was mobilized to clean up and to plant trees and shrubs. Merchants and civic-minded citizens contributed time, money, and muscle. Trees were planted around the library, school, ballpark, church, along the parkway, and in the yards of many private homes. Ground covers, annuals, and bulbs were planted everywhere.

Projects like the preceding are designed to bring beauty to ugly or barren places. But plants have also been put to work to educate while they beautify. The following projects were carried out with the idea of teaching both young and old something about plants and planting as well as achieving a broader understanding of the natural environment.

One of the most sophisticated efforts in this direction was undertaken in Evansville, Ind. There, 18 members of the local garden club created an Outdoor Learning Environment Center on 20 acres of land adjacent to the campus of Indiana State University.

With the help of university officials, they cleared the land to make trails, labeled trees, and made a research map of the land which is being preserved in its natural state. The property includes a lake and many plants native to that part of the country.

The result is a natural outdoor museum which can be used by students, teachers, and all nature lovers. It is of interest to the scientific investigator and amateur naturalist alike.

Another ambitious educational project was launched in Freeport, Ill., by the Civic Garden Club. Although their primary aim was to restore trees which had been destroyed by storms and disease, garden club members decided to combine this with a plan to teach all school children in Freeport something about conservation.

During one week last April, 3,500 students were transported by bus to sites which had been chosen for planting trees and shrubs. These included three city parks, the municipal golf course, and schools.

Each child was permitted to plant his own tree, which was marked with his name, and he was responsible for taking care of it until it was established.

All plantings were supervised by garden club members, park personnel, and school administrators. Throughout the project the club worked closely with the personnel of the board of education and the park district.

A total of 2,000 seedlings were planted in this way on school property, and 3,500 larger trees were planted on park property. In all, more than 9,000 trees and shrubs were planted, while the children learned a great deal about their responsibility to nature and the mechanics of reforestation.

The dollar cost of this project was negligible. Most of the plant materials, labor, and services were donated free of charge.

In Lincoln, Nebr., education was aimed at adults in the community. The garden club there launched a citywide project of beautification. Homeowners were encouraged to landscape and beautify their yards by competing for the awards.

Public areas were beautified with the help of 4-H boys and girls who planted trees and shrubs. Businessmen and industrial managers were encouraged to clean up and landscape their grounds and the shopping centers around them. Both public areas and private yards were planted with thousands of tulip bulbs.

Meanwhile, a landscape designing course was offered to homeowners to teach them proper planting methods. They learned, among other things, what to plant, how to plant it, and how to maintain their gardens. Hundreds took advantage of this course, which covered a period of weeks. Since it is a continuous project, still more citizens will continue to participate in years to come.

Finally, in Winter Park, Fla., members of the garden club formed a high school gardeners group as part of a 5-year plan to educate the young people and beautify their city.

Landscape plans were drawn and plots assigned to the students who then worked out their own planting plans with the help of a landscape architect. The county agent provided advice on soil conditions and improvement.

At least 150 oak trees and 1,000 slash pines were among the trees and shrubs added to Winter Park's landscape, while the high school students received valuable experience in landscaping and planting.

Beautification, recreation, and education—all have been accomplished with plants by relatively small groups of determined people across the country. But one other target of plants in action deserves mention here, and that is preservation.

Savannah, Ga., is perhaps the best known example of historic preservation. Citizens from all walks of life have pooled their time, energy, and resources to rescue the city from the ravages of time and neglect.

Plants have played an important role in restoring the city's unique squares to their rightful place as beautiful centerpieces in the historic town plan. Some enterprising Savannahians have even turned a crumbling old cemetery into a lovely park.

Other large cities are now doing what they can to salvage and preserve all that is old and beautiful within their boundaries. But preservation is by no means limited to big cities.

On the outskirts of Taos, N. Mex., for example, lies the little village of Talpa, rich in Spanish-American history. In it are ancient farms and chapels, including one which is among the few remaining unrestored chapels in New Mexico. Talpa has a prehistoric Indian tower, archeological sites dating back to Indian occupation, and other relics of the past.

The Talpa Garden Club was organized in the late sixties by a group of concerned citizens who wanted to restore and preserve the ancient village. By registering its 50 buildings and having the entire village declared a national historic landmark, they hope to save it for future generations.

In the meantime they are creating a plaza near one of the most historic chapels. Flagstone walks, stone walls, a cactus garden, and flowering crabapples and juniper have replaced the dirt, weeds, and rocks that were there. A watering system was installed to maintain the plantings.

In short, you find plants in action everywhere in the seventies. They offer all of us a chance to pitch in and help accomplish something useful or beautiful. And yet, much of the difficult, significant work will continue to be done by trained specialists.

According to one authority, ". . . environmental management is going to be the fastest growing area of industry, public services, and the economy for at least the next decade and probably much longer."

Landscape architects will continue to play an important part in putting plants into action. One expert estimates that by 1980 we will need 6,000 more landscape architects—a total of 14,500.

We will also need new kinds of professionals. At least 17 new environmental specialties have already been identified, and more will emerge. Besides, the "oldtimers"—like landscape architects—will have to keep broadening their outlook and their training.

Landscape architects, for example, used to make their living beautifying the already beautiful estates of millionaires. But during the depression years of the 1930's, there was a quiet revolution in landscape architecture which moved its practitioners right into the middle of the workaday world. They rolled up their sleeves and began taking on public jobs such as slum clearance projects, State parks, children's playgrounds, and roadside development.

Today I am the dean of a school of environmental design which trains landscape architects to deal with the real problems of the seventies. They are learning to work with others in a team effort and to understand the political arena in which our public work is conducted.

But right now we do not have enough environmental specialists to keep up with the demand and need. That is why I think the Landscape Design Study Course program has been so useful.

The aim of this nationwide program is to create a civilian army of environmental watchdogs capable of exerting a constructive influence on local, State, and national affairs. Begun in 1958, the program is sponsored by the National Council of State Garden Clubs which makes it available to its membership of 375,000.

More than 2,000 garden club members had completed the 2-year program in June 1970, and had earned the certificate designating them as landscape design critics. Another 24,000 persons had taken at least one of the four courses by the middle of last year.

This small but well-informed group of people has already made itself felt by speaking out in favor of highway beautification, wilderness areas, national seashores, historic preservation, and other environmental improvements in every State.

Graduates of the program serve capably on park commissions, zoning boards, and other groups with responsibilities for the health and beauty of the landscape, both urban and rural.

For example, Mrs. Charles Yarn of Atlanta was appointed by the governor of Georgia to serve on the Citizen's Environmental Design Commission. Mrs. Gerald J. Pierce of Utica, N.Y., serves on the Mayor's Committee for City Park Planning and Beautification. And in Fort Worth, Tex., Mrs. Howard Kittel serves on the Texas Park and Recreation Board.

We have always recognized the beauty of trees, shrubs, and flowers, but perhaps the seventies brought us a new awareness of the *power* of plants in action: their power to change and improve the quality of our lives.

If there is a lesson here, perhaps it can be stated this way: never underestimate the power of a plant or the power of the men and women who are determined to put plants into action on behalf of people and the earth they inhabit.

For further reading:

U.S. Department of Agriculture, *Forestry Activities: A Guide for Youth Group Leaders.* Program Aide 457, Superintendent of Documents, U.S. Government Printing Office, Washington, D.C. 20402, 1970. 20¢

──────────, *Teaching Conservation Through Outdoor Education Areas.* Program Aid 837, Superintendent of Documents, U.S. Government Printing Office, Washington, D.C. 20402, 1970. 35¢

garden clubs and everyone else pitch in to landscape a school

THANKS to the Bearden Ecology Student Team (BEST) and the best efforts of the community, the modern Bearden High School building in Knoxville, Tenn., lies on beautifully landscaped grounds. Students, parents, teachers, garden clubs, civic groups, and businesses all worked together on this "do-it-ourselves" project.

Bearden High School's landscaping success story is proof that determined amateurs can achieve excellent results for a reasonable cost. Professional guidance is invaluable, but inexperienced people can plant successfully with help from practiced gardeners.

Landscaping a school is an ambitious project, but at Bearden High it turned out to be easier than it looked. Although the original plan called for spreading the work over 3 years, donations of money and trees and shrubs came so quickly that the planting project was nearly finished in one year. Garden clubs, individuals, and local businesses were eager to help. The gifts of trees, shrubs, plants, and fertilizer were worth about $850, and the cash contributions amounted to nearly $1,000.

It all began in a spring board meeting of the Parent Teacher Student

Organization (PTSO), when Mrs. Elizabeth Regas—later named chairman of the beautification committee—suggested asking the local garden clubs to adopt the grounds of the one-year-old school.

Obtaining professional advice seemed to be the first requirement. With an unplanned assortment of trees and of shrubs coming from several sources, the school grounds might have begun to look more like a plant catalogue than a harmonious campus. Even too much well-organized planting would have been undesirable. School grounds, after all, are meant to be used, not just admired. And the simple fact that trees grow makes planning essential.

On the advice of one of the area's garden clubs, the board sought assistance from the Agricultural Extension Service on the University of Tennessee campus. The Extension Service is one of the few consulting services which doesn't charge a fee. The extension horticulturist soon met with the principal and the members of the parent-teacher-student group to discuss the special considerations involved in landscaping schools and the special needs of this particular school. The PTSO's Ecology Beautification Committee assumed a leadership responsibility for getting the project underway.

A good landscaping plan for a school recognizes both functional and decorative requirements. Trees and shrubs can separate areas used for different purposes, so that students can make better use of the grounds. Landscaping can either integrate the school with the surrounding community or separate it from its surroundings—the choice depends on the nature of the community. Trees and shrubs can screen out undesirable views, but unless they are placed with an eye to future growth, they can obscure the good views, too.

Author DONALD B. WILLIAMS is Professor and Head, Department of Ornamental Horticulture and Landscape Design, University of Tennessee, Knoxville.

Coauthor Jane Clausing is a writer in the Information Division, Agricultural Research Service.

After all had agreed on the general direction to take, the extension horticulturist obtained a blueprint of the school grounds, and indicated on it the location of all the various trees and shrubs he thought were needed.

With this blueprint in hand, the Ecology Beautification Committee had no trouble gaining the wholehearted support of the Parent Teacher Student Organization and the school board. Having specific goals from the beginning of the project was a great help.

Excellent planning and organization proved to be the keys to the "BEST" results.

Members of the PTSO saw that here was a perfect situation to build school and community spirit that would serve Bearden High well in the future. Students had an unusual opportunity to participate in getting the new school off to a good start. They adopted the project enthusiastically.

Working from the "landscaped" blueprint, Mrs. Carolyn Woods, president of the PTSO, made an itemized list of all the trees, shrubs, and other plants needed. The list was sent to three nurseries with a request for bids.

The local garden clubs deserve a large share of the credit for the success of "BEST." Just after the start of the new school year, the Ecology Beautification Committee sent letters to presidents of the garden clubs describing the plan and inviting them to a meeting at the school.

Representatives of six garden clubs attended the meeting and pooled their knowledge of the community's resources. Provided with copies of the itemized list drawn up by Mrs. Woods, they could make detailed reports to their clubs.

A $150 contribution from the HANDS project sponsored by the Sears Foundation came as an unexpected outgrowth of this meeting. HANDS stands for Home and Neighborhood Development Sponsors. This national organization is active in Knoxville, where it works closely with garden clubs to provide financial impetus for beautification projects.

A large and completely unexpected donation came about through an announcement at a Parent Teacher Student Organization meeting. One of the parents in the PTSO happened to know of someone who might be willing to help even though he lived in another city. Charles Browder of Sweetwater donated 32 trees and shrubs valued at $375. The PTSO itself voted to contribute more than $450 to BEST from membership dues and the proceeds of a special rummage sale.

Students also were involved in the round of meetings. Leaders of student organizations and the president of the student body decided to offer a plaque to the class that contributed the most labor and one to the school club that contributed the most money. Those plaques later went to the senior class and the French Club.

Local news media were kept abreast of the progress. Newspapers and radio and television stations informed the community of the project, requested help and contributions, and provided encouragement through their reporting.

Local businesses helped by contributing money, food for workers, and plants. In addition, civic groups pro-vided financial help and sent members to help supervise the planting.

The excellent planning and cooperation that were evident through the whole project culminated in two Saturday "labor days" held in December. These were full days, with time out for the lunch donated by local businesses. Since everything had been assembled beforehand, the work went on smoothly and efficiently.

All the labor was volunteered. With more than 200 adults and students pitching in, it took only four days to do all the planting. At $1.65 an hour, the 800 man-hours spent digging, planting, and fertilizing were worth over $1,300.

The first job was digging holes for the trees and the shrubs donated by Charles Browder. A caravan of trucks driven by Bearden students transported the trees and shrubs to the school in the morning. The husband of the PTSO's president marked the location of every tree and shrub, and he and their son then staked the trees that required support. Two thousand tulip bulbs were also waiting to be planted.

On the second "labor day," the amateur gardeners planted 7,000 loblolly

Some of the volunteer student labor.

ine seedlings and 63 other trees and shrubs. Although it was hard work and sometimes a little monotonous, it was fun, too. Civic club members who came to work were so inspired by the students' enthusiasm that they returned to their clubs to recommend that they give more money to "BEST."

After only 2 days, most of the work was done, and the results of all the effort were right there to be seen. Another work session in March lasted only a few hours. The students decided to plant two Norway spruce trees as living memorials to two young servicemen from the school, rather than installing the customary plaque.

Additional funds were needed before the project could be finished in the spring. The garden clubs and the Parent Teacher Student Organization cooperated in holding a benefit card party and style show in the mall of the new school in April. By this time, there were flowers in bloom. Theme of the party, appropriately enough, was ecology and gardening. Proceeds from the party went toward 200 eleagnus shrubs to screen out a view of an auto sales and service center.

Of course, a project like "BEST" is never really finished. Fertilizing, pruning, and everyday care continue. For-

tunately, the planners recognized the need for on-going maintenance. So part of the proceeds from the benefit party was saved as a maintenance fund.

The students' pride in a job well done will last long beyond the time they graduate. What better setting could there be for a reunion? Some students will use their knowledge of landscaping on their own yards. The people who live and work near Bearden High School will enjoy this growing monument to school and community cooperation for years to come. Other schools in the community have been encouraged by the success of the "BEST" project to landscape their schools.

The ingredients of success would be no different for other schools in other places: planning and organization, professional advice, people with green thumbs, and people who are willing to do the hard work. In every community there are people and organizations willing to lend a helping hand for a worthwhile goal. Probably more important than anything else is a positive attitude—"Let's get together and get it done!"

For further reading:
U.S. Forest Service, *Arbor Day*. FS–64, Washington, D.C. 20250, 1970.

metro forestry's growing role in the urban environment

AS THE QUALITY of life in our cities faces new perils, metropolitan forestry looms as an important factor in enhancing the urban environment. Metro forestry is defined as a category of forestry designed to foster the selection, cultivation, management, and protection of trees in metropolitan areas in a manner which will provide maximum benefit to urban society. In essence, it adapts sound forestry principles and techniques to physiological, sociologi-

cal, and economic conditions that are peculiar to metropolitan areas.

A major portion of our country's population is concentrated in cities, and migration to urban centers continues at the rate of approximately 2 million people each year. Because of crowded conditions and deterioriation of the natural environment, trees are becoming increasingly important to all city dwellers.

Urban residents value their shade trees, wooded tracts, and park areas

Tree mover saves 25-year-old evergreen tree that otherwise would have been cut down as a result of land use changes. This and other trees were taken to a company nursery for later use in a suburban development.

highly. They are interested in protecting them from insects and diseases, as well as from damage which often results from lightning, ice storms, construction equipment, and chemical pollutants.

The metro forester renders a valuable service to city dwellers by inspecting shade trees that are suspected of being infested by insects or stricken by disease. When a malady is detected and diagnosed, the metro forester offers technical advice and assistance in solving or alleviating the problem.

Metro foresters also assist urbanites in assessing other damage to trees. Where appropriate, they recommend

---

Author JOHN W. MIXON is Atlanta Metro Forestry Coordinator for the Georgia Forestry Commission.

Coauthor HARRY B. SEWELL is Atlanta Metro Forester for the Commission.

treatment and sometimes are able to propose actions for preventing or minimizing recurrence of similar damage.

Metro foresters encourage land owners and developers to preserve the maximum number of trees possible when wooded tracts in metropolitan areas are transformed into commercial or industrial sites. They offer technical advice and assistance designed to accomplish this objective and stress the long-range economic and ecological advantages of retaining the trees.

In too many instances, all the trees on the large tracts are bulldozed out and replaced by buildings, concrete, or asphalt.

In other cases, substantial numbers of trees are left standing on residential lots or apartment areas but they are damaged so severely they can't survive. This damage may come from mechanial injury to the tree trunk, excessive dirt fill around the trunk, or changes in grade which adversely affect the roots.

Metro foresters help persons contemplating home building to develop landscape plans that will preserve the shade trees and prevent damage during construction. They furnish designs for tree wells and for barriers which will protect the trees from construction equipment.

Requests for assistance also come from owners of new homes whose fondness for trees was a significant factor in purchase of the homes. The metro forester reacts to the requests by conducting inspections similar to those made for insects and disease. He then gives advice and assistance for correcting the adverse conditions in an effort to save as many trees as possible. Unfortunately, several months sometimes elapse between the period of damage and the time the metro forester is informed.

As popular interest in metropolitan forestry expands, requests for advice in selecting shade trees are increasing. Metro foresters furnish information concerning the adaptability of various shade trees and ornamentals to specific climatic and soil conditions. They also give advice relating to the suitability of different species for the purposes desired, and provide data pertaining to the susceptibility of each species to disease and other natural enemies.

In Atlanta, an Arborist Association has been established and the heads of leading tree service firms are supporting it. The association has adopted a code of ethics and is pressing for legislation that will require State registration for the arborist profession.

When arborists experience difficulty in resolving a shade tree problem, they frequently will request guidance from metro foresters. Progress resulting from this cooperation has resulted in better service.

In speaking appearances, metro foresters emphasize the value of the tree as an ecological instrument and explain the use of trees for abating noise, reducing water and air pollution, protecting watersheds, preserving wildlife, and for enhancing the beauty of recreational areas.

In his presentations to young people, he stresses the importance of trees to the future environment and economy, and he explains how to protect trees against their natural enemies.

Members of garden clubs are given instruction in selecting, planting, and cultivating shade trees and ornamentals.

As an additional means of focusing attention on metro forestry, floats are entered in major parades, and exhibits are displayed on various occasions.

Metro foresters cooperate with civic groups in planning and implementing many types of projects that relate to forestry and ecology. Such activities include establishing nature trails, arboretums, and esthetic plots.

Cooperation between metro foresters and City of Atlanta officials has resulted in a tree planting project which has added considerable beauty to the heart of the city.

A full-time entomologist has been employed jointly by the Georgia Forestry Commission and the City of Atlanta.

Future metro foresters at work.

A Forestry Information Center located on the top of historic Stone Mountain attracts thousands of visitors from all States of the Union.

Cooperative projects with women's clubs, garden clubs, and the Boy Scouts are resulting in large-scale tree planting at various highway intersections in the Atlanta metropolitan area. This planting not only produces favorable ecological results, but the blending of the flowering species with pines and various hardwoods will add greatly to future beauty of the areas.

Metro forestry is still in its infancy and is not a panacea for the numerous environmental problems of our cities. However, the tree is our best natural ecological instrument and the proper development of its potential through metro forestry will result in a major contribution to improving the urban environment.

For further reading:
A Symposium on the Role of Trees in the South's Urban Environment, Jan. 31– Feb. 3, 1971, Center for Continuing Education, University of Georgia, Athens.

how a state helps cities, towns to plant trees

COMMUNITY FORESTRY we call it in Missouri. It's a State program of providing tree planting savvy, and it works.

The professional foresters, landscape architects, and insect and disease specialists of the Missouri Department of Conservation serve as consultants to local government units.

After receiving a formal request from a city official or the governing body responsible, we prepare tree planting and maintenance plans. Our services are limited to public land and lands of public concern.

Public land includes parks, park lawns (streets), courthouse squares, school grounds, and industrial parks. Property of public concern (for which a specific request must be made from the city with approval of the land-owner) includes railroad rights-of-way, creek banks, old quarries, junkyards, industrial sites, and trailer parks and private campgrounds.

In small cities (under 10,000 population) we are willing to prepare a community-wide plan. For larger cities, however, we work only on specific areas.

The work we do includes disaster aid following wind or ice storms. We

evaluate damaged trees to determine those worth saving and those to be cut. We also recommend replacement trees. We get the word out to tree service concerns, nurseries, newspapers, and private property owners on pruning, fertilizing, and wound treatment. Other work in a normal day includes evaluation and control of insects, diseases, or environmental damage; providing planting plans for specific areas; and planning for problem areas (eyesores).

We also participate in special projects such as downtown beautification, approach plantings, and Arbor Day projects.

In our tree plans for towns we first inventory existing trees and determine needs. From this a planting and maintenance plan is designed. It includes specific recommendations for species, sizes, and types of stock to be planted.

We give detailed planting instructions since we have found that trees planted on public property seldom receive adequate care. We try to com-

Author OSAL B. CAPPS is State Forester, Missouri Department of Conservation, Jefferson City. He is Past President, National Association of State Foresters.

ensate for this at planting time by uggesting staking, wrapping, mulching, nd, when necessary, fencing. Fencing s necessary to protect trees from mow- rs—the biggest enemy of a young tree.

We have found it highly desirable o include a financial section in our lan. We estimate costs based on pre- ailing nursery prices. This helps com- nunities plan for funds. Many towns ay they have no funds, so we also uggest ways and means of raising the unds.

In community forestry we are not rying to usurp anyone's job. We go ut of the way to work with local urseries, tree service companies, and ity foresters.

Incidentally, in many small com- nunities there is no local expertise to all on. This is one of their problems. andscape architects and ornamental iorticulturists are rather scarce, as are vell trained arborists.

We currently assist all areas in Mis- ouri. St. Louis and Kansas City metro- olitan areas are serviced by foresters vith no other duties. The remainder of he State is served by a staff of foresters vho have primary responsibilities for orested areas outside of towns. All the oresters are given training and assist- nce as needed by our central office

staff, which includes an insect and dis- ease specialist, a landscape architect, and a specialist in ornamental trees.

Here are some examples of recent work of the Missouri Department of Conservation.

1. Our St. Louis forester helped de- sign and lay out a nature trail in Forest Park, a large tract with some heavily wooded areas in the heart of the city and within walking distance of the underprivileged.

2. He also laid out five nature trails on the grounds of Maryville College (for girls) in West St. Louis County.

3. As an Arbor Day project in 1971, a seedling tree was given to each child in the fourth grade in St. Louis and St. Louis County. Cooperating on this were the schools, the Greater St. Louis Nurserymen's Association, and our de- partment. Some of these trees may only live as long as is possible in a paper cup or coffee can in a tenement win- dow, but each will be some child's very own tree.

In Kansas City, the same sort of project was carried out through the Kansas City Park Department. A total of 80,000 seedlings were furnished by our nursery at no charge to the St. Louis area, St. Joseph, the Kansas City area, and Jefferson City.

Planting and tree maintenance plans are prepared for public lands as a part of Missouri's community forestry program.

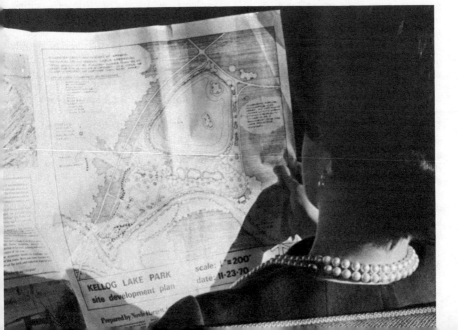

KELLOG LAKE PARK
site development plan   scale: 1"=200'   date: 11-23-70

Prepared by Norstan H.

rent-a-garden projects beginning to spread

YOU WILL FIND the sweetest carrot or the most fragrant rose growing in your own garden. And a place or opportunity for gardening may in time become available to just about everyone.

During World War II, some 40 million people working in victory gardens were an important part of the war effort and supplied essential fruits and vegetables for many families. Numerous gardens were continued long after the need to grow our own food ended.

Once again, there is a great resurgence of interest in gardening. It is now used as recreation, for exercise, or to fill the natural desire to be creative, as well as to provide fruits, vegetables, and flowers for home use.

Gardening is not limited to persons with large yards. You even may have a yard not suited for gardening. But in and adjacent to cities and towns, fertile lands can be found that are well suited for growing plants. Suitable garden plots may be found in various places, just as the victory gardens were planted in parklands, vacant city lots, church grounds, State or Federal land, unused industrial areas, and numerous other locations.

Similar garden plots are still available. In fact, such plots have been established and used in some cities since the early 1960's. Gardens have been planted on vacant lots divided to accommodate several gardeners, or on farmland and other land many acres in size. Owners or managers advertise availability of these rental garden plots in newspapers during the late winter and early spring months.

Rent-a-garden projects have been combined to form a program which has been operating for more than a decade in East Lansing, Mich. This was started by people in the Horticulture Department at the University of Michigan, but it is completely independent of the university.

Originally there were 25 garden plots, each 50 feet by 50 feet in size. After a few years, the plots were taken over by two or three graduate students and expanded from 25 plots to 450 plots, occupying 22 acres. The plot size was reduced to 25 feet by 50 feet as requested by the renters. The more avid gardeners—or those with large families —rent two plots, but many gardeners found the smaller plots more manageable. Credit for the success of this project is due to the interest and work of many people.

A private homeowner and the manager of an apartment complex have requested information about the management of these garden plots, and have expressed an interest in starting their own gardening organizations.

Rent-a-garden projects, while relatively new in the United States, are similar in some respects to garden projects in many of Europe's cities. There, city dwellers have long enjoyed the gardening pleasures and benefits often considered the privilege of people living in the country. In Europe, municipal and privately owned lands on the fringes of cities sometimes are divided into small plots and rented for gardening.

No national information center exists for rent-a-garden projects. The best sources of information at present are local Cooperative Extension Service offices.

***

Author ROBERT A. WEARNE is a Horticulturist with the Division of Agriculture and Natural Resources, Extension Service.

Rent-a-gardens can vary in size. Some may be 20 feet by 20 feet, some 25 feet by 50 feet, or adjacent garden plots may be combined to make larger gardens. People who garden as a hobby may want to rent only a small plot, while a family with children may rent a larger plot or combine several plots. Rental fees for garden plots will vary according to locality, plot size, and equipment and services furnished with the plot. Rental fees may range from $7 a month to $25 per growing season.

People learn about available rent-a-garden plots primarily from friends that have them, newspaper articles, or occasionally from radio and TV programs. After rent-a-garden plots are available, advertising seldom is needed, because there is a waiting list of anxious gardeners. In established programs, renters from the previous year are notified by mail and given preference each spring to sign up and also choice of plot location.

The people renting garden plots pay for their use in the spring, and some places they sign agreements as to rules and regulations that will be followed. Some of the most common rules are: do not grow poisonous plants; do not use herbicides; stay off others' plots; and remove stakes, plastics, and plant debris from the garden plot in the fall when the growing season is over.

Among the problems encountered with garden plots have been theft and vandalism. It may be desirable to have garden plots fenced with the gates locked at night. When only the renters have keys, no serious troubles have been encountered.

One rent-a-garden operation issues a car decal to gardeners and any unauthorized drivers can be asked to leave. In some garden areas, persons have been assigned to protect them; this has reduced theft and vandalism. All gardeners in a program are encouraged to become acquainted with one another and thus likely to recognize trespassers.

Occasionally a gardener will be unable to care for a plot after it is planted. The plot is either assigned to another gardener or the gardeners using adjoining plots take over.

Cost of land preparation such as plowing, discing, and so on, is included in the rental of the land. The gardeners supply fertilizers, stakes, garden tools, and other equipment needed. Garden plots in or adjacent to cities and towns may be irrigated from city water systems. Garden plots in the country are watered from wells, ponds, or irrigation ditches, or may depend on rainfall.

All sorts of strange vegetables can be found growing in rent-a-garden plots, because people with many different tastes rent the plots. The most commonly grown vegetables, however, are tomatoes, sweet corn, peas, radishes, lettuce, snapbeans, carrots, and beets.

A garden plot can supply fresh produce from early spring until late fall. The greatest benefits will come from a well-planned plot.

As soon as the ground is plowed and prepared in the spring, peas, radishes, onions, swiss chard or lettuce can be planted.

Several weeks later and after any danger of frost, sweet corn, carrots, and snapbeans can be planted. Also about this time, tomatoes, eggplant, and pepper transplants can be set out. These transplants may even be planted where the radishes, onions, or peas had been growing.

Vegetables such as collards, mustards, radishes, or onions can be planted about the middle of the growing season and harvested in the fall, even after some light frosts.

A rent-a-garden plot can be fully utilized by replanting rows as the vegetables are used.

Local authorities, and gardening publications developed by your State or the U.S. Department of Agriculture, should be consulted.

Individual homeowners, managers of apartments, and community representatives can develop management plans for garden plots and organize gardening groups. Usually these garden committees will consist of volunteers interested in gardening. Experienced gardeners may be asked to participate and help the beginners and novices by showing them how to plant their gardens, and even conduct garden classes.

Some newly planned cities and residential developments are providing gardening sites for their residents. Gardening sites are as important in the overall planning and development as the other recreational or cultural opportunities. In some planned communities, the designated gardening areas are located throughout the community, making them readily available and convenient for the gardeners.

Homeowner associations or nature centers in these cities may organize and coordinate the gardening activities. Educational programs are planned to help new gardeners, and publications and bulletins with tips on gardening are assembled and furnished to the registered gardeners.

Gardening should be a family activity. Most of the garden will be cared for by adults, but a portion of it should be made available to the children. They can plant their favorite flowers or vegetables, be involved in cultivating and harvesting, and learn to enjoy and appreciate gardening and plants.

For further reading:

U.S. Department of Agriculture, *Growing Flowering Annuals*. Home and Garden Bulletin 91, Washington, D.C. 20250, 1967.

——————, *Growing Flowering Perennials*. Home and Garden Bulletin 114, Washington, D. C. 20250, 1968.

——————, *Minigardens for Vegetables*. Home and Garden Bulletin 164, Washington, D. C. 20250, 1970.

——————, *Growing Tomatoes in the Home Garden*. Home and Garden Bulletin 180, Washington, D. C. 20250, 1970.

——————, *Exploring the World of Plants and Soils*. 4-H Series, Plant and Science program. Available from Cooperative Extension Service offices in your State.

Many excellent State publications are available through your State's Cooperative Extension Service.

small gardens in europe make cities livable

AMERICANS traveling in Europe have for many years been impressed by the large areas around cities that are devoted to small garden plots.

To the casual observer these appear to be simply clusters of miniature truck gardens with scattered fruit trees. More discerning travelers are impressed by the obvious care lavished on these plots. Gardens are weed-free, crops are bountiful, fruit trees are carefully pruned, hedges are clipped, huts and toolsheds—if present—are usually neat and well-tended, and every square foot is carefully utilized. Many garden areas have a festive air, with flags flying.

Try as he will, the traveler will find little reference to these garden areas in guidebooks, on guided tours, or in tourist information bureaus. There are few readily available sources of information for the American on the small-garden movement in Europe.

The small gardens and small-garden areas referred to in this chapter are not the garden plots of today's suburban householder. Rather, the focus is on community efforts to develop gardening areas for city people whose living quarters provide little or no space for gardening.

Names given to these areas in Europe vary from the general (such as "garden colonies"), to the manner in which they are allocated ("allotment gardens"), or the facilities they include (such as "hut colonies," which refer to the toolsheds or small houses on garden plots in some countries). Often these collections of individual garden plots are referred to as "workers' gardens." Many simply are called "small gardens" or "small-garden areas."

For centuries people have needed to live in cities and towns in order to find jobs—yet have desired the greenery, the cleaner air, and the opportunity to garden that rarely are available except in rural or rural-urban fringe areas.

Living space has always been at a premium in cities and towns; there has been little green space—and even less space for gardens. During the Middle Ages, when cities were walled for protection, there was little open space of any type within the walls, and gardens flourished in front of city gates.

Similar crowded conditions occurred several hundred years later when the industrial revolution forced rapid city growth. Ground space was at a premium so that houses were squeezed together side by side, pushed behind into alleys and inner courtyards, or forced up—into five- and six-story buildings with several apartments on each floor.

Many rooms had no outside light. Ventilation was almost nonexistent. Added to this were other poor health conditions, including a general lack of sanitary facilities, inadequate heating, and meager and unwholesome food— all compounded by the terrible crowding as the workers and their families swarmed into the cities. Lack of air, lack of sunlight, and unsanitary, overcrowded conditions were a way of life for most working people.

One of the measures provided to relieve people living in such unhealthy conditions in England was a law in 1819 that provided for leasing land for small gardens to the poor and unemployed. Later, other countries in Europe promulgated laws regarding provision of small-garden areas for city people.

Author JEANNE M. DAVIS is a planning consultant residing in Columbia, Md. For 11 years she was an urban planner with the Economic Research Service (ERS).

Coauthor RICHARD C. MCARDLE is an Economist in the Foreign Regional Analysis Division, ERS.

Gardens for working people, the poor, and the unemployed were provided as a health measure by city governments, philanthropists, and some factory owners. Gardens also became a way to help ensure social stability by providing a link to the countryside that the workers had left, as well as a means of improving the quality of life.

By the mid-1800's the small-garden movement had appeared in most European countries, either as an independent effort to meet the local conditions, or influenced by work in neighboring countries. The movement continued to grow into the early 20th century and began to be considered as a factor in planning urban areas.

Community gardens, called allotments, were provided in the garden cities developed according to the ideas of England's pioneering town planner, Ebenezer Howard. For Letchworth (commenced in 1903), the plan included allotment gardens and children's playgrounds behind groups of houses.

Allotments also were included in Welwyn Garden City (begun in 1919).

During the 1920's and 1930's, there was increasing interest in town planning, particularly in the use of open green spaces to add light, air, and form to cities. Small-garden areas were included in new residential districts of many large European cities.

Lewis Mumford, in *The Culture of Cities* (1938), wrote about the small gardens in the then newly developed Römerstadt area of Frankfurt. "One of the earliest applications, beginning 1926, of modern methods of planning and building communities: so far probably the best. . . . The low-lying land beneath the parapet . . . shows the individual cultivation gardens with their trim, collectively built, tool sheds: part of the green belt that sets off this community on two sides. . . ."

World War II caused a great increase in small gardens. In city parks, school and hospital grounds, vacant lots, idle land on the city's edge, and on unused space around factories, gardens were tended by the elderly, the very young, and people in between. In

Europe, as in the United States, the wartime gardens had a three-fold purpose: to give the individual citizen a sense of participation in the war effort, to improve the economy of families and nations, and for the food itself.

The U.S. Department of Agriculture estimated in 1944 that approximately 40 million gardeners were growing vegetables in victory gardens in the United States. Data are not available concerning the number of gardens or gardeners at that time in various European countries, but evidence shows that gardening efforts were great. New gardens were added and in the existing small gardens, vegetables were grown in space formerly used for flowers.

In this country after World War II there has been only sporadic interest in community gardens. Today, clusters of gardens are found on a few schoolgrounds, at some veterans' hospitals, and in a few remnants of victory gardens in city parks. Others appear in vacant lots in inner-city redevelopment areas, in city blocks on closed-off alleys, at homes for the aged, on farms in rural-urban fringe areas, and in a few of the planned communities now under construction.

In Europe the small-garden movement has continued to flourish. There was a temporary decline in availability of gardens in many countries as close-in sites were taken for urgently needed housing. A temporary lag in the demand for small gardens in some countries resulted from the effects of increased incomes and mobility. Despite these declines there has been a steady interest in small gardens.

The International Association of Small Garden Organizations, originally founded in 1926, was re-established after World War II in 1947. Principal members of the association include the following countries: Austria, Belgium, England, France, Germany, Luxemburg, the Netherlands, and Switzerland.

In many European countries there is a continuing interest in small gardens within and on the edge of the older cities and towns. The type of garden varies from country to country, but the basic idea remains the same—gardens for health, esthetic pleasure, family enjoyment, and, of course, for the fresh vegetables and fruits.

In France the gardens are of three types: workers' gardens, similar to the small-garden areas in Germany; individual family gardens purchased or leased from a farmer or other landowner outside the city; and industrial gardens, provided by factories.

In England, the gardens are principally one type, "allotment" gardens. These are rented from the local government for a small fee. Some allotment garden areas are part of open-space areas within cities; some form part of greenbelts surrounding cities.

In the Netherlands, small-garden areas are found around most cities.

Many have a small cottage where families spend the weekend or even the entire summer. Other gardens are on land that in most countries is wasted—such as land along railroad lines. These usually are quite tiny, and haven't space for the smallest toolshed. Even so, they produce quantities of vegetables and some flowers, with not a foot of space wasted at any time during the growing season.

In Denmark and in Sweden, small gardens usually are on the edge of built-up areas. These generally have a cottage for weekend and summer use.

Some Danish "garden colonies" are laid out like small towns. Gas, water, and electricity are available for each garden. The entire colony may be set in parkland and surrounded by trees. A playing field, a children's playground, a swimming pool, a "village hall," and a "village shop" are not uncommon. The Federation of Colony Garden Associations in Denmark acquires land by purchase or long-term lease, plans the garden colony, and leases gardens to members.

Cities and their surrounding regions have experienced vast changes during the middle of the 20th century. The impact of technology has been great. For example, increased use of the automobile has resulted in residential areas being spread outward from the city, and

Garden colony with cottages in Denmark.

in the scattering of industrial and commercial areas in both Europe and the United States.

But some of the problems of the industrial revolution are still with us. The inner cities still are crowded and lacking in open space. All too often city living and working conditions are deficient in clean air and sunlight. And these deplorable conditions affect everyone in the city—not just the poor, the unemployed, or the undereducated.

Pressures of an expanding population, the need for more efficient use of limited resources, and a growing concern for the quality of our environment have aroused much interest in the renewal or redevelopment of our cities and towns.

Old, dense, but habitable city areas are being rejuvenated by provision of open space and other amenities. Some of the worst parts of cities and towns are being completely redeveloped to provide good housing; schools, shops, and other community facilities; improved street patterns; and much-

needed open space. A few of these redevelopment areas—"new towns in town"—contain all the facilities needed for urban living. And in rural-urban fringe areas, "new towns" and "planned communities" are being constructed, using advanced sociological and technological concepts to provide better living conditions.

Provision of small gardens in redeveloped and renewed areas, and in new communities, can make a number of useful contributions far outweighing their minimal cost in terms of land, money, and community effort.

Some of the planning concepts being proposed today actually were in use a hundred years ago. For example, during the latter half of the 19th century, several far-sighted factory owners in England built model villages to house their employees. Copley Model Village, built near Halifax in 1844-53, and Akroyden, commenced in 1861, were planned according to principles stated by their owner, Colonel Edward Akroyd. Cottages were grouped closely together and did not have individual kitchen gardens; instead, small allotment gardens were grouped on the edge of the villages.

Ebenezer Howard, the Englishman who has contributed so much to the development of today's new towns through his efforts to build the first garden cities (Letchworth and Welwyn Garden City), insisted that these cities provide a small front yard and private back garden for each house. In addition, as was mentioned previously, both Letchworth and Welwyn included allotment gardens.

It also should be noted that this utopian yet practical thinker suggested in *Garden Cities of Tomorrow* (1902, reissued in 1945) the transformation of London as well as the building of new cities. Howard recommended that slums be cleared "and their sites occupied by parks, recreation grounds, and allotment gardens."

New towns built in Britain since World War II also include allotment gardens. Gardening, whether in a private space behind a house, or in one of the community's allotment gardens, appears to have helped people from densely built areas of London and other cities adjust to their new way of life.

In Newton Aycliffe, built in northeast England, the Gardens Guild was the first organization established. In addition to monthly meetings during the nongardening season for films, lectures, and discussions of many aspects of horticulture, the guild provides a gardeners' cooperative selling many gardening materials in a small shop at the entrance to allotment gardens.

Frederick J. Osborn and Arnold Whittick, in *The New Towns—The Answer to Megalopolis* (1963), mention the use of allotment gardens as a way in which residential areas in Hemel Hempstead were given variety. In one instance cited, the allotments were behind groups of row houses that faced a small, central open space. In another example, the groups of row houses faced outward, and the inner area had allotment gardens at one end and a children's play area at the other.

The usefulness of small-garden areas to provide space for needs not always foreseeable even in well-planned new towns also is illustrated in Hemel Hempstead. At the time Hemel Hempstead was being built—the early 1950's —so few people owned cars that few spaces were provided for them. During recent years the number of cars has greatly increased and space for them has had to be found. In Hemel Hempstead some land once set aside for allotment gardens, presently not in demand, is being used for garages.

Compared with other uses, the total area for small gardens need not be large. Location may vary according to topography, soil quality, density of development, site plans for residential areas, or provisions for transportation or various open-space uses.

Runcorn, now being developed southeast of Liverpool as a new town of 90,000 to 100,000 people, will provide additional employment opportunities, housing, and amenities for people from the Liverpool area. The master plan calls for a total of 2,060 acres of land for various open space uses. Allotment gardens will utilize 30 acres of this space.

Some of the new satellite communities in the Netherlands and in the Scandinavian countries also include small-garden areas, primarily for people living in apartment buildings.

But perhaps Germany is placing the greatest emphasis on providing small gardens for people who will be living in new communities. Increasing attention is being paid by planners to ensure that small-garden areas are available for people moving to the new satellites as well as those who live in older cities.

This planning effort is backed by the Association of German Small Gardeners. A legal foundation is provided by the small-garden law of 1919 with its subsequent revisions and amendments, together with laws and regulations of the individual German states.

From Bremen in the north to Munich in the south, cities are expanding through planned development of satellite communities that include all the

Small-garden plot in Germany.

facilities people need and many of the amenities they wish for. Open space for community gardens and other recreation uses is an integral part of the plans.

Small-garden areas exist in some of the new communities being built in the United States. Usually they result from efforts made by people who want to garden but lack space for it, rather than from plans by the developers.

In Columbia, Md., a new town being built between Baltimore, Md., and Washington, D.C., a group of people interested in gardening were able to obtain from the developing company permission to use land as yet not devoted to residential or other purposes. The gardens are shifted to other areas as schedules for development change. Small-garden areas were not included in the original development plan, nor have they as yet been granted a permanent area by the civic association which allocates space and facilities for recreation uses.

On the other hand, in Reston, Va., a new town also being built near Washington, D.C., the developer deeded to the homeowners association a parcel of land which is being used for small gardens. This is an excellent example of multiple use of land; the garden site is on the right-of-way of an underground natural gas line.

Gardening in Reston is proving to be popular. A waiting list contains names of a number of applicants for gardens, and a permanent site for a second small-garden area is now being sought.

Through practice, Europeans have found that small-garden areas should meet certain criteria to be successful.

The community garden should be near the residential area it serves, although this principle is being modified as a result of increased ownership of automobiles.

Natural features, as well as trees and shrubbery, can be used effectively as separators between the groups of small-garden plots and between the small-garden area and adjacent uses, such as for highways, industry, and residences.

Sufficient space must be provided for a minimum number of individual gardens. Some planners indicate the minimum number is 20, others would have no fewer than 50 plots in one area. The individual gardens should be large enough to provide space for an adequate selection of plants to be cultivated—including flowers, berry bushes, and even small fruit trees.

Desirable facilities include a clubhouse or other meeting place, parking space on the periphery of the area, space for sports and other active recreation, and provision for irrigation.

An important factor in a successful small-garden program is to ensure that the garden area will be relatively permanent. It is essential that the gardener have some assurance that his work toward soil improvement, his investment in perennial plants, and his feeling of attachment to this garden will have a chance to last for a relatively long time. He cannot be expected to pack his soil, plants, and compost pile off to another area should development plans change and bulldozers destroy the gardens in preparation for construction of new roads or buildings. Protection against an increase in rental fees also is needed.

The small garden has evolved from a device to provide sunlight, fresh air, and food for the underprivileged to a modern means of providing everyone in an urban area with a higher quality of living through the beneficial environmental effects of green, open space.

Among the uses of open space—and one for which community gardens are eminently suited—is that of giving form and structure to urban areas. One method links small-garden areas, sports fields, and other open-space uses into extended green strips that tie residential areas to neighborhood and community centers. Community gardens also are excellent buffers between disparate uses, such as residential areas and intensely used commercial areas, or between residential areas and highways.

Europeans are becoming as concerned about their environment as Americans, and small-garden areas are being suggested as effective barriers to smoke and dirt, noise, and odors. The presence of green plants in cities also is looked upon as a source of oxygen. Further, plants provide visual relief from the harsh outlines of the concrete and brick structures in today's cities.

As outlined in the objectives of one European association, the small garden provides the individual with improvement in physical health and well-being, a way to relieve the tensions of modern living, and, of course, a supply of nourishing fruits and vegetables.

For children, the small-garden area can serve as an introduction to the wonders of nature. For the elderly, small gardens provide a sense of doing something useful. For everyone, the community small garden offers one answer to the problem of using increasing amounts of free time in a pleasant, meaningful way.

As America moves increasingly toward an urban-oriented culture, the individual plot in a small-garden area can provide a tie to the open countryside that cannot be found on asphalt playgrounds, concrete parking lots, or even in the often overcrowded city parks.

WHO
CAN
HELP

current gardening information:
where you can find it

ONCE AN INTEREST in home gardening has been kindled, good garden talk seems to be everywhere—over the fence with the neighbors, in the programs and chats with garden club members, in your newspapers, in regional and national magazines, on radio and television, in bright, new garden books that appear every year in bookstores and in your library, and of course in the perennially tantalizing plant and seed catalogues.

Surely more is being *said* about gardening today than ever before. As a talk sport, gardening is bigger than baseball (some gardeners will argue that it's a faster game). Fortunately, gardening is one thing that everybody —the young, the old, even the blind and other handicapped—can work at with satisfaction and delight. Along with all the good talk, a lot of good gardening is being done.

Even if you are a novice gardener, you have no doubt discovered the universality of gardening interest. While you may agree it's fun to talk about gardening, your basic question is, "How can I have a better garden?" This gets down to such practical matters as what to plant, where and how to plant it, and how to keep it adequately fed, watered, and healthy.

This type of practical information will be found in the sources closest to you—your neighbor, if he has gardening expertise; your local garden clubs; your county agent or Extension Service horticultural specialist; your local newspaper and other publications; and of course your nearby nurseryman or garden supply dealer.

This leaves a world of information to be explored later—for example, the garden book collection in your favorite bookstore or library. But in home gardening there are good reasons to learn what you can nearest home first.

Foremost of these reasons is the sharp variation in soil and climate conditions within a few miles, especially if those miles lead to higher or lower altitudes. The United States has about every type of climate and soil to be found in the world; spring comes late in some regions, early in others; growing seasons may be short or long, rainfall heavy or light. National publications offering gardening information have difficulty being specific and timely for gardeners in various sections of the country.

Just now your problem may be the drainage in your backyard, which spots get the best sun, and what is most likely to grow in your neighborhood even if you do nearly everything wrong. To mulch or not to mulch? That may be the question. And your local mulch-seller will say, "Sure, mulch." But your neighbor can tell you which mulch is best, how deep to mulch, where, and why *in your particular location*.

A visit with a successful, experienced, and enthusiastic gardening friend or neighbor will help a novice gardener get a correct start, or keep on the right track.

Good gardeners participate in local gardening clinics or workshops, have memberships in garden clubs or horticultural societies, and read gardening literature. These people know what cultural practices have made their own gardens successful and as a rule will

Author ROBERT A. WEARNE is a horticulturist with the Extension Service.

Coauthor GLENN WHITE is an information specialist in the Office of Information.

gladly demonstrate and discuss their techniques.

Probably most important for the new gardener is that gardening friends and neighbors speak frankly about sources of reliable plants and gardening equipment. This exchange of information helps gardeners avoid poor-quality materials, gimmicks, and many gardening disappointments or failures.

For the same reasons, membership in a local garden club is valuable and a pleasure. If membership is not convenient, reading the nearest garden club or plant society bulletin can be helpful. Another source of garden information geared to specific needs in a countywide area is the Cooperative Extension Service, a quite extraordinary Federal, State, and county partnership with access to resources of the land-grant colleges in each State and the U.S. Department of Agriculture.

The Cooperative Extension Service has an office in 3,150 county seats, or in nearly every county in the Nation. You will find it listed in your phone book under the county government. Most county extension offices have for distribution a supply of USDA garden publications and the many fine publications prepared for laymen by State university horticulturists and others.

Many extension agents have gardening articles and personal columns in local newspapers; some conduct regular radio and television garden shows. Some also offer soil testing services, usually for a small charge, and sponsor lecture series and correspondence courses open to the public.

In several regions the Extension Service produces and operates garden tip-a-phone tapes, changed weekly or more often, which give current gardening advice. If you live in one of these areas,

Knowledgeable neighbors can help in gardening.

Nurseries are a source of garden information and equipment, properly cared for plants, and customer service.

you can dial a number on your telephone and hear an expert tell you what you should be doing in your garden *right now.*

In some instances, the tape will also record your request for publications to be mailed to you. One of these is in Pierce County, Wash., where the "Dial-a-Home-and-Garden-Tip" program of the county Extension agents gets 40,000 calls a year.

While local sources are of practical importance for the home gardener, garden editors of large-circulation national magazines use much the same sources —and in much the same way. When it comes to real gardening, the "green thumb" is as rare as a magic wand. Nobody has one—he learns by doing, sometimes by doing wrong.

How do the experts become expert? Where do garden editors get their information? Marybeth Weston, garden editor for the magazine, House and Garden, answers this way:

"By talking to good gardeners and by digging in the soil, weather and weekends permitting. Of course, we read what others have to say about gardening, in all the magazines and books we can afford or find in the library. I read with great respect a local column in our up-county newspaper (Paul Casson in the *Patent Trader,* Mt. Kisco, N.Y.) and watch "The Green Thumb" on a New York TV station on Saturday mornings.

"But you learn most by asking gardeners about *their* methods and by haunting good local nurseries and arboretums. Oh, yes, I often call my county agent for advice, but I'll keep asking neighbors' help, just as I did when I was a safely anonymous amateur."

Nearly every daily newspaper in the United States has a full- or part-time garden editor, or an editor-writer for whom gardening is one of several continuing assignments. Usually these editors are experts, with years of practical gardening experience. Very few write about gardening who do not practice it, or who are not at the very least, gardeners *emeritus.*

These writers prepare reliable and timely gardening information for their area, and are aware of unique differences in soils, climate, or other local factors met by their gardening readers.

Garden editors usually base their writings on personal experience and their association with other gardening and horticultural experts.

They tell the gardener when and how to perform such chores as soil preparation, liming and fertilizing, pruning, weeding, mulching and composting; what plant varieties are most suited for the area; and what disease and insect management schedules to follow.

They give the reader this information well in advance, so that gardening chores can be well planned.

Some indication of the diversity of gardening communications can be seen in the membership of the Garden Writers Association of America—400 members employed as newspaper editors and columnists, magazine writers, book authors, radio and TV performers or programmers, free-lance garden writers, and public relations specialists.

Most garden editors encourage their readers to call or write to them for advice. They keep their readers informed about the time and place of garden workshops, clinics, and tours. These editors also know what garden clubs, plant societies, and other gardening associations are active in their area, and then can help an interested gardener obtain membership.

Among the most entertaining sources of gardening information are television shows, one of the earliest and most notable being that of Thalassa Cruso, who conducts "Making Things Grow" on Boston's WGBH/TV and a large portion of the other public television stations (PTV).

In Honolulu, Extension specialist Fortunato Teho has been conducting radio and television garden programs for 14 years (plus newspaper and magazine garden columns). Other garden telecasters and writers include Aileen Lubin in Washington, D.C.; Frank Atwood, Hartford, Conn.; Ed

Hume, Seattle, Wash.; Dewey Compton in Houston, Tex.; Judson Francis in Fort Myers, Fla.; and Orville Gillespie in Berkeley, Calif.

The U.S. Department of Agriculture contributes public service tapes and video tape features to innumerable radio and television broadcasts. Many of these deal with one or another aspect of home gardening. Extension agents in many counties, especially in urban counties, make frequent radio and TV appearances or supply gardening information to broadcasters. All of these draw upon the research resources and publications of the Agricultural Research Service, Cooperative State Research Service, Forest Service, and Soil Conservation Service, as well as university and commercial resources.

Garden books and booklets increase in number and attractiveness each year. As noted, your best source for free or inexpensive government and university leaflets and booklets on home gardening and related topics is the nearest office of the Extension Service. Lists of similar Federal publications may be requested from the Superintendent of Documents, U.S. Government Printing Office, Washington, D.C. 20402.

Magazine articles generally contain information that is current, as most magazine publishers depend on regional writers to assure that readers will be given the most accurate information.

Only after a reader has some gardening experience and knowledge will he know what publications are reliable, when information is out-of-date or just a rehash of material published elsewhere, and how to adapt useful information to the local situation.

State and Federal publications are periodically revised and updated. U.S. Department of Agriculture publications are general, and are not prepared for any specific area. Publications issued by State extension services or universities are written for local use and thus the information applies specifically to a relatively limited area.

Much gardening help may be found in the publications of commercial plant, seed, and fertilizer companies. Some of these, or addresses to which to write, may be obtained from garden stores or nursery centers. Once your name is on several mailing lists you will not lack garden reading material, though not all of it will be offered free of charge.

Two national horticultural societies in the United States are the American Horticultural Society and the American Society for Horticultural Science.

There are also 40 national plant societies, such as the Chrysanthemum Society, Rose Society, American Rhododendron Society, American Rock Garden Society, and African Violet Society of America, Inc. Besides these, there are numerous State societies and some international plant societies.

The American Horticultural Society (AHS) publication, *Directory of Amer-*

Some supermarkets offer information along with potted plants sold in their produce department. Each plant in this Florida store has a plastic "spike" stuck in its soil with gardening advice from the nursery.

324

ican Horticulture, tells where to turn for information or assistance in any aspect of horticulture and gives names and addresses of the numerous plant and garden societies.

Objective of the AHS is to unite the many phases of American horticulture and to supplement their efforts, to represent horticulturists nationally and internationally, and encourage and promote horticulture and kindred interests. The society supports horticultural and botanical gardens, such as the New York Botanical Gardens, in New York City; Colonial Williamsburg, Williamsburg, Va.; Kingwood Center, Mansfield, Ohio; Strybring Arboretum, San Francisco, Calif.; and Callaway Gardens, Pine Mountain, Ga.

Other AHS activities include a seed service, an annual Horticultural Congress, a quarterly journal, and special publications, such as handbooks on holly, daffodils, and peonies.

More information about this society may be obtained from O. Keister Evans, Executive Director, American Horticultural Society, Inc., 901 North Washington Street, Alexandria, Va.

The mission of the American Society for Horticultural Science (ASHS) is to serve as the professional society for horticulturists and to promote and encourage scientific research and education in horticulture.

This society publishes two bimonthly publications which contain detailed results of scientific research in all phases of horticulture.

Correspondence regarding membership or other information should be directed to Cecil Blackwell, Executive Director, American Society for Horticultural Science, P.O. Box 109, St. Joseph, Mich. 49085.

Women's garden clubs foster both the esthetic and horticultural aspects of gardening. Their programs include such activities as developing a conservation curriculum guide for schools, developing slide programs in landscaping or flower arranging and design, and providing speakers at adult workshops and teachers for youth programs.

The women's clubs initiate and support many community improvement projects. They may purchase trees or shrubs for a park, contribute their time and talents to cleanup drives, plant roadsides at the entrance to cities, or plant and maintain areas around municipal buildings and schools. Many members improve their gardening and artistic abilities by enrolling in flower shows and judging schools.

Garden club members also participate in therapy programs for physically and mentally handicapped people and provide them the necessary materials and instructions for growing and enjoying plants.

The National Council of State Garden Clubs, Inc., 4401 Magnolia Avenue, St. Louis, Mo. 63110, or local clubs can provide advice and help.

Another organization, Garden Club of America, aims to preserve natural beauty spots and green areas for future generations. Each month more than 1,200 conservation education packets entitled "The World Around You" are sent to schools all over the world. These packets are intended primarily for students in the fifth, sixth, and seventh grades.

Garden Club of America showed concern for our environment in 1930, when money was raised for the purchase of endangered redwood areas of California, now known as the Garden Club of America Grove. In Philadelphia, this organization planned and planted a garden around Independence Hall. It gives the U.S. National Arboretum, Washington, D.C., financial assistance for procuring plant materials and conducting educational programs.

More information about the club's horticultural and environmental programs can be obtained by writing to: Garden Club of America, 598 Madison Avenue, New York, N.Y. 10022.

The objective of Men's Garden Clubs of America is to bring better gardening to more people. These clubs consist of men who share a common interest in home gardening and want to learn more about plants, soils, flowers, trees, vegetables, and the art and science of growing things.

Local chapters organize programs for civic beautification. Members often participate in planning and zoning commissions, and parks and recreation commissions. They also support or take leadership in projects such as rose and chrysanthemum test gardens, indoor gardening for the residents of high-rise apartments, and touch-and-smell gardens for the blind.

Local men's garden clubs also sponsor youth gardening projects. Youth gardening is dramatized nationally with "big pumpkin" and "giant sunflower" contests in which thousands of young gardeners participate. These clubs also provide some project leaders for 4-H garden clubs and hope to expand this activity.

Local chapters provide flower and garden judges for fairs, and stage flower and garden shows.

Members of the Men's Garden Clubs of America receive *The Gardener,* the official magazine, and other how-to-garden information. They also have access to the club's loan library.

Hundreds of horticulturists from the clubs are available at any time, by letter or phone, to give advice and consultation on gardening problems. A list of speakers for any gardening occasion is available from the regional or national offices. Each of the 17 regions has at least one—and usually two or three—regional conferences each year.

Men's Garden Clubs of America maintain national headquarters at 5560 Merle Way Road, Des Moines, Iowa 50323. Lyman E. Duncan, Executive Secretary, will answer inquiries about the organization's activities.

People who are in the business of growing and selling plants have knowledge and experience that can be helpful to every home gardener. Garden clubs, neighborhood gardening organizations, plant societies, and individuals should seek the advice of these plantsmen and benefit from their horticultural expertise.

Commercial plant growers should be on hand for consultation at home landscaping and gardening clinics. They can provide help on such matters as turf management; selection, planting, and pruning of trees and shrubs; soil management; insect management; and disease and weed control.

Landscape contractors and arborists offer many services, which vary from State to State. They can provide the technical knowledge for installing automatic sprinkler systems, equipment for transplanting or pruning large trees, other landscaping equipment, and spray service. These professionals can also help the gardener diagnose problems and provide planting instructions.

Landscape contractors may or may not grow plants; they specialize in executing landscaping plans or designs. Arborists specialize in maintaining trees and shrubs providing such services as pruning, tree surgery, and treatments for prevention or cure of diseases and management of insects.

The professional landscape architect is not concerned solely with plant material and vegetation. He is a designer who deals with the land much as an architect will deal with a structure. He can help determine appropriate uses for outdoor spaces, which he may regard as an extension of the rooms of a home.

Ideally the landscape architect should be called in as early as possible to work with the architect or builder of a new structure. His services at this early stage will enable him to do a better job, and perhaps make it unnecessary to correct mistakes, usually a costly procedure.

Like other professionals, the landscape architect believes that planning is the key to pleasing results. One important advantage of having a plan is that it may be carried out in stages to produce an effective and satisfying design when completed.

For more information, and names of local professional landscape architects, write to the American Society of Landscape Architects, 1750 Old Meadow Road, McLean, Va. 22101.

Arboretums, botanical gardens, and conservatories are other good sources of plant know-how. Woody plants, trees, shrubs, and vines are grown in an arboretum; many different types of plants are grown in a botanical garden. A conservatory is an enclosed structure where plants are grown under controlled conditions of humidity, temperature, and light.

Arboretums and botanical gardens are sometimes associated with a university or a park department; they may be government operated or privately endowed. Some arboretums and botanical gardens started as private gardens.

Horticulture and gardening can be studied at arboretums and botanical gardens by talking with staff members, attending planned educational programs, or observing the plant materials being grown. They are also places for rest and relaxation, and they provide havens for birds and other wildlife. The home gardener can attend scheduled classes organized by the staff or interested groups to study plant propagation, plant identification, landscaping, native plants, botany, plant breeding, and other subjects.

A guide to gardens and arboretums, *American Gardens—A Traveler's Guide,* prepared by the Brooklyn Botanic Garden, Brooklyn, N.Y. 11225, is available for $1.50. This book lists some of the finest gardens and arboretums in the United States, Canada, Hawaii, and the Virgin Islands.

The 1971 *Directory of American Horticulture,* published by the American Horticultural Society, Inc., 901 North Washington Street, Alexandria, Va. 22314, lists almost 300 gardens and garden centers in more than 40 States. It is available for $5.

Gardeners will find libraries one of the best sources of helpful information. Local libraries usually have a section devoted to gardening, horticulture, flower arranging, botany, wild flowers and native plants, and other subjects associated with gardens. At a library, the gardener has the use of many resources—reference materials, gardening encyclopedias, special book collections, and slides or movies.

Inter-library loan services make it possible for small libraries to borrow from larger ones, opening the resources of many private and university libraries to borrowers in distant locations. This gives dedicated gardeners the opportunity to read a wide range of reference books, gardening magazines and periodicals, and to examine books before buying personal copies.

Libraries perform other services besides collecting books. Some have a referral service, through which inquiries are referred to horticultural or gardening experts or to the best reference library. Some libraries offer a copying service for reproduction of pertinent information.

Libraries also may have a clipping service. The reference division for gardening clips out pertinent news articles and places them in a "vertical file." These vertical files also contain bulletins and other materials not ordinarily cataloged but listed by subject matter as a supplement to other reference materials.

Some libraries collect unique and special gardening references. Nursery and seed trade catalogs, for example, may be found at the National Agricultural Library, Beltsville, Md. 21705. Some of the catalogs in its collection date back to the 19th century. Using these catalogs, it is possible to locate rare seeds, plant species, and varieties.

Facilities of a library often are used for educational activities such as flower shows, gardening exhibits, and displays of new and antique books.

Antaeus Books, Box 153, Granville, Mass. 01034, is a bookfinding service which can supply almost any book on gardening, farming, conservation, and ecology. Environmental Resources, Inc., 2000 P Street, NW., Washington, D.C. 20036, is the publisher of *Yellow Pages —A Guide to Organized Environmental Efforts,* which lists more than 3,000 regional and community environmental organizations.

For further reference:
Many garden books are wonderful to own, but they can be costly. Most book-lovers are patrons of libraries as well as bookstores. Among many others, the Time-Life *Encyclopedia of Gardening* is offered by mail (four 176-page volumes at $4.95

each). So vast is the supply of garden literature that a brief selected bibliography of recent books can only be a subjective sampling. Such is the following:

Abraham, George, *The Green Thumb Book of Fruit and Vegetable Gardening.* Prentice-Hall, New York, 1970.

Baker, Samm Sinclair, *The Indoor-Outdoor Grow-It Book.* Random House, New York, 1969.

Biles, Roy E., *The Complete Illustrated Book of Garden Magic.* J. G. Ferguson, Chicago, revised 1970.

Brooks, John, *Room Outside.* Viking, New York, 1970.

Budlong, Ware, *Indoor Gardens, A Collection of Novel Ideas for House Plant Grouping.* Hawthorn, New York, 1969.

Darlington, Jeanie, *Grow Your Own.* The Bookworks, Berkeley, Calif., 1970.

Elbert, George and Hyams, Edward, *House Plants.* Funk and Wagnalls, New York, 1969.

Heriteau, Jacqueline, *The How to Grow and Cook It Book of Vegetables, Herbs, Fruits, and Nuts.* Hawthorn, New York, 1970.

Howard, Sir Albert, *An Agricultural Testament.* Oxford University Press, New York, 1970.

Lees, Carlton B., *Gardens, Plants, and Man.* Prentice-Hall, New York, 1971.

Leighton, Ann, *Early American Gardens.* Houghton Mifflin, Boston, 1970.

Miklos, Josephine von and Fiore, Evelyn, *The History, the Beauty, and the Riches of the Gardener's World.* Random House, New York, 1969.

Pirone, Pascal P., *Diseases and Pests of Ornamental Plants.* Ronald Press, New York, 1970.

Wyman, Donald, *Wyman's Gardening Encyclopedia.* MacMillan, New York, 1971.

NEW GUIDELINES FOR THE WELL-LANDSCAPED HOME, a 14-minute USDA color film, available to organizations on loan from State film libraries (usually at State universities), 1967.

COLOR IT GREEN WITH TREES, 50 frames, slide sets and filmstrips available. Some of the "do's and don'ts" of tree planting, 1970. Address inquiries to the U.S. Department of Agriculture, Office of Information, Photo Library, Room 412A, Washington, D.C. 20250.

 # where to turn to obtain information on land planning and development

DEVELOPING LAND under planning principles that are sensitive to human needs yet in harmony with nature is a primary purpose of sound land use planning. This relatively recent approach has its roots in landscape architecture, city planning, architecture, and the environmental sciences.

Today there are several public agencies, private organizations, and university-based groups that a person can contact for information on land planning and development. Often the best sources for such information are the ones closest to home. These sources are usually familiar with local conditions such as soils, weather, water supply, housing, and other critical factors important to anyone who is considering land development.

Sources identified in this article will be helpful in learning more about housing, commercial and industrial development, and resort and recreational uses. Recently the concept of complete "new towns" has become an important addition to the land planning and development field.

Local planning departments of the city, county, or region where you live are usually a good place to start looking for information. Usually these departments have both personnel and library facilities that can greatly assist anyone interested in land planning, zoning, subdivision regulations, and in development opportunities.

Further information and standards for land development on such items as streets, sewers, and water supply can be obtained from local public works departments and public health agencies. Often these are in the same city, county, or regional office building as the planning department. These agencies are the ones you would be dealing with should you undertake a land development program.

Local public libraries may not have a great amount of material on land development, but they often carry several "trade" magazines related to the field. Some of these are House and Home, Architectural Forum, and the periodicals of national associations and professional societies such as the American Institute of Planners, the American Society of Planning Officials, the American Society of Landscape Architects, the Urban Land Institute, the American Institute of Architects, the National Association of Home Builders, and the Association of American Geographers.

Almost every community has a home builders council and a chamber of commerce with some research and data-gathering activities. Both should be contacted for their insights regarding land development, current trends, and the strong or weak markets in your area. Directions of urban growth and development are well known to these organizations and they may verify information gathered elsewhere.

Depending upon your interest in actual development, you may find the services of a professional land planning consultant well worth the investment. Most consultants are located in major and secondary cities but often they service an entire State or several States from their home office. The local planning department can tell you which consultants are most active in your area and how to get in touch with them. The State planning office should also have a list of consultants on file, particularly if the consultants are providing services through local planning assistance programs administered by the State.

Author ROBERT L. WILLIAMS is with the Gulf Oil Real Estate Development Company. His office is at Reston, Va.

Nearby universities are often an excellent source of technical and conceptual information on land development. If you are lucky your institutions will have undergraduate or graduate degree programs in community planning, architecture, landscape architecture, or environmental studies. Their libraries are also rich collections of historic and current information on planning for development. The faculty members often do consulting work when university regulations permit.

Some engineering schools have good resources on land development, transportation, surveying, etc.

When checking the universities be sure to find out if they have research bureaus on land economics, real estate, land development, or urban studies. Most bureaus publish the results of their studies and the material is usually available at a modest price. Often the research is of a fairly local nature and may contain invaluable data on your area.

Graduate schools, research bureaus, and educational centers often sponsor technical conferences and exploratory seminars on land planning and the environment. You may wish to get on their announcement mailing list.

Counterparts to local planning and development agencies exist in almost every State. The more urbanized and populated States usually have rather large agencies with technical personnel able to assist you. Try the State planning office and the State development commission first. They will help and then guide you to other sources. All of these are probably headquartered in the State capital.

On large scale land development programs the projected development for the State highway network, water supply, flood control system, and other major public works are important. They may have great impact on the type and timing of private land development throughout the State.

Also to be found in the State capital are State affiliates to many national organizations having a direct interest in land development. Although they are usually in the State capital to represent their organizational point of view and to protect the interests of their members, they also are excellent sources of current data with valued insights on upcoming legislation or developments of interest to anyone considering land development.

Such groups include the National Association of Counties, the National League of Cities, and the National Association of Real Estate Boards. These groups also publish their findings and recommendations.

At either the State or multi-State level are the regional or district offices of the U.S. Department of Housing and Urban Development and the U.S. Departments of Agriculture and Interior. HUD is particularly able to respond to inquiries on land development as discussed in this article.

Any U.S. office or post office should be able to provide you with the location of the regional headquarters nearest your home.

Federal Government reorganization in recent years has placed most of the land development and planning responsibilities in the three Federal departments previously noted. Both HUD and the Agriculture Department have important home mortgaging functions and concerns for rural-urban balance through Federal policies and actions.

All three departments are concerned, to one degree or another, with large scale developments including "new towns" and the resulting impact upon prime agricultural or environmentally fragile lands.

All of these departments are headquartered in Washington, D.C. Along with the U.S. Department of Commerce they also carry out research activities related to land and area development. For obvious reasons dealing with urban growth, the greatest emphasis has been placed in HUD where a major research activity has been established.

More information can be secured by writing directly to the Federal departments or by contacting their regional offices nearest you. Technical bulletins and other materials are available from the agencies, or from the Superintendent of Documents, Government Printing Office, Washington, D.C. 20402, for a nominal charge.

Several national organizations involved in planning and in land development can be of immense help to anyone interested in the subject. Those headquartered in Washington, D.C., include the American Institute of Planners, the American Institute of Architects, the American Society of Landscape Architects, the Urban Land Institute, the land development departments of the National Association of Home Builders, the Urban Coalition, and the American Society of Civil Engineers. The American Society of Planning Officials has excellent publications; its headquarters is in Chicago.

Both private corporations and universities have recently established "new town centers" for the study of large scale new communities built upon the later concepts of social, economic, and cultural mix. Such centers have been established in several locations including Reston, Va., and Columbia, Md.

For further reference:

U.S. Department of Agriculture, *Know the Soil You Build On.* Agriculture Information Bulletin 320, Washington, D.C. 20250, 1967.

——————————, *Soils and Septic Tanks.* Agriculture Information Bulletin 349, Washington, D.C. 20250, 1971.

——————————, *Protecting Shade Trees During Home Construction.* Home and Garden Bulletin 104, Washington, D.C. 20250, 1971.

MUD, 20-minute color film. Gullying erosion and lake siltation caused by careless builders and how these problems can be solved. Available to organizations on loan from the NACD Environmental Film Service, Box 855, League City, Tex. 77573.

PLANNING FOR
GROWTH
CENTERS

techniques for planning
tomorrow's landscapes

EVERY GARDENER is concerned with the appearance of his garden. Gardeners also are interested in the visual and esthetic aspects of the total landscape of the nation. It is no accident that garden clubs throughout the United States have been in the forefront of the fight for conservation and good planning.

Beautiful landscapes which we admire today within urban areas were designed by landscape architects who encouraged and inspired planning in American cities.

The tools they used were simple—maps and drawings—but they had a clear concept of what they were striving for.

These people were attuned to the needs of their environment. And they had a sensitivity for what was "right" and appropriate. They were instrumental in bringing many aspects of the natural landscape into the city.

Planning tools of today still include the earlier, simpler methods, but have taken advantage of modern technology. Let us explore the planning process and some of these present day tools and techniques for planning . . .

A number of small groups of people hover around what looks like a gigantic chess board. They study the disposition of the "chess pieces" on the board, and confer within their groups. An emissary from each group goes to others and confers with them. Some decisions appear to be made, and the emissaries return to confer with their own groups.

What is all this activity? A "game" for adults—a simulation of reality—and a means of learning about the problems inherent in developing a city or town, a county, or even a State or region. Many of the lessons learned and

the insights gained are directly related to planning tomorrow's landscapes.

These games have evolved from planning and strategy games used by the military. Early forms of urban and regional planning games were developed at Cornell University, Michigan State University, and other institutions. At present such games are being developed and run by entrepreneurs, consulting firms, and metropolitan or regional centers, as well as universities. Their clients range from business groups to government agencies. Players include planners, real estate brokers, bankers, business executives, personnel of government agencies, and elected local, State, and Federal officials.

Each type of game has different rules and different methods of play. Some have visual aids such as the "chess board" mentioned above, with squares on the board denoting city blocks or areas of undeveloped land, and with "chess pieces" variously colored and shaped that represent the physical and economic facilities of the geographic area or government unit.

Brown cubes, for example, might represent a four-story apartment building, and a stack of five of these a 20-story apartment building, while a small yellow cube might represent a single-family detached house and a green Christmas tree shape might stand for a parcel of wooded land. Tapes of various colors and widths might represent watercourses, streets and highways, rapid transit lines and railways, and utility lines.

———

Author JEANNE M. DAVIS is a planning consultant residing in Columbia, Md. For 11 years she was an urban planner with the Economic Research Service.

At the outset, each group is given a different amount of capital, debt, and income. Each also is given a different combination of real property—which may include heavy or light industry, downtown department stores or suburban shopping centers, apartment buildings or single-family housing, or undeveloped land.

All groups receive instructions about the type of game they are playing. Players also are given hypothetical but specific "laws," tax policies, community goals, a comprehensive plan, zoning ordinances, and so forth.

The condition and the value of each piece of property is noted—new, run-down, obsolete, and so forth.

One group may find itself with a great deal of money in the bank, a few parcels of bypassed land in a deteriorating part of the city, and a downtown department store, while another has little money in the bank, a valuable site with an obsolescent factory, and high taxes. Still another group may have a moderate amount of money, high taxes, but a good income from well-located apartment buildings in good condition, and a new shopping center. A fourth group might find itself rich in land, with numerous parcels in the rural-urban fringe, but with little income, high taxes, and very little money.

The ways each group seeks to improve its own position—while adhering to or seeking to avoid the laws, goals, and plans for the city—are entertaining and very informative. Often, playing the game becomes remarkably like real life.

Each "round" of the game represents a given period of time. For example, an hour may represent a year in the life of a city.

Conditions under which new development or redevelopment may occur are provided in the rules of the game. A rule might require, for instance, that no development is permissible unless there are water and sewer lines within a specified distance of the site considered for development. Then, if the owners of a parcel of land wish to build a factory, they must apply to the proper local government authorities for permission.

Often the landowners must spend much time to convince players owning nearby land that the factory will be a benefit to the community and will in no way create a nuisance or lessen the value of adjacent property. They must also convince players representing the utilities commissions, and taxpayers with differing and possibly conflicting interests, that extending the water and sewer lines to the site in question will benefit others.

The "wheeling and dealing" that goes on is remarkable. Vote trading often occurs—and bribes are not unknown.

Other games are played with highly sophisticated equipment and utilize a computer to determine the end results of each round of play, rather than highly trained clerical workers manning ranks of calculators who compute results of the manual game described above. Instead of putting results on a chalkboard or on tabular forms, a high-speed printer may be used to write out the results, show them on electronic display boards, or describe them graphically on electronically produced maps.

Whatever the degree of complexity or sophistication, these games are an exceptionally good tool for helping people understand many of the problems and the possibilities inherent in planning in general, as well as those involved in planning the future of a given area. Such games are versatile. They may include any combination of residential, industrial, commercial, and other land uses. And they may include any combination of regulations affecting land use and development—or no restrictions.

If there are no regulations concerning development, players soon learn the problems *laissez faire* engenders! Simplified versions of the actual regulations pertaining to a county or other political unit may be used; again the results of these soon become evident. Or the games may include specific policies, plans, ordinances, subdivision regulations, building codes, capital programs, tax policies or budgets—in various combinations—in order to discover the possible effects any or all of these might have on the physical, economic, and even the social development of the area.

Everyone who participates in these games with an open mind learns something from them. Often what is learned is quite different from what you might expect. Sometimes one's concepts of how decisions are made or what decisions are made under a certain condition are shredded. The results of a single day's play might be similar to the following, which were noted by participants in one game:

No matter how altruistic or community-minded people may be, unless there are enunciated goals, policies, and plans (that are both comprehensive *and* comprehensible) to guide growth and other change, development is likely to be far different from what is needed or desirable.

It is very difficult to interest people in long-range planning that does not in some way reflect their personal interests and goals.

Goals which are too general are impossible to meet; everyone interprets them in his own way. Vague, over-generalized goals are easily misunderstood or deliberately distorted to serve personal or corporate goals.

Long-range plans have little effect on today's decisions unless there are strong measures for implementing the plans.

Today's decisions can effectively preclude or restrict medium- and long-range opportunities. For example, a sewer line built to serve a fringe-area housing subdivision encourages many kinds of development along the line, thus preventing use of the land for open space and other community amenities that may seem unnecessary one year but in later years become important as the city expands.

Plans must be static enough so that they can be a basis for individual, corporate, and public agency decisions. Yet plans must be sufficiently flexible to meet needs of the community as they change over time.

Many regulations concerning development are too antiquated for today's needs; some actually encourage illogical growth.

Planning and regulating methods often are too cumbersome to permit the community to react quickly enough to today's rapid changes.

In areas of rapid growth a moratorium on development is useful and sometimes imperative to allow time for policies and plans to be made.

Resources—physical and economic—are finite. Demands on them can become virtually infinite. Rational use of all our resources must be planned very carefully if increasing demands from an increasing population are to be met. Uses of air, water, and land are major determinants of the present and future quality of our landscapes and our lives.

"What do we have now?" "What do we need?" "What can we afford?" are among important questions that must be answered as part of the planning process for cities, counties, States, regions, and the Nation as a whole.

In order to maximize opportunities for all Americans, the planning process, at any level of government and for a geographic area of any size, must consider the needs, resources, and technology available within a given time frame.

Principal steps in the planning process are formulation of goals and objectives, making inventories, evaluating alternatives, creating the policies plan and the comprehensive plan, and finally, putting plans into action. At each step the public should be consulted to ensure that the results will benefit a majority of the present and future population in the area for which the plans are made.

One of the first steps in the planning process for any geographic area or political unit is the formulation of goals and objectives. Because goals and objectives express values, they are difficult to determine and difficult to state. They should be general, rather than specific.

For example, an air quality goal for a region might be, "Clean air throughout the region, of a quality not at any time injurious to people or plants." An example of a housing goal for a county might call for, "Adequate housing for all people in the area." Notice that these are general, rather than detailed. The housing goal does not mention housing types, costs, or locations; the air quality goal does not call for maximum levels of various chemicals or of particulate matter.

These goals, which are to guide the future of the planning area, should be formulated by the elected representatives and appointed officials, the general public and representative community organizations, and the professional planning staff and its various consultants. Goals formulated for any area or political unit without the assistance of all three of these groups acting and reacting together are likely to remain unmet. A very important part of the planning process, and one which often takes a great proportion of funds allocated to planning, is the acquisition of data for inventories.

Inventories of present social, economic, and physical resources are imperative. These should be qualitative, as well as quantitative, and should be keyed to specific geographic locations. There is little worth in noting that a State has seven airports and 25 parks unless you know their size, condition, location, and accessibility. Similarly, there is little value in knowing that a county has x percent of its area in farmland, y percent in forest, and z percent is idle. What is the quality of the land? Are the farms and forests economically viable? Why is land idle? What is the distribution of these land uses? What benefits, other than the most obvious ones, do the farm and forest lands provide to nonfarm people?

Measurement of present demand for resources, facilities, and services are needed. Projections of future demand for and availability of resources also are necessary.

Information about legal and institutional aids or constraints that may affect the carrying out of policies should be collected and evaluated.

The planning process should include evaluation of different ways to meet specific foreseeable needs, such as that for adequate quantities of clean water. Weighing alternative patterns of development also is a necessary part of this phase of planning.

In considering alternative patterns of development for cities, counties, and larger areas, it is useful to have sketch plans that illustrate the general location of various land uses, facilities, and so forth, and their relationships to one another.

As part of the evaluation process for different schemes of development, the following types of questions are among those that should be asked:

What are the public economic costs and benefits of parkland versus a new shopping center? What are the economic costs and benefits to individuals? Who bears the major costs? Who benefits?

Can the costs of parkland to individuals, in the form of higher taxes, be partially offset by user fees? What are the social costs and benefits? To whom are these likely to fall? Are the social and the economic benefits of significantly more value than the costs?

In what ways is parkland better than a shopping center or a new residential area on a particular site? Or is there some way in which the beneficial aspects of parkland, a shopping center, and a new residential area can be combined in a new alternative—with the social and economic costs minimized and the benefits maximized?

Using data derived from all the foregoing steps, together with information about community attitudes toward the various types of possible development, a policies plan should be formulated. This enunciates in general but clear terms the goals or objectives for the area's future; it may recommend—also in non-specific terms—ways to meet these goals. The policies plan states the basic policies that will guide future social, economic, and physical change and growth, and provides a framework for more detailed planning and for its implementation.

The policies plan should be adopted by the legislative body or bodies concerned. This does not mean the policies plan cannot be changed should that become desirable. But adoption does give the policies plan more weight, and the plan thus becomes a benchmark against which future decisions can be measured.

Using the policies plan as a guide, the comprehensive or general plan should be prepared. (This type of plan has been, and sometimes still is, called a master plan. Misuse of this term by applying it to functional plans, such as for schools, has made it unclear.)

The comprehensive plan should include long-range plans for land use; water and sewer plants and lines; transportation—mass transit as well as streets and highways; schools; recreation; and other community facilities and services. These are physical plans, but included within each is consideration for the social and economic well-being of the area and its inhabitants.

This comprehensive plan, as well as the policies plan, should be adopted by the requisite governing body so that it can be an official guide concerning future development.

The comprehensive plan should be reviewed at stated intervals, such as 5 years, to ensure its relevance as a guide. Social and technological changes may necessitate corrections in or additions to the comprehensive plan several times before its 20- or 30-year target date is reached.

Shorter-range steps lead to implementation of the policies and the comprehensive plan. These implementation steps include specific plans for geographic areas and specific plans for functions, such as a detailed plan for open-space uses in a city or for the location of schools in a county. Designs for neighborhood improvement or for the redevelopment of a deteriorated commercial area are other examples of this level of the planning process.

Zoning ordinances, subdivision regulations, building codes, and taxation policies are among the tools used to implement the comprehensive plan, as are capital improvement programs. The latter outline how much of the public's money is to be spent, on what, and when. Capital improvement programs should reflect all major interests of the community as indicated in the goals, the policies plan, and the comprehensive plan.

The last stage in the planning process involves immediate action. Such action includes acquiring land for open-space or other uses, commencing neighborhood improvement programs and redevelopment projects, constructing new segments of the transportation system, rebuilding old water-treatment plants, building new schools, and so forth. These depend, of course, upon schedules in the capital improvement programs mentioned earlier and upon the funds allocated in the town, county, or State annual budget.

Other activities in the action phase of implementing the plans include enforcement of the zoning ordinances, subdivision regulations, and so forth, as new residential, commercial, and industrial areas are planned and built by private enterprise.

Implementing the policies plan and the comprehensive plan is a vital aspect of the planning process. Unless the plans are implemented, they are a waste of time, talent, money, and other precious resources.

Numerous tools and techniques are useful in preparing inventories of the social, economic, and physical resources of a planning unit. Others are required to measure demand. And additional tools and techniques are needed to make reasonably reliable projections of future resources and estimates of demand for them. Space limitations permit mention here of only a few of these tools and techniques. Maps, for example, are a basic tool.

Much of the data for physical inventories is available and needs only to be compiled. Maps are excellent sources for much of the basic data needed.

Geologic maps from the U.S. Geological Survey can provide information in addition to that concerning the underlying geologic structure. They show the sources of minerals, and probable sources of underground water supplies. They are useful in determining areas that may be subject to earthquakes and to earth slips and slides.

Topographic maps from USGS have a high degree of both horizontal and vertical accuracy and can be used for measurements. Besides showing the topography of an area, such as the shape and steepness of a mountain, topographic maps indicate forest areas and lakes, rivers, streams, and swamps. They also show cultural features—cities and towns; highways, streets and trails; quarries; airports; and even such detail as individual churches, schools, and houses in non-urban areas.

Because of the long time required for preparing these topographic maps, they are sometimes out of date and should be used with caution for all except the basic topographic and other physical data. Between the time the map was compiled and the time it was printed, many changes may · occur—houses built, wooded area logged, new quarries commenced.

Since years elapse before maps are updated (time and cost of preparation prohibit more frequent revision), other changes are probable. Many of them may be major changes; others, although small and therefore easy to overlook, may in the aggregate create problems if not included in the inventory.

Relatively new maps are desirable, but old topographic maps remain an excellent base for compilation of additional and more current data.

Because planning requires precise and up-to-date information, airphotos are used by planners to supplement map data.

The quality of airphotos is continually being improved, and additional uses for them continue to be found. The U.S. Department of Agriculture and other government agencies have long used aerial photography. Airphotos are available from USDA's Agricultural Stabilization and Conservation Service, Forest Service, and Soil Conservation Service; combined, the photography from these agencies covers nearly all of the Nation.

Aerial photography is especially valuable for making rapid and economic surveys of areas that are relatively inaccessible. But it has many and diverse uses for all rural and urban areas.

Included among the many applications of airphotos for planning are the following: The airphoto itself may be used as a type of map; the airphotos, with identifying marks and annotations shown on the photo itself or on an overlay, may be used as a map base; a number of overlapping airphotos may be connected to form an airphoto mosaic; and airphotos may be used as information and education devices. Overlapping pairs of photographs—in which the same area is shown on both photos—can be seen in three dimensions with the aid of an inexpensive stereoscope.

Relatively simple photogrammetric methods can be used for many measurements. For example, one can ascertain data such as the length and slope of shoreline at sites considered for a waterfront park or the number of square feet (and the approximate number of parking places) in center city parking garages, or the heights of trees and buildings in airport approach and takeoff patterns.

Aerial photo interpretation is a very helpful technique for such diverse purposes as traffic surveys, identification of sources of air or water pollution, inventories of outdoor recreation facilities, determination of extent of flood damage, delineation of areas containing dilapidated housing, and estimates of the rate of change from rural to urban land uses.

Photo-index sheets, mosaics, and airphotos are an excellent means of becoming familiar with the general area within the planning unit, and are very useful for study of an area before fieldwork is commenced. In the field, they are used first for orientation, and

City officials use aerial photos during field trip in Farmington, N.Mex.

then to verify land uses, delineate and code land uses, note changes in land use since the photography was flown, and so forth.

The use of airphotos and airphoto techniques for many aspects of planning studies for both urban and rural areas is time-saving, costs less than other methods, and makes greater accuracy possible. Aerial photography is one of the most versatile and least expensive tools for inventorying, measuring, describing, mapping, and planning any area. Where existing recent photography is available, the cost per square mile is very low. And, when all uses are considered, the overall cost for new photography also is low.

Photo-index sheets are a type of uncontrolled mosaic compiled so that most image details of the individual airphotos match. Because index sheets contain errors in both position and scale, reliable measurements cannot be made from them. Index sheets are very

inexpensive and are quite useful for obtaining information about land use, however.

Controlled mosaics are compiled from airphotos rectified to eliminate distortions caused by tilt; they are constructed so that image details are well matched, and position and scale errors do not exceed specified limits. Within these limits, precise measurements can be made from controlled mosaics.

When new aerial photography is ordered, the contract for it must be carefully written to ensure that the quality of the photography will be suitable for the uses to be made of it. Photography to be used for topographic or planimetric mapping should be taken with an optimal combination of available camera types, lens focal lengths, and film and filter types to provide the scale and type of photography needed.

Every step in the process—from determining approximate flight lines and altitude, through exposure of the negative, developing and printing the photograph, and on to the preparation of the map manuscript—must be made with care if the printed map is to be accurate.

Ordinary panchromatic black-and-white photographs are generally used for most planning purposes. For special purposes, however, other films are superior. Infrared black and white films are especially useful for forest and other vegetation studies, and for certain soil and water studies—such as watercourse delineation, determination of extent of soil erosion, and water pollution studies.

Airphotos in color are easier to interpret than prints from black and white films. The lower cost of interpreting color prints may offset the higher cost of the color film and prints. Landforms, cultural features, vegetation, variation in soil types, variation in water depths, drainage patterns, and many other images important in planning for tomorrow's landscape often are recognized and studied most easily on color photographs.

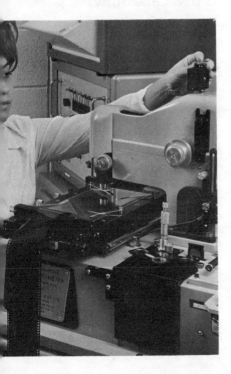

Two other films are useful for special-purpose studies. Orthochromatic black and white film is good for showing underwater obstructions in harbors, rivers, along shorelines, and in reservoirs. And infrared color film helps in detecting diseased or insect-infested trees and to determine strata underlying terrain features.

Acquisition of imagery and data for planning purposes will be helped by the use of even newer technology in the years to come. Use of earth-orbiting satellites will permit vast areas to be covered in short periods of time and at relatively low cost compared with other survey methods. The satellites will carry different sensing devices. These will include photographic and television cameras as well as scanners which convert data derived from patterns on the earth below to coded symbols that will be stored in computers, then analysed automatically.

But there is no need to wait for the future—existing tools and techniques are seldom used to the fullest extent of their capabilities. One example of good use of present techniques is the New York State Land Use and Natural Resources Inventory. Prepared for the New York State Office of Planning Coordination by the Center for Aerial Photographic Studies at Cornell University, the inventory was completed in 1970, but additional information may be added at any time.

The objective was to compile a wide range of information about the State's land uses and natural resources in such manner that, utilizing a computer system, it can be recalled as individual items or combinations of items for any area. Land uses are divided into more than 50 categories. Also included are 70 items, called point items, which identify measurements of distance or

USDA technician operates machine that measures film emulsion density differences in aerial color infrared photos, a technique that may speed collection of surface data from aircraft or satellites.

quantity, types of land use, and so forth.

Approximately 85 percent of the information in the inventory was gathered from aerial photographs. Additional information was collected by field studies and interviews, as well as from such supplemental sources as maps, planning reports, fact books, and lists. Topographic maps were used as a base for recording the data collected from airphotos.

In order to summarize map information quantitatively, all data were summarized by grid cells. The Universal Transverse Mercator grid, in which each square or cell is one square kilometer, was used as the base unit for computerizing all of the material in the inventory.

Four major types of products are available from this inventory:

(1) map overlays which can be reproduced as opaque prints or as transparencies;
(2) raw data concerning each cell, printed on work sheets;
(3) graphic displays of data, in map form, prepared by computer graphics programs;
(4) computer analyses and tabular summaries.

A great variety of uses have been found for information available from the inventory. Many directly or indirectly affect New York's landscapes.

Use of these and other techniques for planning can provide a framework for orderly and rational development of our limited resources. It also can help ensure better utilization of those features of our national landscape which contribute so much to our physical, mental, and emotional well-being.

comprehensive state planning
based on land use capability

AMERICA is experiencing a new interest in land planning.

This is due to a convergence of increasing congestion within our largest metropolitan centers—to the point of diminishing returns in many of them—with a growing concern about pollution of our natural environment. And the focus is increasingly on State government as the cornerstone of our Federal system.

Regulation of land, not mentioned specifically in the Constitution as granted to the national government, is a power reserved to the States. States, in turn, have delegated much of that power to local governments, but this does not diminish the fact that it is basically a State responsibility (local governments are created by State law). And States are coming to realize they have often delegated too much responsibility to counties, cities and towns,

which have neither the perspective nor the authority to handle effects cutting across local boundaries.

Presently, land development is an aggregate of thousands of unrelated decisions being made by single-purpose agencies, local governments, and private landowners without regard for each other or for regional, statewide, and national concerns. The imperative is to develop policies taking into account the needs of both people and nature.

The last several decades have seen the decline of rural communities and deterioration of central city cores. An in-city migration of the rural poor with migration to the suburbs of high- and moderate-income people has resulted in social and area polarization, and a phenomenon called "the urban crisis." Improper land use controls such as exclusionary zoning exercised by suburban cities and counties plays a large part in this urban crisis.

Accompanying the increased congestion in megalopolises, and socio-economic disparities in metropolitan areas, is increasing concern about pollution in rural areas and incursions of development into rural landscapes.

These developments—total planned new communities, second-home and recreation complexes related to water or mountain location, and isolated developments based on exploitation of resources or defense—must be built right for minimum damage to the natural ecology. In most cases they are being located in areas of fragile environment, so that extra special pains must be taken in location, siting, and design.

While the Federal Government has some control over these developments when they locate on public lands and through "environmental impact statements" which must accompany applications for Federal aid, it is increasingly recognized that only the State can enact basic procedures for assuring the proper harmony between growth and the natural environment.

This recognition of State responsibility is resulting in both Federal and State action.

Congress has been considering legislation which would establish a national land use policy and authorize the Department of Interior to make grants to assist States to prepare and implement statewide land-use plans.

This legislation was reported out by the Senate Committee on Interior and Insular Affairs in the 91st Congress (1970) and is being considered by both the Senate and the House in the 92nd Congress.

Two approaches to land-use planing are evident, and both would be aided by the Federal legislation. One uses State investments and regulations to create the infrastructure within which proper land development takes

Author DAVID K. HARTLEY is a governmental affairs consultant in Washington, D.C., specializing in State Government.

place. The other is regulation of sensitive areas subject to development pressure. A major tool in the first approach is capital budgeting, the primary tool in regulation is zoning.

Both the approaches require State administrative and legislative action. Capital budgeting is based on optimal planning of 20 to 30 years corresponding with the useful life of large public investments.

Hawaii, New York, Connecticut, and Wisconsin are States where economic vs. resource pressures have led to an "optimizing" type of State land-use planning, along with local "regulatory" planning. Intricate processes of land analysis (often using aerial photography), resource planning, social service policy, and public facility planning are brought together into long-range land use and settlement plans. They seek land use "capability" for various levels of population, with guidance through efficient infrastructure. These procedures have achieved legislative sanction and broad acceptance by the business community.

Hawaii is the only State with statewide zoning. New York is the only State to have created a State land agency, with broad powers of land condemnation, acquisition and development, and utilizing State credit for financing. This is the New York State Urban Development Corporation.

Although States have granted the power of regulation of land uses to local governments, few have developed the capability for the "optimization" planning so necessary to fit the local regulation into broader statewide perspective involving both growth and direction.

The American Law Institute, a research organization related to the American Bar Association, has been working on a Model Land Development Code which will soon be available for adoption by State legislatures. The code updates the standard land-use and zoning code proposed by the U.S. Department of Commerce in the 1920's and since adopted by most States.

The model code proposes several new State institutions. A State land planning agency would establish the rules and standards governing development having State or regional impact. Anyone seeking permission to undertake such development, however, applies to a local land agency which makes an initial decision. The State land planning agency may participate in the hearing. Developers and State and local government may appeal to the State land adjudicatory board.

The system preserves the benefits of community control by assuring the local agency of the right to make the initial decision in each case. It allows the State land planning agency to concentrate on policy-making functions and participate in individual cases only to the extent necessary to defend state-wide policies. And by allowing the State appeals board to review local decisions on the record made in local hearings, the system avoids the necessity of creating an expensive and time-consuming procedure for hearings at the State level.

This model code was being readied for consideration by 1973 State legislative sessions.

Similar legislation is being recommended by the Council of State Governments.

A good example of direct State assistance to a land development in a rural area is the Big Sky of Montana project. The project is based on careful attention to the capability of the area to support the proposed development. This involves studies of geologic structure, the soils, hydrology, climate, present land uses, economics, transportation facilities, and necessary social infrastructure.

Big Sky is a tourist and second-home development in an isolated area midway between Bozeman and West Yellowstone, Mont., in the Gallatin River Valley. The project involves 11,000 acres, with development confined to a Meadow Village oriented to golf and summer mountain recreation, and a Mountain Village oriented to skiing.

Formal announcement of the project was made in early 1970, but this was preceded by a year of preliminary site preparation aided by agencies of the State government. The Governor and the Montana State Department of Planning and Economic Development supplied technical information and coordinated cooperation from the other State and local agencies.

The State has taken the lead in gathering landowners and local elected officials into a consensus leading to formation of a zoning district along the Gallatin River Valley. This will be necessary to prevent strip commercial development and pollution of the valley by many small, unrelated tracts.

The project is benefiting from an independent study being conducted by a multi-disciplinary team of scientists at Montana State University with support from the National Science Foundation. The first phase, completed in 1970, was devoted to establishing physical baselines from which change can be measured. The second phase, to last 3 years, will expand the number of variables under investigation and measure socio-economic and environmental changes accompanying actual operation of the project.

Information is being gathered to measure impact upon water quality, geology, soils, climate, fish, game and recreational land use. As the data is gathered and interpreted, it is utilized by the developer in refining the basic plan. The university scientific team is using data collected earlier by the developer in project planning.

The project is also benefiting from a Gallatin Valley Planning Study which is supported financially by funds from the U.S. Government (HUD Comprehensive Planning Assistance Program), Gallatin County, City of Bozeman, State of Montana, and the developer. The study has professional staff and consultant advice and is oriented to the basic data collection and planning which will lead to local regulation.

The Regional Planning Program of the Federation of Rocky Mountain States is a good example of interstate cooperation in land-use planning.

This Federation is a nonprofit co-operative endeavor of the State governments of six Western States (Colorado, Idaho, Montana, New Mexico, Utah, and Wyoming) and leading businesses concerned with proper development of the region. It works through planning, research, education, and communications in such areas as transportation, natural resources, non-commercial television, agribusiness, export promotion, and the arts and humanities. An office and professional staff are maintained in Denver.

The Federation's Regional Planning Council, whose membership consists of each Governor's chief legislative and planning aide, oversees regional planning studies and assists the officers, staff, and functional committees of the federation in identifying problems and establishing projects and priorities.

The Regional Planning Program is a long-term effort to assist member States in identifying and finding solutions to problems unique to the Mountain West. The 1970 effort was an 8-month intensive study of three significant but interrelated problems—transportation, new communities, and housing.

Focus of the second year is on State land-use planning. This includes procedures for land-use analysis, classification, and projections; land-use change monitoring; model legislation for land-use planning and regulation; and joint planning arrangements between State and Federal land-use agencies.

It also includes a site certification system by which each State will establish an office to provide one-stop service in harmonizing State requirements on large land developments (such as water pollution control, sanitary sewers, water supply, transportation and access, soils testing, moderate-income housing assistance, air pollution abatement, taxation and fiscal responsibility); and consistent procedures for socio-economic projections as a beginning on regional growth models.

Implementation will be accomplished through specific administrative and legislative actions taken in each State, but in a coordinated framework reflecting the unique characteristics and potentials of the West.

Thus it is clear that States are moving to live up to their responsibilities in providing the legislative and administrative framework for use of land. The 1970's will be the decade in which land will be recognized as one of the country's most valuable commodities, and the government and private sector will be developing techniques to harmonize development and growth into appropriate patterns.

citizens, computers, clusters;
a way to parks and housing

MOST OF THE PROBLEMS that go with suburban development are now familiar to local officials across the country. Woodlands are bulldozed and stream valleys are cut into private lots, while lakes, brooks, and rivers are polluted by mudflows from construction sites.

In addition, many small townships around the country are approaching bankruptcy. This is the result of poorly planned, sprawling subdivisions which simply cost more to service than they pay in taxes.

Citizens are understandably unwilling to pay higher taxes for more of the same. Many towns have used restrictive zoning as a kind of "conservation" effort—they simply oppose and delay every new housing plan. But the courts have indicated, and good sense tells us, that we can't solve these problems by ignoring the need for new housing.

This chapter describes a watershed conservation program designed to improve environmental quality, reserve public parkland, and accommodate development demand at the same time. I believe the new techniques developed for the Wissahickon watershed will suggest timely solutions for similar situations elsewhere, both public and private.

Wissahickon Creek winds its way through a 34,000-acre watershed in suburban Montgomery County, Pa. The Wissahickon joins the Schuylkill River in the heart of Philadelphia's Fairmount Park.

Since the prerevolutionary era the watershed has been dotted with the large estates of wealthy Philadelphians. Washington skirmished with Howe over the Wissahickon Valley approaches to the city. In the mid-19th century, railroad lines encouraged the growth of small farming communities which shared the landscape with the large estates. In the period since World War II, however, new expressways have encouraged suburban subdivision which now threatens to encroach upon the stream valley itself.

Concerned residents of the area formed the Wissahickon Valley Watershed Association as a private effort to preserve the creek as a recreational resource. The association asked our firm to develop a workable conservation program focusing on the stream valley.

Our first objective is to preserve a greenway along the creek as a public parkland, while we also seek certain restrictions on adjacent land use. The stream valley provides the most logical focus for a regional park because it is both a satisfying retreat and a pleasant pedestrian route.

The natural features of the wooded stream valley provide privacy for many, while they help satisfy the wanderlust in

Author JOHN RAHENKAMP, a landscape architect, is chairman of the Pen-Jer-Del Open Space Committee and President of Rahenkamp Sachs Wells and Associates Inc., a Philadelphia-based land planning firm.

Coauthor ANDREW WOLFFE is a staff member of the firm.

others. For kids the park is hide-and-seek, tag, and king-of-the-mountain. For adults it's the sights, smells, and sounds of nature, remote from the office and automobile.

But a good park can't be just a minimum greenway. In order to control the quality of the mainstream, many other areas must be subject to conservation and ecological review. The floodplains of important tributaries, marshlands, steep slopes, and uses adjoining the valley must be controlled with respect to erosion and siltation caused by runoff from impervious cover. This enlarged concept sets the frame of reference for our conservation program.

Traditionally, conservation programs have used public purchase and private philanthropy to gain open space. But in a very large area where real estate is costly, funds are limited, and pressure for development is increasing, these methods and this philosophy are simply not adequate. We have based our watershed plans on the idea that good development represents the best conservation. By "good" development we mean construction based on natural systems; preserving open space and drainage patterns.

Too often, conservationists vainly oppose any and all development. Inevitably, the bulldozer follows the pent-up demand for new homes. The objective of planning in the watershed is to accommodate new development while reserving open space and protecting natural systems. Because we are willing to support quality construction, several additional tools are available to us. The key to this program is an active role for the Wissahickon Valley Watershed Association in the development process.

This approach requires a very solid information base. If a citizen group wants an active role in the development process, it needs up-to-date, authoritative information. The watershed association must know which lands have conservation value, which lands are under immediate pressure for development, and what kinds of uses or restrictions are appropriate.

In addition to data on conservation values and development demand, the group must be aware of local taxation and service costs in order to work effectively with local government.

As a first step, we mapped the watershed in terms of "conservation demand." Six criteria were studied and each was given a numerical value based on its relative importance in maintaining conservation standards.

The six factors are as follows:

Existing open space	1
Forest cover	2
Visual corridor	3
Erodible soil	3
Slope, 15 percent or greater	3
170-year floodplain	6
Total possible value	18

The composite of these factors shows lands of maximum, moderate, and minimum importance to natural systems. Our studies showed that a "Wissahickon Valley Park" would have to include over 4,800 acres, with controls on the adjacent land necessary to protect the stream valley itself. Clearly, the association cannot focus on all the important land at the outset of the program. The need for priorities led us to evaluate "development demand."

In order to pinpoint lands under imminent pressure for development, we made a different kind of evaluation. This analysis involved both positive and negative elements.

First we studied those factors which encourage development—water service, sewerability, and potential highway capacities.

Next we compiled a composite of the natural building restrictions. We analyzed these restrictions from the standpoint of a developer, not that of a conservationist. Natural restrictions included depth to bedrock (1 to 3 feet), slopes over 20 percent, 50-year floodplain, and seasonal and permanent high water table.

The 50-year floodplain includes all land which has been (or would be) flooded by a storm that is statistically likely to happen once in 50 years. This is the floodplain commonly mapped by

the Corps of Engineers and considered the legally defensible minimum restriction. However, flooding in Montgomery County in September 1971 reached 100-year proportions.

Finally, we subtracted the sums of the values of these restrictions from the sums of the factors which encourage development. The result, based on present data, was a composite locating areas of development demand in the watershed.

When conservation and development demand were added together a *composite of conflict* resulted, indicating where conservation and development demand are in direct competition for land use. This composite determined priorities of the association—"Where must we act right away?" The composite requires updating as new sewer, water, and access facilities are added. It serves as a dynamic and rational model of priorities for a 25-year program, an up-to-the-minute guide to "where the action is."

Conservation and development demand indicate the areas of immediate concern to a conservation group. But if the group is to work effectively with local authorities, it must also consider the political service costs that affect local government. Both natural and manmade systems—such as access, sewer, water, schooling, and market demand—must be considered.

The sum of these evaluations, continually updated, yields a dynamic development impact model. Although these considerations are primarily the concern of local officials, the Wissahickon Valley Watershed Association must evaluate them in order to work within the give and take of local political processes so as to finally obtain a beneficial residual—"open space."

The development impact model differs from traditional town planning in two important ways. First, it is based on the unique natural and economic resources of a given locality. And secondly, it is not a fixed plan which merely projects past trends into the future. It serves to suggest the logical patterns of development and open

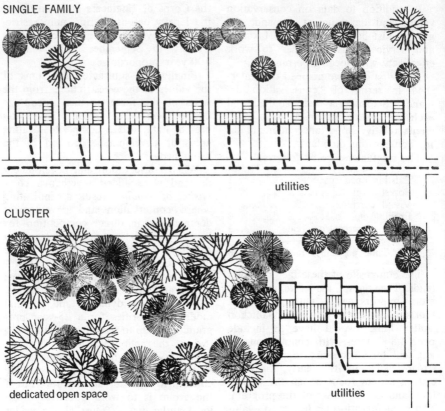

SINGLE FAMILY

utilities

CLUSTER

dedicated open space   utilities

Single Family vs. *Cluster* comparison shows open space gained by clustering homes.

space with respect to stream valleys and natural systems, and also to locate the logical placement of industry, highways, low-cost housing, and the whole spectrum of growing public services.

It can be used not only at a township level, but also at the State and regional levels.

The impact model relates to a given site plan in much the same manner as the computer "test-flying" of a new aircraft design before it leaves the drawing board. Its primary purpose is to provide standards by which local officials can evaluate development proposals; but groups such as the Wissahickon Valley Watershed Association also need this kind of information to identify conservation requirements and the possible "community cost" of implementation.

The watershed association quickly realized that the scale of its objective required something more than the

traditional methods of conservation or public policy. Our experience in planning cluster development reminded us that land value can be substantially improved by rezoning and still leave 20 to 50 percent open space. Why not apply a similar technique to realize a profit in both dollars and public parkland? The answer to the watershed problem lies in private enterprise for public purpose.

In combination with conventional methods, the association could use some of the tools of private enterprise—landbanking, the identification of markets and computer capability—in order to achieve its goals. Based upon our firm's proposal, the association received a grant of roughly half a million dollars towards the creation of a Wissahickon Valley Park.

This program was a response to the inadequacy of traditional governmental

346

tools. Condemnation is prohibitively expensive in a relatively wealthy area such as the Wissahickon Valley watershed. It is also politically untenable. The association's program requires the backing of residents and local authorities. Clearly the use of eminent domain would merely embroil them in devastating political squabbles.

Traditional zoning techniques are also inappropriate, because they typically encourage dividing open space into private yards. Parks, after all, are not made of 1-, 2-, and 4-acre lots, and conservation practices are thwarted by subdivision. The remaining conventional methods—public purchase, philanthropy, and conservation easements or restrictions—are useful tools, but only partially adequate. Clearly, additional methods are needed.

The development process is essentially the same whether it is for private profit or public purpose. A developer purchases land, or an option to buy land. Then he may seek rezoning for higher densities. If achieved, this produces a profit. The Wissahickon Valley Watershed Association may take the same kind of action, except that this group seeks conservation restrictions and its profit is the portion of the site retained as public parkland. The value of the land is constantly rising, due to development pressure. It will also increase further because of rezoning and because of the park's creation.

The association can share in this increase in land values, while at the same time securing land use controls essential to the park. With a relatively small amount of seed money—approximately $480,000—the association can begin a land-banking operation which would result in green spaces in the stream valley, controls over land use in upland properties resold to developers, and adequate funds available for park maintenance. This proposal was accepted by the association.

It isn't enough to understand development pressure in 1971. If the association is to use its data base effectively, and if townships and developers are going to come looking for support in exchange for compliance with restrictions, then the information base must be both accurate and up-to-the-minute.

We began with information on maps and in manuals, but the need for computer capacity quickly became obvious. Computers are appropriate when an organization with a small staff seeks to constantly update a large body of systematized information. Such is the case in the Wissahickon watershed.

Land-banking and computer use are important techniques in the Wissahickon project. It is estimated that the program will break even after 4½ years, and reach its goal after 25 years. The association will obtain control, and replan 3,600 acres over 25 years at an estimated average cost of $10,000 per acre. After replanning, this land will be sold with 30 percent restricted open space (1,080 acres) at an average of $14,000 per acre.

This program will require that the Wissahickon Valley Watershed Association become part of the local leadership to plan and execute a total park program. Its activities must include continuous overall planning, initiation and backing of public and private action, the acquisition and resale of buffer land, and park development and maintenance.

Two sites have been evaluated, verifying the regional plan in practice. Each of these sites is approximately 130 acres. They represent estates typical of the land along the Wissahickon.

In each case we evaluated natural criteria to determine acceptable impervious coverage for various portions of the site. We then studied various possible mixes of housing types and chose a mix of garden apartments, townhouses, and single family homes. The site includes housing areas, private open space, and public park along the stream valley.

The site plan chosen represents a marketable and profitable program, with a good chance for local approval. It respects both natural restrictions and can be implemented by the association can be implemented by the association directly, or by a private developer.

In summary, the Wissahickon Valley Watershed Association is a citizen's group practicing private enterprise for public purpose. It uses the techniques of land-banking and computer capability to implement a program of park development determined by a regional, up-to-date information base. Its activities are grounded in the realization that the only practical route to large-scale conservation is through an active participation with the private developer and local government to obtain good development.

hope for tomorrow's landscapes depends on our acting now

THERE is obviously an acute need to improve the American environment and its landscapes *now*. Problems are increased, not alleviated, by delay. We must begin immediately the long and arduous task of improving our environment, if we are to have any real hope that tomorrow's landscapes will be at least as good as those of today. We must make better use of our resources. And we must recognize, accept, and utilize the forces of change that affect our resources and our landscapes rather than merely adjusting to them.

Man must understand that he is part of and dependent upon a complex, interlocking series of cycles. Each change in any of these cycles has impacts on others. We must stop behaving as if renewable and nonrenewable resources are a "free good" to be used and misused as we wish. We have to learn to work within the requirements of nature. Destruction of delicate ecological balance in the name of economic efficiency or "highest and best use of the land" is shortsighted.

Too often, decisions based solely or primarily on economics result in damage that is expensive and difficult or impossible to repair. The so-called economic efficiency may benefit an individual or a corporation (and often even this benefit is an illusion), but the long-term costs are borne by all of us, and short-term costs that may have to be paid by people living in the area of immediate impact may be astronomical.

For example, construction of garden apartment buildings on a flood plain may pay the builder and the owner high returns on capital invested. But buildings on flood plains restrict the flow of water during floods, preventing the water from spreading out and thus having a chance to slow its speed. Downstream areas therefore are more subject to damage. And the people living in that unwisely located garden apartment may lose all their possessions—possibly even their lives. Of course, the owners of the apartment projects will also suffer some losses.

We are predominantly a metropolitan nation. If present trends continue, it is quite likely that by 1975 three-fourths of the U.S. population will live in metropolitan areas. Like population, jobs of many types are primarily metropolitan focused. Rural people, and especially those who are poor and under educated, move to metropolitan areas in search of work, education, and other opportunities that are in short supply in many parts of rural America. They settle in the cities, where they can find housing at lower cost than in the suburbs.

Unfortunately, however, the jobs are moving to the outer parts of urban areas, and real opportunity may be as

Author JEANNE M. DAVIS is a planning consultant residing in Columbia, Md. For 11 years she was an urban planner with the Economic Research Service.

much of a dream for the poor and low-skilled city dwellers as it is for those still in depressed rural areas.

The people left behind in both the rural areas and the center cities are, in general, those least able to support an acceptable quality of education, health, housing, recreation, and other facilities and services which comprise a livable environment. A well-planned, long-term effort is needed to correct these rural and urban ills. The longer they remain uncorrected, the more harm is done to people and to the environment. Neglected rural areas become increasingly derelict as more and more people leave; the dilapidated and congested parts of urban areas become more so.

If rural and urban landscapes and other elements contributing to our total environment are to be improved, new, strong, and sustained efforts must be made by all parts of the private sector and all levels of government working together. Most of the efforts made thus far have been limited in outlook and sporadic rather than sustained. Worse still, many of the efforts to improve the quality of our environment work at cross-purposes.

But there is hope that we will not continue landscape misuse in the future. More people are becoming aware of the problems and the need to correct them. They are also becoming aware of the need for a national land-use policy to provide a basis for: (1) a national land-use plan which would be a framework for national level program decisions, and (2) a framework within which to fit multi-State regional, State, and local comprehensive plans.

To be successful in protecting our landscapes, a national land-use policy should consider the esthetic character of various landscapes as well as the physical characteristics of the land itself. The effects of location and of climate also need to be considered.

The national land-use policy needs to be backed by State, regional, and local policies and comprehensive plans. In terms of protecting America's landscapes, these plans should contain provisions for ensuring that environmental quality is maintained at a high level. Such plans should take into account:

• Ecologically fragile land and water areas that should not be developed for any purpose.

• Areas less fragile where intensive development is not desirable because of probable adverse impacts upon the landscape or upon the environment in general.

• Areas most suitable for particular types of development, such as: Specialty crops which depend on unusual microclimates; power plants, with their special needs and impacts; heavy industries with particular requirements, such as steel mills and oil refineries; regional airports; and large year-round recreation facilities accessible to urban areas.

• Areas having physical and economic attributes most suitable for development of new cities or balanced new towns.

• Existing small cities and towns which could become socially and economically viable growth centers (in effect, new cities or towns), either as expanded individual units or where several existing towns could together become the nucleus of a new city.

Similar considerations are being taken into account in some of the plans being prepared today.

We need to use our landscapes as well as to improve them. Growth is occurring. It will not stop. Even if we were to achieve zero population growth, there would be new housing, new factories and shops, new recreation facilities. The question is, will new growth enhance the landscapes of our Nation or harm them? Where will growth occur? When? What will the style and quality of that growth be?

Much new growth can be accommodated within the existing cities and towns, or as well-planned adjuncts to them. Other new growth may best be accommodated as a part of new communities. What is the difference between this type of development and the suburban sprawl around cities today? Some suburban areas that now contain little more than housing, schools, and

Above, landscaped pool of shopping center in Farsta, a Stockholm satellite, is a focus of community life. Residential areas are nearby. Below, green space between buildings enlivens mix of housing types in residential area in Vällingby, another Stockholm satellite.

some shops can be restructured as satellite communities. This can be done with a minimum of urban renewal, and the resulting economic and social costs, if there is very careful planning for the location of needed new facilities.

Because these suburban areas need close ties to the city on which they depend, thought must be given to establishing a rapid transit system. At the beginning this might be no more than an express bus system picking up passengers at a limited number of stops in the suburban community and delivering them to a limited number of stops in the city.

Strips of shops along a street may be revitalized by rerouting traffic, closing the street, and landscaping it as a shopping mall. Installing a library and community meeting rooms here, together with construction of office buildings and possibly a high-rise building to contain new, small, light industries, would help make the former shopping street a focal point for the community. And adding apartment buildings would bring life to the area at night and on weekends.

Mini-parks should be developed to provide the positive values of open, green space. If no other space is available, mini-parks can be installed on the roofs of underground or low-rise parking garages.

"New towns in town" can be created through urban redevelopment. These should include all, or at least most of, the facilities of a relatively self-sufficient new town. Urban redevelopment projects have usually produced only a few portions of a community: high- or medium-priced housing and possibly a few shops and offices.

The "new southwest" in Washington, D.C., an example of public planning and private construction, and Universal City, in Los Angeles, an example of private planning and construction, might be considered as steps toward "new towns in town," but neither has the range of facilities a new town requires. A planned example of new towns in town is Fort Lincoln, designed for construction on undeveloped land in Washington, D.C.

Satellite communities contain many of the facilities of the relatively self-sufficient new town, but have strong ties with an existing city. There is a substantial flow of traffic between the city and its satellite, with a good deal of cross-commuting.

Although a well-planned satellite community includes offices and industry, many inhabitants commute to city jobs—and city people commute to work in the satellite. Cross-commuting usually is less extensive in satellites that provide a variety of housing, work, shopping, and cultural opportunities.

Examples of existing satellite communities include "suburban districts" of Stockholm—such as Vällingby, Farsta, and Skärholmen. In France, eight satellites are to be built in the Paris region by the year 2000.

The relatively self-sufficient new community may be based primarily on a single industry, but is more likely to survive in times of economic difficulty if it has a diversified economic base. There needs to be a variety of industries and offices, so that a high proportion of wage earners living in the community would have the opportunity to work there.

Such communities must include all needed educational, recreational, and commercial facilities; housing of various types and a wide range in prices; health facilities; cultural and social facilities; and should have a public transportation system.

In effect, a new town is a miniature city and has many of the city's attributes. Support for the needed facilities and services is unlikely if the community is planned for less than 50,000 people; a population of 100,000 or more is desirable if the community is to be balanced and self-sufficient.

The new town may be self-governing, or it may lie within the jurisdiction of a local government. Columbia, Md., and Reston, Va., are integral parts of counties in which they are being built, as are Irvine and Mission Viejo in California.

The geographically isolated (in terms of distance or travel time) new town or new city requires a complete range of facilities and services of course. Few such new towns have been attempted in the United States recently. One reason is that our new communities are located, planned, and built by private industry—and it is easier to sell land to prospective residents and to entice commercial and industrial investment to the areas where a large market already exists.

The relatively isolated and independent new towns which have been started here in the past decade have as yet not succeeded in developing according to their original schedules. Lake Havasu City, Ariz., was planned as a balanced new town. Great efforts are made to attract industry to this isolated site (the nearest town is Kingman, 60 miles across the Mohave Desert) on Lake Havasu—a reservoir formed by damming the Lower Colorado River in the late 1930's. A few industries have settled here, but Lake Havasu City at present is primarily a resort and retirement town.

Expansion around small cities, towns, or a group of towns can be planned and built to provide all needed facilities and services for a much larger community. When such *planned* expansion equals or is larger than the original population, the community falls within the category of new towns.

Most of Britain's new towns actually are vast expansions based on older villages or towns. Recently designated as new towns are the existing cities of Milton Keynes (1967 population in the area was nearly 41,000) and Peterborough (1965 population was 81,000).

Expanding existing towns and small cities by planned development offers much hope for revitalizing America's nonmetropolitan areas. It would permit people from rural America to remain there, yet still enjoy many of the opportunities they seek in the large cities.

Many towns and small cities could accept a great many more people by a carefully planned and programmed growth. The basic physical, economic, and social infrastructures and needed institutions exist; well-planned expansion would increase the quantity and the quality of opportunities for present citizens as well as offering newcomers an interesting and economically viable community in which to live.

In the Netherlands a large proportion of all new growth is occurring in this way. Carefully planned and scheduled expansion of towns and small cities utilizes existing facilities more fully—and there are additional taxpayers to share the costs.

New development at Örebro, Sweden, is in planned units which have greatly enhanced this small city.

A multitude of criteria must be considered when planning any type of new community—whether it is a new town in town, a much-expanded existing town or city, or an isolated new city. Our concern here is for the factors affecting the landscapes of tomorrow.

Every new community will, of course, have a great impact on the adjacent land and will completely change the site of the community itself.

The most vital resource of all—air —is ignored much more often than it is considered when sites are selected for any type of development. It should be obvious that meteorological aspects must be considered when selecting a site for a new community where thousands of people will live for generations yet to come. And it is equally true that microclimates should be considered when sites are selected for satellites or for areas in which to expand existing towns.

Areas subject to frequent air inversions that would trap and hold pollutants should not be developed. The building of a new community downstream in an airshed that already contains a city or other source of air pollution will lead to unnecessary hazards to people and also to the plants used to landscape the new community.

Water requirements for the proposed size and type new community usually are considered during site selection, but increasing demand for water and foreseeable conflicting demands from other users have often been discounted or ignored.

Land is the third of the major resources that must be considered. There must, of course, be sufficient acreage for the type of new community to be built, that is, whether it is to be self-sustaining or a satellite. Self-sustaining towns need space for more facilities than a balanced satellite requires. The population size planned for and the overall intensity of land-use in the new community also are major determinants of total acreage required.

Somewhat less obvious as a determinant is the development capability of sites considered. Construction sites need not be flat, but excessive slopes, unstable soils, impervious soils, and wetlands all pose problems that must be considered in selecting a new community site and in determining acreage needed.

Esthetic factors also are important. Terrain, vegetation, and watercourses affect the landscape's appearance and livability of the new community.

The plan for the new community should provide for rational and efficient use of space, remembering that the new community is planned for people—not for machines of any kind. Arbitrary segregation of residential land use from commercial or even industrial uses is generally based upon outdated thinking. Light industry, office buildings, and shops can be good neighbors for residential areas if properly planned. Separation of apartment buildings from single-family housing is archaic—again, it is *how* uses are combined that makes the difference between desirable and undesirable living conditions.

Good circulation for people is imperative. If the new community really is planned for people, some facilities must be within walking distance and most others should be readily accessible by a public transportation system. Pedestrian and bicycle pathways should have the most direct routes, and they must be segregated from streets and highways. Public transportation has to be readily accessible and inexpensive if it is to succeed. Realistic provision must be made for parking automobiles and trucks, as well as for their movement.

Provision for all needed facilities in sound and tastefully designed structures is desirable. An important aspect of the landscape in a new community is the appearance of its buildings. There is little excuse for badly designed houses, factories, and office buildings or shops. There is no excuse for architecturally inferior schools, community centers, and other public and semipublic buildings. Good architecture costs no more than that of low quality.

Well planned and executed landscape architecture also is important. A new community without trees, shrubs, and grass would be a community with little grace. Lakes and pools can have a soothing effect, and streams and fountains add liveliness and sparkle wherever they occur. Well-designed signs, lights, benches, trash containers, and paving also add much to the quality of the landscape.

Steps taken to preserve the environment during construction of roads and buildings can save much of the cost of post-construction landscaping. Leveling hills and filling wetlands generally is an affront to the environment. Removing or damaging trees and scraping off topsoil on all areas except those actually used for construction occurs because of ignorance, carelessness, or misunderstanding of the real costs resulting from such actions. Excessive runoff of rain falling on land scraped by the bulldozer results in soil erosion and in silting of streams and rivers.

Montgomery County, Md., has a sediment-control program that tackles this problem. The program was developed cooperatively by Soil Conservation Service officials, the Montgomery County Soil Conservation District, the County Council, the Maryland National Capital Park and Planning Commission, the Washington Suburban Sanitary Commission, and the local builders associations. In large construction projects, development is in harmony with natural topography and drainage patterns. For all construction projects natural vegetation is saved wherever possible, exposure of scraped soil is brief, and seeding or other ways to re-

353

place plant cover is done as quickly as practical. Where necessary, basins are used to catch and retain sediment that otherwise would flow into streams. Prevention of pollution is imperative for all new development. New communities must not contribute to further pollution of air, water, or land. It would be foolish to subsidize directly or indirectly the construction of any new community that will damage our landscapes, decrease our well-being, or add to the costs of cleaning up our environment.

Problems of transportation, heating, trash disposal, and sewerage treatment must be faced and solutions sought. New communities are logical places to try out well-formulated experiments that attempt to solve such problems. So far, we have to look outside the United States for most of the workable examples in new communities.

In Britain, Washington (near Newcastle) has precluded the visual pollution caused by television antenna and telephone poles. This in itself is not unique—but read on. A communication network has been designed that can include telephone, television, radio, and data transmission. Cables now installed in Washington houses presently provide telephone, television, and radio service. Data transmission can be added later without the cost or disruption of adding cables.

Several American new towns have cable TV, but these do not include provision for future transmission of data.

Also in Britain, Runcorn (near Liverpool) has been planned to encourage people to walk, bicycle, or bus from home to work, schools, shops, and so forth. The majority of people living here will be within 500 yards, or 5 minutes walking time, of a bus-only route that can provide point-to-point travel times rivaling those of automobiles, which must go the long way around.

Reston, Va., Columbia, Md., Litchfield Park, Ariz., and a few other new towns in the United States have pathway systems. Columbia has an unusual

bus system which presently utilizes scheduled service during the workday, with Call-A-Ride door-to-door service in the mornings, evenings, and during weekends.

In Sweden the Gothenburg satellite communities of Biskopsgården and of Västra Frölunda include central boiler houses that incinerate refuse (collected in paper containers and trucked to the boiler-houses) and provide heat and hot water to the community's apartment buildings.

Planning for and development of growth centers is a major way of acting positively to assure hope for tomorrow's landscapes. There are many other positive steps that can be taken by governments, corporations, clubs and other organizations, and individuals to improve the quality of our landscapes and our total environment.

Dozens of books and hundreds of magazine and newspaper articles have been written recently that tell tales of woe and emphasize the gloom and doom facing us should we not do this, that, or the other about our environment. Shock tactics may shake some people out of their disinterest in their own environment. But engendering a crisis attitude may do more harm than good by causing people to believe there is little hope for today's—much less tomorrow's—landscapes and environment. And this is simply not true. A few examples indicate the scope of action to improve the quality of our environment.

What is the value of a tree? A view? Birdlife? The Tahoma Audubon Society, Tacoma, Wash., has prepared a report on the destruction values of various components of a particular landscape. The site is 4,150 acres, the delta of the Nisqually River where it flows into the southern part of Puget Sound.

Members of the Tahoma Audubon Society, under the guidance of Robert W. Ramsey, a Tacoma landscape architect, carefully established the dollar values of most components of the Nisqually Delta's landscape. The point of this effort was to awaken Tacoma

A landscaped island where neighbors
collect their mail is the heart of this
housing cluster in Columbia, Md.
Columbia's trees contrast with the facade
of the Post Pavilion, provide shade
for a pathway, and create a cool spot to wait
for a community minibus.

area people to the values of the landscape that would be destroyed if a proposed port is built on the delta.

The authors estimated at $4,000 per lot the value of views that would be lost if the port is built. The total view loss for 530 lots would be $2,120,000.

Using the National Shade Tree Conference value of trees as $9 per square inch of the tree's diameter at 4½ feet above the ground, together with an assumption of 10 trees of 6-inch diameter for every 1,000 square feet on a 300-acre reforested portion of the proposed port site, the tree destruction value was estimated as $6,657,000.

Valuation of birdlife was $115,000 for the hunting that would be lost and $18,750,000 for an estimated loss of 75,000 new birds per year, computed at $5 per bird over the expected 50-year life of the port.

Loss of grass, soil, and other landscape components were included. The total values that would be destroyed were put at $40,617,000.

The Landscape Destruction Value Doctrine propounded by the Tahoma Audubon Society states that developers "should pay to a public body of jurisdiction a destruction penalty equal to the appraised ecological loss incurred." It further recommends that such funds be used only to administer programs for land acquisition, and for protection, management, and maintenance of greenbelts, wetlands, shorelands, etc.

The Metropolitan Fund, Inc., is a nonprofit research corporation which has the aim of accomplishing "through research, the physical and social goals for a better metropolitan way of life" in southeast Michigan. The area concerned includes Detroit and six counties. In 1971 the fund released a report that may have far-reaching impact on future development of new towns. *Regional New-Town Design, A Paired Community for Southeast Michigan* establishes the concept of simultaneously developing a pair of new towns— one in town and one out of town.

The report proposes that "the many advantages of 'new-town' development as a planned growth policy be coupled with the need and desire for concurrent peripheral development and city development in the concept of a paired new-town . . . the creation of a united community within the region which simultaneously grows on two sites, one within the central city and one on the suburban fringe."

The report includes detailed examination of the social, physical, economic, and governmental needs, possibilities, and realities of developing a new town in this unusual manner. It concludes that a paired new town is both desirable and feasible.

The plan is for 100,000 people living in a pair of socially and economically balanced communities. The in-town component would have a population of 25,000 and the out-town component, 75,000.

Goals for the paired new-town include: action and interaction of the two components as one community; a full expression of the sense of community based upon as widely diversified economic, educational, racial, age group, and population mix as is possible; citizen participation in governing the new town; extended opportunities for education and jobs; and material contribution to redevelopment of the city.

The in-town component would have a looped, linear form with five "environmental areas," of 5,000 population each, and a town center arranged along a loop transit system like beads on a necklace.

The out-town component would have three villages with 25,000 people in each, and a town center that would include housing as well as commercial, cultural, and recreational facilities plus a community college and a hospital. Each of the three villages would be designed as a cluster of three communities (8,000 population each) focused on a community center and linked by a loop transit system similar to that of the in-town development.

It is proposed that a high-speed transit system link the town centers of this paired new town.

There is a long way to go before construction of a paired new-town can actually begin. Possible sites must be selected and evaluated. A general plan for development must be prepared and ways to implement it determined. And then at last comes the design and construction stage, which includes the preparation of site plans and the careful timing of all development.

Whether all these steps will be taken for the development of one or more paired new towns in southeast Michigan is, of course, unknown. But one thing is certain—this planning concept and the work supporting it is a significant contribution to solution of the interrelated problems of urban redevelopment, suburban growth, and the need for better quality landscapes for tomorrow.

Urban redevelopment has become a fighting term in recent years as the result of some admittedly bad mistakes and an often misplaced zeal on the part of a few people who cling to all that is old, whether it is worth saving or not.

In most instances, it is ridiculous to tear down dwellings that are habitable or can be made habitable. And destruction of especially historic sites, excellent examples of various architectural styles, or areas with high quality landscape features is senseless—and in the long run, uneconomic.

On the other hand, there should be logical (rather than emotional) reasons for retaining buildings, open spaces, or other features of our towns and cities if their original purposes are no longer valid.

One of the better urban redevelopment projects is Charles Center in Baltimore, Md. A large number of rundown or disused buildings and an outdated, no longer functional street and alley system have been replaced by an improved street pattern, high-rise buildings of good to excellent architectural quality, and well-designed and landscaped open spaces. This area, once dead at night, has become dynamic because of the introduction of new hotels, apartment buildings, restaurants, and a theatre.

Urban renewal improves the environment of towns and cities by rejuvenating deteriorated housing and commercial, educational, or industrial areas. Most urban renewal projects are carried out under the aegis of local government; such projects have been described in books and in many articles. Much less attention has been paid to the projects initiated, carried out, and financed by nongovernmental groups.

If private urban renewal projects help meet the community's goals and implement its general plan, they can be a distinct contribution to the community's environment and perhaps a contribution to its economy. Numerous private urban renewal projects for housing have been attempted. Some succeed, some fail.

Pittsburgh, Pa., has an excellent example of housing renewal that provides sound housing at moderate cost to the inhabitants and also is a financial success. The Allegheny Housing Rehabilitation Corporation, owned jointly by 40 of Pittsburgh's largest businesses, has rehabilitated more than 800 dwellings during the past 3 years. Nearly 500 additional units have been bought and will be renewed.

But this success story goes further. Previously unemployed or underemployed men are becoming skilled in various building trades through on-the-job work under an apprentice training program.

In too many rural and urban areas the landscape has been damaged by man's neglect. More harmful to the landscape than neglect are the effects of much road construction, land scraping and re-forming for building sites, surface mining operations, and so forth.

Culver City, Calif., is planning a park on a 5-acre tract under a State highway interchange that presently is a small valley criss-crossed by highway lanes supported on concrete pillars. This wasted and ugly bit of land will be landscaped.

Trees, shrubs, and grass will improve the area's appearance and diminish traffic noise. The landscaping, together with a wading pool and play equipment for children, and a shaded sitting area for adults, will help transform the site

Developer of apartment complex above in Indianapolis used an excavated area for storm water storage, recreation, and for scenic value. Storm water is routed into this area and released through an outlet at a retarded rate. Right, improper disposal of surface water caused gully threatening a home in Des Moines. Below, sediment and debris fill channel of small stream where it passes through a development in Washington State.

to a useful park accessible to several thousand people.

This has been made possible by a new California law that permits cities to lease non-operating parts of State highway right-of-way for public parks. Culver City will pay the State $100 a year for the lease. And the State will provide nearly $30,000 from its highway landscaping fund for the city's park—the first plan accepted under the new law.

Sites adjacent to highways or their interchanges generally are not very good for small parks and play areas, but this project is important because it

358

Much surface-mined land can be restored to an acceptable level of landscape quality. Some mined areas now are used for forests, wildlife habitat, and forest recreation; other uses include ponds, golf courses, and building sites. Planning for future use before mining commences can make it possible to restore the land more rapidly.

One aspect of America's landscape problems is directly related to our affluence. Only a country with a high economic standard of living is afflicted with litter. In many less economically developed nations the newspapers, bottles, and cans that we throw away are carefully hoarded and reused until they are beyond any utility. People in these countries could not imagine a place where automobiles, stoves, and furniture end in a junkyard, a county's landfill, or on a city street.

Recycling paper to make new paper products, ground glass for new bottles

will bring a usable recreation place close to people who presently have no park nearer than 2 miles away.

Surface mining has damaged more than 3 million acres of America's landscapes, and there has been a rapid rise in such mining during the past decade. Some surface mining areas no longer in use are safety hazards, many affect the quality of water for miles downstream of the site and also reduce stream flow, and nearly all are eyesores for years after mining ceases.

The U.S. Department of Agriculture's Forest Service and Soil Conservation Service, foresters in affected States, reclamation associations, and individual firms and their associations are working to reduce the impact of surface mining on the mined area's landscape. A number of States now have laws requiring restoration work or use other regulations to limit the problem. How well they work remains to be seen.

Top, lush crop of weeping lovegrass growing in test plot on a strip mine spoil in West Virginia. Right, fishing in lake formed from coal strip mine in Pennsylvania.

Beautified highway intersection near Clarksdale, Miss.

or to pave streets, and similar measures will help reduce the demand on resources. Recycling also should help reduce the costs of picking up litter. The magnitude of this problem is almost unbelievable.

June 5, 1971, was Scouting Keep America Beautiful Day. There were two objectives. One aimed at an immediate improvement in our landscapes by cleaning up. The other objective was educational—for litter prevention (or lessening!) in the future.

Throughout the United States on that one day more than 2 million youths and adults cleaned up trash along 200,000 miles of roads and stream banks, and on more than 400,000 acres of parks, recreational areas, and other public places.

They collected more than 1 million tons of litter, ranging from candy wrappers to automobiles. This represented more than 200,000 truckloads of trash! And that, to repeat, was done in a single day. This, unfortunately, gives us only an indication of the magnitude of

Soil scientist checks sample from an auger while mapping soils near Aiken, S. C.

Boy studying microhabitat of a stream at Izaak Walton League's Environmental Science Center in Minnesota.

the cleanup campaigns needed. Next year the Scouts will try again.

Scouting Keep America Beautiful Day was part of Project SOAR (Save Our American Resources), which is a year-round effort that includes many Scout unit and individual projects that help Scouts earn the Conservation of Natural Resources Merit Badge. Scout Troops and Cub Packs throughout the Nation have been encouraged to initiate and work on many projects, such as these: to clean and beautify vacant lots, stream banks, and so on; to develop a nature trail in a park, camp, or community forest; or to plant roadcuts to prevent soil erosion. Each of these

efforts is a positive step toward better landscapes in the future.

Our country's best hope for tomorrow's landscapes may lie in the realm of education. We need more, and better trained, professionals and technical assistants in a wide range of fields that directly or indirectly affect our rural and urban landscapes and our total environment.

An even greater need is for educational programs that will help all Americans learn to understand, appreciate, and care for our environment. Such programs must be extensive in subject matter and geographic scope; they must be imaginative so that people

361

will want to learn. They must be tailored to fit local problems, opportunities, goals, and needs.

Perhaps most important, each environmental education program has got to include ways to involve many segments of each community's population in action to bring visible and rapid improvement in that community's landscapes. Such reinforcement is needed in order to interest people in long-term or less visible landscape improvements.

Educational programs for children offer a great hope for tomorrow's landscapes. Teaching a child about conservation and landscape design can influence him; his interest and enthusiasm can influence his family as well.

The Izaak Walton League of America operates a number of programs designed to educate young people. The Bethesda-Chevy Chase (Md.) chapter has cooperated with the USDA's Forest Service and the Maryland Department of Game and Inland Fisheries to sponsor a series of youth conservation days. These were field trips to several properties of the chapter. Youngsters learned, for example, how a tree grows and why trees are important.

In 1969 the Des Moines chapter held a fisheries workshop. More than 4,000 children learned what fishing is all about, and why clean water is important to fish and to people.

In 1970 the Minnesota Izaak Walton League established an environmental science center in the Minneapolis-St. Paul metropolitan area. The center cooperates with elementary and high schools in the area; environmental classes are invited to the center to learn about conservation.

Lack of research and ignorance of end results is no excuse for failure to act to solve our landscape problems. We cannot wait until next year, 1980, or the year 2000 to plan for intelligent use of all components of our landscape. We must commence now, utilizing the best available knowledge of a great variety of specialists. Our resources are finite; we have got to learn how to use them best.

As the foregoing examples indicate, steps of a number of kinds have been taken toward preserving or improving America's landscapes. Many concerned citizens, individually or in groups, are actively working for landscape and environmental improvement. It is efforts like these that will preserve our landscapes for future generations—and for ourselves.

PHOTOGRAPHY

Major thanks for the photography in this Yearbook goes to the U.S. Department of Agriculture lensmen, who took the bulk of the pictures.

Many other photographers also have made fine contributions to the book, and the editor is most appreciative.

David F. Warren of USDA's Office of Information was visual coordinator for the 1972 Yearbook. He was mainly responsible for the concept of the photo section at the front of the book, and for selection of pictures for this section.

Prints of most of the USDA black and white photos in the book may be obtained from the Photography Division, Office of Information, U.S. Department of Agriculture, Washington, D. C. 20250. Duplicate color slides of many of the color photos may also be obtained from the Photography Division. In requesting prints or slides, please refer to the 1972 Yearbook, give the page number, and describe the photo briefly if there is more than one photo on the page.

Please note that no page numbers appear in the photo section at the front of the book. However, for photo credit purposes, Page I is the first page on which a color photo—a picture of a small child coming up steps between banks of forsythia—appears. Pages II and III carry one photo across the two pages. Roman numerals continue consecutively through Page XXXII for the remainder of this photo section. Arabic numerals in the credits indicate page numbers in the main part of the book.

Photographers are given credits wherever their names are known.

Vincent Abbatiello, Rutgers University, 197, 198, 201

Claude A. Alkire, 11 (bottom)

Jim Allen, 360 (bottom)

American Association of Nurserymen, 82

American Plywood Association, 41 (top), 67, 68 (top and bottom)

Harris H. Barnes, Jr., XI (top), XX (small photo), XXIX (top right), XXXI (top), 360 (top)

Howard Behrens, U.S. Government Printing Office, IV (bottom small photo), VI (center small photo), VII (top), XIII (bottom), XVI and XVII (photo across two pages), XX (bottom), XXII (top)

363

Robert C. Bjork, xxviii (center), xxix (lower right), 17, 18, 363 (photo of USDA photographer James D. Strawser)
Robert B. Branstead, vi and vii (photo across two pages)
Hugo Bryan, 14 (top), 115
Wilbur Burkhart, ix (bottom), x (lower right), xi (bottom), xiii (top)
Lord & Burnham, 214 (top photos), 215
Burpee Seeds, 106 (bottom photo), 109
Erwin W. Cole, 358 (center)
Al Conradi, xxvi (small photo)
John L. Creech, 175 (top)
Loran L. Danielson, 148, 149
John's Dewkist Nurseries, Apopka, Fla., 324
DPA (German press agency), 317
Richard H. Drullinger, 12, 34
Eckbo, Dean, Austin & Williams, xxvi (bottom), 296 (top, lower left)
Gene K. Eisenbeiss, 96 (right)
O. Erwin, xx (top)
Herbert O. Evans, 33
Max Evans, 358 (top)
John Fichter, xxi
G. M. Fosler, x (top)
Max Fullner, 358 (bottom)
David Gates, 296 (lower right)
L. N. Gooding, 184 (right)
Karl E. Graetz, 184 (left)
H. C. Green, 258
Ron Green, xxii (bottom)
Betsy Harnden, D.C. Department of Recreation, 256
Robert Hartmann, 23 (sketch), and 26 (sketch)
Jack Hayes, i, xxiv (top), xxiv and xxv (across bottom of two pages), xxv (small photo), xxvi (top), xxvii
Charles E. Herron, 359 (top)
Joseph J. Higgins, 175 (bottom)
Colin A. Hogan, 86
Don Holt Photos, 289
Jimmy James, 298 (top)
Allan J. de Lay, 77 (top)
Murray D. Lemmon, xii, 133 (top), 243, 245, 339

Raymond E. Leonard, 8
B. C. McLean, 6 (bottom), 13
Malak (Ottawa), 102, 103, 125
Ray Matjasic, Cleveland Plain Dealer, 288
Milwaukee City Park Commission, xxx
James N. Nash, 11 (top)
New York City Housing Authority, xvi (top inset photo), back endsheet, 4 (bottom), 278, 279, 281
Al Nottorf, 14 (bottom)
Terence K. O'Driscoll, v, xxviii (top), xxix (top and bottom), 190, 208, 221 (both photos)
Robert D. O'Hara Jr., Environmental Science Center, 361
Pan-American Seed Company, 106 (top), 108 (top)
Hermann Postlethwaite, 58
C. J. Price, 15
Steven Glenn Prindle, 283, 284, 285
Larry Rana, xix (two lower left photos), 269, 321
Russell Reagan, Missouri Dept. of Conservation, 309
Gary Robinette, 24, 25 (top and bottom), 27
Roche (Caldwell, N. J.), 169
Gottscho-Schleisner, Inc., 64
Jack S. Schneider, xxxi (bottom 2 photos), 322
Donald C. Schuhart, 261
Gordon S. Smith, 32, 306
Paul Steucke, ii and iii (photo across 2 pages), xxiii
Robert N. Stewart, iv (large photo and top two small photos)
James D. Strawser, vi (bottom), viii, ix (second from top), xxxii, 213, 238
Swedish Information Service, 350
Morton Tadder, 355 (center right)
Tideyman Studios, 294
William R. Van Dersal, 177
David F. Warren, 71
James L. Wells, Jr., D. C. Recreation Department, 255 (top left)
R. E. Wester, xiv (top)
J. M. Wise, 359 (bottom)

INDEX

LCC No. 4–18127

U.S. GOVERNMENT PRINTING OFFICE: 1972 O – 441–067

FOR SALE BY THE SUPERINTENDENT OF DOCUMENTS, WASHINGTON, D.C. 20402—
PRICE $3.50   STOCK NUMBER 0100–2441